EDWARD ABBEY

MATTER JOURNAL 13

WOLVERINE FARM PUBLISHING

FORT COLLINS, COLORADO

WOLVERINE FARM PUBLISHING is a 501(c)3 nonprofit organized for literary, educational, scientific, and charitable purposes. To learn more about our organization, please visit www.wolverinefarmpublishing.org.

Dust jacket front/back photos © Milo McCowan/Lyman Hafen
Book cover front/back illustrations © Ryan McKee
Title page photo © John Blaustein
The Fell Types used in this book were digitally
reproduced by Igino Marini: www.iginomarini.com.

Parts of this book are works of fiction, and any resemblance to actual persons, living or dead, is purely coincidental. The opinions expressed herein by the many varied artists and authors do not necessarily reflect the collective opinion of those who live and work at the Wolverine Farm. However, their opinions combined make a fairly accurate aggregation of Edward Abbey, the man and the myth. And in Abbey's case, what good is one without the other?

Drawing upon inspiration from Edward Abbey, our aim is to outlive the bastards. We got involved in river protection, small farm salvation, and bicycle jubilation simply because they are more enlivening than the alternatives: dams, industrial agriculture, and automobile congestion. Now that we know the bastards do not play fair, what next?

Floyd Dominy died on April 20, 2010.
The Deepwater Horizon oil spill in the Gulf of Mexico began the same day,
and is still on-going one month later as we send this book off to the printers.
Clearly, we have not left some eras behind us.

For more information please address:
Wolverine Farm Publishing, PO BOX 814,
Fort Collins, CO 80522.

FIRST EDITION
12 11 10 9 8 7 6 5 4 3 2 1

Printed in Cheyenne, WY on recycled paper according to industry standards established by the Green Press Initiative.

ISBN: 978-0-9823372-5-7
ISSN: 1548-1841
LCCN: 2004-214172

Get Out.
Dig In.

This book was just thrown through
something big and glassy.

TABLE OF CONTENTS

VISUAL ART & PHOTOGRAPHY

WOLVERINE FARM PUBLISHING

MATTER STAFF
Sue Ring deRosset : Managing Editor
Charles Malone : Poetry Editor
Chelsea Aaron, Sara Eden : Interns
Aaron Espe, Abby Goodman : Interns
Todd Simmons : Publisher/Editor/Design

BOARD OF DIRECTORS
Anne Macdonald, Bryan Simpson, Gary Wockner

SPECIAL THANKS TO:
Beth Kopp, Heather Manier, all the Matter Bookstore
volunteers who make this possible, The Bean Cyclers,
Megan, Leopold & Harper, the Tiny House Farm
Office, Jason Shelman, New Belgium Brewing, Rick
Knight, Erzsebet Gilbert & David Rozgonyi, Steven
Schwartz, Fort Fund, M. John Fayhee, & Jack Loeffler.

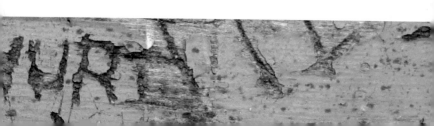

Antler, Milwaukee Poet Laureate 2002-03, has poems in the recent anthologies *Poets Against the War*, *Comeback Wolves: Western Writers Welcome the Wolf Home* and *Best Gay Poetry 2008*. In May 2010 he read with Robert Bly and Ray Gonzalez in Minneapolis as part of the Centennial Celebration of the Poetry Society of America.

Heidi Blakenship spends a great deal of time wandering around on the Colorado Plateau, helping protect areas Abbey and Ruess enjoyed. Her poetry has appeared in *The Lynx*, *The Fourth River*, *White Pelican Review*, *The Avocet*, and *Mountain Gazette*.

John Blaustein began his photography career as a river guide photographing the Grand Canyon. His classic book, *The Hidden Canyon*, traces the path of the Colorado River from river level throughout the entire canyon.

Jerrod E. Bohn is currently completing his MFA in Poetry at Colorado State University. His poetry has previously appeared or is forthcoming in *Touchstone*, *Kansas English*, *May Day Magazine*, and *Suss: Another Literary Journal*.

Dorothy Burk teaches naughty children, frolics in the desert, and collects animal skeletons. She lives in Northeastern California and is studying for her MA with The New School.

Jeana Steele Burton earned her MFA from Colorado State University, where she now teaches. She lives in Fort Collins with her husband, Matthew, and their two dogs. Her short story, "This Most Certain Future," will appear in the upcoming *Laurel Review.*

Tabitha Dial earned an MFA in Creative Writing from Colorado State University in 2009. Her first publication in *Matter Journal* is a found poem made from the first page of Edward Abbey's short story, "Doc and Bonnie Go Shopping." Most of her writing is created with less direction.

Mark Easter lives in Fort Collins with his wife Jan and cats Ink and Lewis, where they maintain a big garden and micro orchard, ride their bikes, drink good beer, and try to get the hell out of town and off to wild places whenever possible.

Sara Eden is graduating from Colorado State University in May 2010 with a degree in English Literature. She interned with *Matter* Fall semester 2009.

Hollis Evans grew up in the South. Ed Abbey exploded his worldview.

Robert Fillmore is a geology professor and recently had an essay published in *Mountain Gazette* called "Meeting Cormac McCarthy in a Bar."

Denis E. Foley is a lifelong hiker, backpacker, camper, rafter, geologist, hunter, world traveler and wanderer of wild places. Denis is happily married to Rozolen Stanford and lives/works/walks in downtown Denver. Professionally, Denis helps heat your house as a consulting petroleum geologist.

Dennis Fritzinger is the Poetry Editor for *Earth First! Journal*.

Pam Furumo lives in Bellvue, Colorado.

Adam Garry lives with his family in North Carolina.

David Gilbert is a senior creative writing major at Colorado State University. He is the editor and publisher of *Wolf Boy*, a local underground writing and art 'zine.

Emma Goldman, 1879-1940—and reincarnated in the 21st century into a former Stegner Fellow just long enough to pen a letter—was a feisty writer, anarchist, and feminist who advocated for birth control. Today, "Red Emma" is mad as hell at the use of drones in war, at wars as solutions, at decisions that permit corporations to have the same rights as persons—freedom of speech, for example—and at the patenting of life.

Noah Eli Gordon teaches in the MFA program at the University of Colorado-Boulder. His seventh book, *The Source*, is forthcoming in 2011 from Futurepoem Books.

Drum Hadley lives in Arizona.

Kristopher Hite lives in Fort Collins, Colorado.

Lauren Howell currently works for the state of Colorado creating landscape designs for rural communities.

Laura Katers did not do that yet.

Michael Kellett is executive director of Glen Canyon Institute, a nonprofit organization based in Salt Lake City, Utah.

Christoper Ketcham divides his time between Brooklyn, New York, and Moab, Utah.

Sean Leisure grew up in northern Michigan, travels extensively, and longs for his own darkroom.

Michael A. Lewis is an anarchist, environmeddler and part-time curmudgeon, veteran of the Exxon Valdez oil spill, searching for that which cannot be found in a world where it no longer exists. His observations on Life, what passes for Civilization, and the Wild can be found at http://hayduke2000.blogspot.com/

Susie Martinez is a poet writing in Fort Collins and is currently attending the Colorado State University MFA program in poetry. Her work has recently appeared in *TRNSFR Journal*.

Ryan McKee loves his family and friends and resides with and around most of them in Fort Collins, Colorado.

Jane Miller is the author of numerous collections of poetry, including the National Poetry Series selection *The Greater Leisures* (1983), *Memory at These Speeds: New and Selected Poems* (1996), and the book-length poem *A Palace of Pearls* (2005).

Paul Miller is editor of *Colorado State Magazine* at CSU in Fort Collins. His essays and fiction have appeared in *High Country News, Orion,* and books including *Pulse of the River,* Tallgrass Writers Guild publications, and *Going Green.* He's currently working on reducing his footprint by going barefoot more often.

David Mitchell is fond of old film that crinkles.

Rico Moore lives in Fort Collins, Colorado, where he is a candidate for an M.F.A. in Poetry at Colorado State University.

Ned Mudd lives in Alabama, writes fiction and the occasional song. He has no dog at the moment, but has his eye out. Much like his stories, his bio is very brief.

Sergio Ortiz grew up in Chicago, studied English literature at Inter-American University in San German, Puerto Rico. His work has been published in *POUI The Cave*, *Origami Condom*, and periodicals in Puerto Rico.

Laura Paskus is a writer living in Albuquerque, New Mexico.

Meghan Peot is a Wisconsin native, living in the West for the past twelve years. She is passionate about family, travel, learning and being outside. Meghan is a lover of the arts, both natural and cultural.

Jeff Poniewaz taught "Literature of Ecological Vision" via UW-Milwaukee from 1989 to 2009. Allen Ginsberg praised his work for its "impassioned prescient ecological Whitmanesque/Thoreauvian verve and wit." His book *Dolphin Leaping in the Milky Way* won a 1987 PEN "Discovery Award."

Dylan Quint wonders if she should withdraw from the slimy, scumsucking, book-writing business to take up an honest profession like boot repair or screwworm management. She lives with her donkeys in Match Pardner, New Mexico, where she is a frequent contributor to *Global Warming*.

Andrew Schelling is a poet, translator of the lyrical verse of ancient India, essay writer, and editor. He teaches at Naropa University where he supervises the letterpress print shop, and currently serves as editor in chief of *Bombay Gin*.

Steven Schwartz teaches undergraduate and graduate courses in creative writing at Colorado State University. His books include two novels, *Therapy* (Harcourt Brace,1994) and *A Good Doctor's Son* (William Morrow, 1998).

Helen Skiba is an English major turned agriculturalist, a native Coloradan fascinated by the language, history, and ecology of the American Southwest. Reading Abbey helped her find a new trajectory toward the study and service of her home, and helped her to not take herself too seriously while doing so.

Ana Maria Spagna is the author of *Test Ride on the Sunnyland Bus* and *Now Go Home: Wilderness, Belonging, and the Crosscut Saw.* She lives and writes in Stehekin, Washington, a remote community in the North Cascades.

David Spiering writes one poem a day. He's been a baker, store clerk, a cook and college professor. His book *My Father's Gloves* is published by Sol books and can be found on web bookstores.

Jordan Twiggs is busy preparing to be an Urban Cowboy via bicycle all over the West.

Faith Walker is a biologist from Flagstaff, Arizona. Much of her wanderings and research have been in wild areas of the Colorado Plateau and Australia.

Maximilian Werner lives in Salt Lake City. His poems, creative nonfiction, essays, and interviews have appeared in several journals and magazines. His book *Black River Dreams* won the 2008 Utah Arts Council's Original Writing Competition for nonfiction and was published in January by Barclay Creek Press.

Joshua Marie Wilkinson's two new books are *Selenography*, with *Polaroids* by Tim Rutili (Sidebrow Books, 2010) and *Poets on Teaching, 99 essays by 101 poets* (University of Iowa Press, 2010). He lives in Chicago and Athens, GA.

Dave Woody is a Colorado-based photographer.

Joshua Zaffos is a freelance writer whose work has appeared in *High Country News, Wired, Miller-McCune, Grist.org, Fly Fisherman, Orion* and *5280.com*, among other publications. Zaffos lives in Fort Collins, and his work and musings are online at joshuazaffos.com.

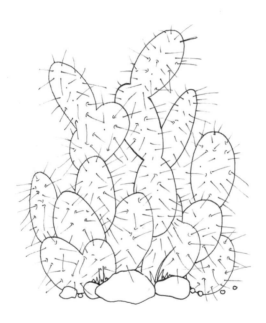

A note about the monkey wrench on the next page: It's day 13 rafting down the Colorado River through the Grand Canyon in March 2010. Eight of us set off through the redwall limestone layer on a steep ascent from the river. We stopped to regroup at the top of the first ridge. My friend Amy was not with the rest of the group. Before I could ask where she wandered off to, I saw her head peak over the top of a house-sized boulder just off the trail. When she stood up I noticed something in her hand. As she passed the object down to the rest of the group I noticed it was a barn-red monkey wrench with an engraved plaque imbedded into the worn wood handle. I felt chills when I read the inscription, "In Memoriam Edward Abbey 1927-1989 Hayduke Vivat."
—*Meghan Peot*

Noah Eli Gordon

Polyptoton for Edward Abbey

until growth's outpaced firstly
the thinking with which it grows
as a thought is not its inflation
a heightened tiny thing inflated
calls the mighty from a high wall
from earthiness as one might
and the earth wrenched
first there was the wrench

The Hunter

Fiction by Michael Lewis

The night is cool and moonless, lit by the stars hanging in their positions of record in the night sky, a slight breeze blows from the mountains to the west, outlining a deeper darkness below the jewel-studded fabric of space.

The hunter creeps silently across barely discernable bunch grass and opuntia between piñon pines. His moccasined feet make no sound on the sandy soil; his dark clothing absorbs light and sound, making him a silent hole in the deep gray background. If he were to look up, which he never did, only the whites of his eyes would betray the presence of a human being disturbing this satiny night.

His prey stands on the near horizon, invisible for now, its exact position known to the hunter through long stalking and planning. The remaining ground between hunter and prey is bare of vegetation, making it easier to avoid detection and alarm.

He stoops forward and begins to crawl, holding in his left hand a complicated arrangement of strings and wood, pulleys and cams, with a large hoop attached at the front. Keeping the tool from scraping across the ground is a challenge, but hours of practice at maneuvering the awkward thing pays off now in a silent approach.

Sounds begin to penetrate the silence, sounds the hunter knows come from beyond his prey, hissing and rumbling sounds as of large objects moving swiftly across hard packed surfaces, sounds occasionally accompanied by a broad sweep of lights across distant mesas. So much the better to mask the tiny whispers of his inevitable approach.

Soon he comes to the base of a slight rise on which his prey awaits. Its dark outline obscures occasional stars beyond. He is in place. It is time to act.

In a practiced effort, he removes a long iron spike from the folds of his clothing and presses its pointed end into the yielding soil. It penetrates a good six inches and then stops as expected. He removes another bulkier, cloth-wrapped object and with several well placed, muffled blows, drives the stake deep into the bosom of the soil, making firm and loving contact with the moistness held therein.

Rising to his knees he fits a slender shaft to the string of the complicated device in his left hand, an aluminum shaft with imitation feathers at one end and a gleaming, sharpened point at the other, catching the distant glint of approving stars. He rises fully to his feet, raises eyes, hand and shaft to the heavens and draws back the string to its knock point at the corner of his mustached mouth. And holds...

For a moment he stands like a statue of an ancient god casting prayers to the heavens, indistinguishable from the constellations above, at one with the Earth, content at the task at hand, focused, relaxed and alert.

Then the smooth, practiced release of string and shaft. The coiled forces in the bow throw themselves through wooden limbs, curving cams and rolling pulleys, the shaft springs forward with an almost audible cry of joy, leaping for the night sky and freedom. Or nearly. For as the shaft rises into the cold desert air, a slender but strong thread follows its path, uncoiling from the reel on the face of the bow, tracing a hissing curve of the arrow's trajectory, up into the sky, over the top of the towering prey, to the peak of its path, the apex of its ambition, the denouement of its escape from the bounds of material being.

Suddenly the thread draws taut, anchored as it is to the iron stake firmly imbedded in terra firma at the archer's feet. The arrow stops abruptly and falls toward

Earth, captivated once again by immutable gravity, its stellar ambitions thwarted, redirected to a nobler cause. As the arrow falls, the thread follows after, downward toward the prey, the tower, the bristling antennae, the circling girders, the electricity pulsing through wire and cable, the radiation broadcast outward in scintillating concentric waves.

The archer leaps back just as the slender aluminum line contacts the tower. Sparks fly out into the night, lightning flares in a clear sky, and electricity, freed from the confines of aluminum and steel and insulated cable, suddenly finds an open path to its unrequited love, the ground, the Earth, the ultimate destination of coursing electrons, deep into the bowels of the earth. The tower shakes with instantly released power, quivers, vibrates, and is quiet.

On the highway below, a sleek, dark automobile purrs smoothly along the Interstate, it's lone occupant holding a small plastic device to his ear. He holds it out in his line of sights, taps it on the dashboard. He looks at the tiny screen and reads the words of doom in glowing green phosphors:

No Service

HURT

YORE

WILD

Dennis Fritzinger

Abbey Recommends

poetry and revolution
before breakfast.
get up, sing a song,
write a poem,
watch the sun come up,
slip on your dark clothes,
blacken your face, pick up your tools,
and go out to meet the enemy—
yellow 'dozers standing in a field,
chill, the dew formed on them,
quiet, cold (it's been hours
since their engines ran),
defenseless.
do your work, slip home,
change softly, shut off the alarm,
make coffee,
oatmeal and raisins,
squeeze some oranges,
have breakfast.

EROSION

Non-Fiction by Ana Maria Spagna

I stand outside a hospital in the grey early dusk of winter holding a shih tzu on a short leash and taking stock. Because taking stock is what you do when a friend is dying of cancer, especially a friend you loved this much, and sometimes hated. I'm standing here trying to breach this gap, a gap hacked open, over several hot seasons, by a machete. And I'm thinking about Ed Abbey.

I didn't attend Abbey's funeral, but I used to think I did.

In 1989 I tore a recruiter postcard off a bulletin board in Oregon to volunteer in a national park. On the application, I penciled in parks I'd visited as a kid—Grand Canyon, Zion—but I was at a loss for the required third choice. Canyonlands. The name sounded right, and the job description sounded manageable: ability to talk to the public, to hike in the heat, to drive a stick. When they offered the job, I took it, and from the moment I arrived in red rock country I felt as though I'd come unsnagged like a vine cut loose from bird netting, like a tendon snapped loose in a massage.

The job was a peach. By day I manned (wo-manned?) the desk in the single-wide trailer that served as a visitor center, and listened to vehicles approach from miles off, tourists strictly segregated by car model: Subaru sporting lycra-clad cyclists, Chrysler vans packed chockfull of Mormons, Hertz rentals with hulking Germans hunched over the steering column. At night I gave interpretive talks around the campfire on the local geology. Sandstone had been deposited by ancient waters—red for rivers, white for seas—then eroded by more recent waters, leaving this shocking army of striped protrusions, distinctly phallic, called, ridiculously, the Needles. If the name were any closer to reality—pillars or columns, silos even—maybe visitors could more easily forget how much they looked like penises. As it was, there was no escaping it.

On days off, I hiked alone, and camped alone, rode my mountain bike on jeep roads, up eroded boulders, down narrow switchbacks, and slept tentless in the sand. I leaned my head back into flash flood water, the color of cocoa, flowing through notches in slickrock, staining my hair, cooling my neck. One night my roommate and I drove a government truck eighty miles to town to pick up two other volunteers to hike to Delicate Arch under the full moon. While we walked a lightning storm moved in and we watched the strikes move closer, faster. I felt giddy, energized, liberated. At home. When we returned to the parking lot to find a dozen grim-faced park rangers—turns out you're not supposed to take government rigs for joy rides especially during lightning storms, especially when two volunteers the previous year had been killed by a lightning strike—I didn't care a whit.

Not that I was purposely emulating Cactus Ed. I'd read him, sure. I was nature-writing obsessed, but I leaned hard toward the northern writers: Lopez, Stafford, Doig. If I related to Abbey in college, it was to *The Monkey Wrench Gang* with its sugar in the gas tank shenanigans and outmoded mores, like the Mod Squad outdoors. *Desert Solitaire*, I'd read and forgotten. When I picked it up again, I finally got it. Not only was it set more or less exactly where I'd landed. Not only was the plot more or less exactly like my life: a job as a ranger in a trailer in Canyonlands. The message was plain: Fuck it, I'm happy here.

I put on a coat and step outside. In the center of the world, God's navel, Abbey country, the red wasteland. The sun is not yet in sight but signs of the advent are plain to see. Lavender

clouds sail like a fleet of ships across the pale green dawn;
each cloud, planed flat on the wind, has a base of fiery gold.

One night late that fall, I went to a party at a Moab ranch, a night I can conjure keenly, vividly, like a movie in high definition, like memory on steroids. I was swept up in the season-ending drama like closing night on Broadway, but also the dry cold desert air and the crowd: all brown skin and brittle blond, slack postured and sculpted. We drank and danced and sat by the creek, high on the smell of sage and sweat and heady happy youth. Even the stars hung close and bright like so many flickering lighters at a rock concert, pleading for an encore.

The next morning a fellow partygoer convinced me that, even though Edward Abbey had died six months earlier, we'd just attended his funeral bash. It was a story good enough to believe.

I planned, after that, to winter in the Northwest, then return to Canyonlands and never leave, but that's not how it worked out. I was working as a temp sending and receiving faxes at an insurance brokerage in Seattle that winter when I got the call. I'd filled out the park service application, all 150 bubbles correctly. Except for one. My application had been tossed out.

So I scrambled. What the hell would I do now? I sat at the kitchen table on yet another drizzly morning considering the parks still hiring.

"You might like North Cascades," my housemate said.

"Which district? There's east and west. Which one do I want?"

"You're from California," he advised. "You'd better choose the east side of the mountains."

Even I knew what he meant: the rain shadow.

Clouds move in from Puget Sound and bunch up against the west side of the Cascades to shed a hundred inches of rain a year or more—nearly twice the amount Seattle gets—then drift over the crest where, as you move east, the average drops from forty to thirty to twenty inches a year and less. Stehekin was on the east side, yes, but aside from that, until I accepted the job, I had no idea where it was exactly or what it was. I certainly had no idea I'd show up in the tiny land-locked valley and never leave. The place was spectacular: glaciers and rivers and forests and more. But that's not why I stayed. I stayed because of Phil.

Phil was the trail crew foreman. He hadn't always worked trails—he'd been a paratrooper and a merchant marine and a farrier—but by the time I arrived, he'd been at it for twenty years. He'd hauled a chainsaw on one shoulder up trails that gained a thousand feet per mile. He'd hiked the equivalent of the Pacific Crest Trail a dozen times over. Maybe two dozen. Now in his fifties, he still spent his days cutting big logs, moving big rocks, blasting, digging, digging, digging. Mostly brushing. In the heat of summer—long strands of hundred-plus days when black flies swirled like dust devils—he climbed the cutbank into a tangle of vine maple limbs and lopped them off, over and over, with a single machete stroke. Hold the limb left, swing right. Repeat. Ten hours a day. I was in awe. I was also in love.

Not with Phil exactly—that summer I also met Laurie, a woman who worked with Phil on trails, and the woman I'd stay with for the next twenty years—but with the whole of it: the scenery, the sun, the sweat, the work. Fuck it, I thought, I'm happy here. I took a job on trails and settled in. I told myself I could live like Phil. And how I tried. One year passed, then ten. Over time, I learned to haul the saw and move big rocks and dig. Come brushing season, I'd swing a brush whip—never a machete, no one but Phil used a machete—day after day, trying to keep up. None of us could.

The majority of living things retreat before the stunning glare and heat of midday.

Not so for Phil. The hotter it got, the harder he worked. He'd peel off his hickory shirt and work in a tank top, his broad shoulders the color and texture of the teriyaki jerky he sometimes ate at lunch. He never carried water, just powdered iced tea in the same dirty bottle. If he wanted water, he'd lie on his belly and lap from the creek.

    I had by then read everything Abbey wrote. And I loved it wholeheartedly. Phil had too—he read voraciously—but he didn't love Abbey quite so much. He disliked grey-bearded radicals as a rule and preferred the more stoic Northern European types: Knut Hamsun, Joseph Conrad, Thor Heyerdahl. We agreed, though, about *The Brave Cowboy,* about how the rejection of modern civilization was as honorable as it was tragic. And Phil was a lot closer to Abbey than he liked to admit.

    "I'm against it," he said often. Meaning, basically, anything: rules, changes, machines. Mostly rangers.

Put the park rangers to work. Lazy scheming loafers, they've spent too many years selling tickets at toll booths and sitting behind desks filling out charts and tables in the vain effort to appease the mania for statistics that torments the Washington office. Put them to work.

Phil couldn't have said it better himself. He'd started

his park career as a ranger and quickly gave it up in favor of real work.

Now rangers tried to enforce rules, and Phil broke them. Rangers hated campfires, and we always had one, no matter what, so Phil could heat the burritos his wife packed wrapped in foil, and out of principle: camping is about being out in the elements, and well, fire is one of the elements. (The prohibition became even more ridiculous as fire policy shifted over time. *Fire is good. Fire is good*, cried the rangers. *But your campfire is bad.*) Rangers tried to remove every trace of humans from the woods—by burning down old trapper cabins and fire lookouts, tearing apart fire rings and hitchrails— and Phil raged. Entire backcountry camps had been abandoned. It was criminal, we thought, and even Abbey would've agreed:

A venturesome minority will always be eager to set off on their own, and no obstacles should be set in their path … But the rest, the majority, most of them new to the out-of-doors, will need and welcome assistance

Once we cut a big log off the trail just across a wide glacier-silted river from one of those abandoned camps. Not wanting to be wasteful, we sawed it long and rigged it across the river; we flattened it and cabled it off. Now we had a foot log. More specifically, we had an illegal foot log. But who would bother with it? A ranger would, of course. A particularly snively ranger, in this case, one whose soft citified manners and persnickety way with rules infuriated Phil. When we returned to see the cut cable and the foot log gone, we worried genuinely, for the first time, about Phil and that machete. The young ranger lived. For better or for worse. By the next season he'd left the park service to become a real estate agent.

Still Phil was not just a rebel. Like Abbey, he was a curmudgeonly savior.

He single-handedly stopped a tall aged dogwood from being yanked out when the park service rebuilt the local visitor center, and he steadfastly refused to kill the rattlers we encountered on the trail. The historic orchard house he and his wife lived in as park housing for forty years leaned off-kilter, and had only a tub, no shower; only a woodstove, no central heat; they never complained; they resisted renovation. And it wasn't just what he opposed, it was what he offered: his wooden signs defined the small valley, hand-routed cursive in knotty misshapen chainsaw-ripped slabs. Phil was the real deal.

By comparison, I decided, Abbey was a fake. He was not only, famously, a half-hearted activist, but a half-hearted inhabitant, too. A city dweller who hiked the canyons in his off-time. For all his raging against tourists, that's what he remained: a tourist. Phil threw his body at the places he loved and answered to no one. Abbey made of himself a caricature, Cactus Ed, who answered to no one, while he himself answered to editors and agents, activists and academics, sometimes his five wives and always the bottle.

If I was hard on Abbey, I had my reasons. The problem was this: Abbey didn't work, he wrote. And though I used to tell Phil that I'd work trails as long as he would, after a decade, I began to get distracted. In my off-time, I wrote a book about wilderness and trail work and finding home, a book that gave not nearly enough credit to Phil or the others who'd befriended me, who'd mentored me, who'd put up with my glaring city girl ignorance until it dulled. Maybe writing a book wasn't as bad as becoming a real estate agent, but it was right up there. According to one story when Phil was first a merchant marine, a young clean-cut Californian, sailors took to calling him: "Hometown." They'd ask him: "You gonna write about this one day?" What they meant was that he was a poser, a wannabe. Phil had proved them wrong. I wanted to do the same, I really did, but my resolve was dissolving.

One season I developed a rash, a reaction to the brush on the trails that doctors diagnosed as poison oak, even though there was no poison oak in the valley. None. Something in me had gone haywire. I wore long sleeves and gloves and put Calamine on my face when the welts appeared. I kept working. But the work was losing its romance. What's worse, my admiration for Phil was beginning to erode. He said often he didn't like strong women, even though he was surrounded by them—his wife, his daughter, his friends—and I couldn't help it, I started to rebel. We fought about Title IX. We fought about Nancy Pelosi. We didn't fight about what mattered most: the fact that he protected me from dangerous jobs he'd never keep the guys from doing. And the constant battle to prove myself grew wearisome and shameful, even as I made coffee in camp and cleaned the shop and kept crew spirits high like a good crew-girl should, like a character in an Abbey novel, like Jerry, say, in the *Brave Cowboy*:

"You men make me sick," she said. "You act like children. Even Seth or that mare out there would have better sense." She dished out the eggs and bacon on to his plate and turned back to the stove to rescue the coffee, already beginning to boil over. "I think you're crazy, that's all."

"You might be right there," Burns agreed. "Question is: what can you do about it?"

Nothing. There was nothing I could do about it.

One night alone at a motel mid-summer, I drank cold beer in the sweet air conditioned comfort—no itching—and watched an old black-and-white movie late into the night in which one soldier said to another, "a man should do what he can do." I decided right then to quit trail crew. After fifteen years. And I felt unsnagged as much as I'd ever felt since Canyonlands, like shedding skin, like dropping a heavy pack after a long hike.

And I landed in a chair. Instead of hacking at brush, I spent my days fiddling with sentences and teaching writing online. Memoir, of all things. From my desk in my cabin in the woods, I was only a window pane away from the wilderness and at the same time in a foreign world. The students were mostly women and their stories were mostly hard: loss and grief, incest and rape and mental illness, and sometimes euphoria. Their stories humbled me, reminded me that while out gallivanting in the mountains I'd been privileged and sheltered and sometimes deluded, thinking that freedom was somehow deserved or earned, and that if my heroes looked down on women or minorities, this was a minor flaw, a quirk, one that did little harm. When I pulled my dog-eared copy of *Fool's Progress* from the shelf after a ten year hiatus, hands shaking, it felt a little like looking at a grizzled old lover, ugly and frightful, wondering what the hell you were ever thinking. From Abbey's alter ego, Henry Lightcap:

Feminism reared its fearsome head, a fright wig crawling with serpents, eyes to paralyze Achilles, the grievance of a million years of servitude glaring from the dark recesses of the female mind.

Who's afraid of Virginia Woolf? I am.

Who was afraid of Edward Abbey? I was.

I was also angry. The desert had spoken to me, but any landscape could speak to anyone; there was no manly patent on ecstatic prose. From the first page of *Mrs. Dalloway*:

What a lark! What a plunge! For so it had always seemed to her, when, with a little squeak of the hinges, which she could hear now she had burst open the French Windows and plunged at Bourton into the open air.

The message is plain: *Fuck it; I'm happy.* If her mood darkens considerably from that point on, it's no darker than Henry Lightcap's and a whole lot less offensive.

That would've been the end of it, I swear it, my twenty year on-again off-again fling with Ed Abbey, except that not long afterwards I was asked to give a talk at a nature writing workshop on finding home, my ostensible expertise, my own story, and I was thumbing through the books on my shelf when I turned to the first page of *Desert Solitaire*.

This is the most beautiful place on earth.

There are many such places. Every man, every woman, carries in heart and mind the image of the ideal place, the right place, the one true home, known or unknown or visionary. A houseboat in Kashmir, a view down Atlantic Avenue in Brooklyn, a gray gothic farmhouse two stories high at the end of a red dog road in the Allegheny Mountains, a cabin on the shore of a blue lake in spruce and fir country, a greasy alley near the Hoboken waterfront, or even, possibly, for those of a less demanding sensibility, the world to be seen from a comfortable apartment high in the tender velvet smog of Manhattan, Chicago, Paris, Tokyo, Rio or Rome—there's no limit to the human capacity for the homing sentiment.

I was stunned. I'd convinced myself that these ideas were my own. But it wasn't true. I'd subconsciously lifted the spirit, if not the words of Edward Abbey, like George Harrison nicking Phil Spector for the melody to "My Sweet Lord." Just as earnest. Just as guilty. Shit. I owed debts that I'd liked to ignore.

None more than to Phil.

He'd retired from trail crew by then. He put a slate roof on his house alone while I wrote a book about civil rights. He rock-faced his chimney while I rock-faced my foundation. Then he came down with cancer.

In *Fool's Progress* when Henry Lightcap gets cancer he sets off for his childhood home, running away in a reassessment as full of self-indulgence as self-recrimination. Phil stayed put. He worked on his firewood. He wrote letters and read books. He eschewed chemotherapy, ate organic, drank juice. And ever single day, no matter what, he walked his dog. Phil had dogs, one after another, as long as we'd known him: a pair of Australian shepherds, males who'd hump at potlucks when they got nervous, a female blue heeler who came with us most days on trails and attacked other female dogs with bloody viciousness. Now he had this prissy all-white shih tzu named, of all things, Vanna White. All summer and into the fall, you'd see Phil carrying Vanna White or biking along the lakeshore in the sun with her in the front basket, ears flapping, underbite-grinning, an image straight out of Norman Rockwell or maybe Martha Stewart.

If he wasn't exactly the Brave Cowboy, I wasn't exactly Mrs. Dalloway either. At some point you've got to be honest with yourself. Identity forms in layers like sandstone: oceans advance and retreat, rivers ebb and flow. There are characters you love from books and people you love in real life, places that draw you in and set you free and eventually wear you down. Erosion happens. So you have to come to terms, compromise and overlook and forgive, precisely the things that Edward Abbey refused to do, ever. That's why we love him, and why—god forbid!—we shouldn't emulate him. Ever.

Phil landed in the hospital, and we kept Vanna White at home for a week or so before venturing out. The nurses were for it even if the doctors weren't, but rules are for breaking, and Phil loved the dog more than any of the rest of us, save his wife of forty years, so we scuttled her in and set her on his lap, and held our collective breath. That he seemed a stranger to her was no surprise. Hell, he was a stranger to himself. That's what cancer does. He'd lost a ton of weight and was draped in tubes—oxygen up his nose, antibiotics in his arm—and smelled, no doubt, like chemicals and rot. Vanna recoiled, then crept forward to lick his face once, tentatively, recognizing what remains, what matters, before curling at the foot of the bed, a safe distance away, but there nonetheless. Still right there.

Antler

Home, Sweet Home

A mouse in its nest inside a moose skull
        looks up at miniature icicles
            dangling from cracks in the bone
        above her head,
Silver icicles inside a moose skull
        as darkness falls
            and the cold wind howls
        while the mouse feels
            safe and warm—
        home, sweet home.
But one night she froze
        and come spring
            there was a mouse skull
        inside a moose skull
            and inside the mouse skull
A spider spun a web
        and lived all spring—
            home, sweet home,
        and when it died
A tiny mite moved in
        inside where the spider's brain was
            and lived all summer—
        home, sweet home,
            before it died,

So there was a skull in a skull in a skull in a skull
    causing a poet's brain in its skull to think
        isn't the Earth in the Sun's skull
    the way his poems
        are in his head?
And the Sun in the Galaxy's skull
    and the Galaxy in the Universe's skull
        and the Universe in the Big Bang's skull
    and the Big Bang in Eternity's skull
        and Eternity in Infinity's skull and…
Home, sweet home.

Christopher Ketcham

Transformation of Rooms

Rooms that are beloved & silent.
The comfort of the small room.
Evening sun in the west room.
We loosened all clothing & light
And we closed away the light
So that it became the color of water & grass.

Darken your rooms. In our wise arms
Lifting nothing for days, no work; we lay down.
The storms move the tree-houses
We have dreamt of since childhood
And in our high rooms in the city we sway.
The rooms out of blankets built, w/in rooms,
Under tables, the tents in the plain,
The snows like geysers, & the roofs made of small feet
& the crows' *eeyaerkk*.

Never belittle them,
Though our waking undoes them.
We do not leave them or come back to them.
They are not the dream of death
Paid interpreters will describe
Nor symbolic of the womb.

In the cabin on the mountaintop,
I have stood for six hours
Keeping the fire hot
While you slept & dreamt
Of the rooms in the snow.

BLOOD
FROM
STONE

One can settle a nomad only by force, by economic or political coercion.
For him, the freedom that the desert gives has no price.
—Ryszard Kapuściński, "Imperium"

Non-Fiction by Laura Paskus

I used to see ghosts, in cities and in dreams, even crouched alongside highway dividers. I have sometimes found bodies, and often found shards of bone. I have inhaled ancient pollen; licking broken pots, I have tucked beneath my tongue the wreckage of someone's dark soul.

Years ago, I crouched inside a tent atop a high desert mesa, fingering the ghost beads around my neck and hoping that the cornmeal I've left outside was adequate in trade for a few hour's sleep. Digging up bodies, wandering deserts, I'd started to see too many things everyone else believed weren't actually there. I have fucked and drank and thrown punches; woken up with bruises and spent days stumbling from too much whiskey.

Nowadays, single mom to a beautiful bright-eyed daughter, I try not to remember those days. Or more truthfully, I try to not remember those days with such longing.

For six years I was a force of destruction. As an archaeologist, I earned paychecks scooping up from the soil potsherds, grinding stones and bones, then depositing them into brown paper bags and marking down their locations. Highways, dams, pipelines, cell phone towers: I cleared the way for all these things. I wiped away the traces of humanity believed to hold progress at bay for those of us who inhabit the land today.

Even in moments of absolute quiet, with neither a shovel nor pickax in hand, I have violated the landscape. Throughout New Mexico, Arizona and southern Colorado, I'd ferret out rock art panels, snug rock shelters where water ollas were cached, or even plod across ridgelines flecked with small stone flakes. Day after day, I would intrude upon a moment of someone else's ancient solitude.

One gray afternoon not far from the tamed Rio Grande, I found the spot where someone had squatted or sat, chipping away at a nugget of chert. He formed the stone into a tool to carry away and presumably put to good use, hunting a rabbit, scraping a hide, perhaps carving the limbs off a small juniper tree.

Centering myself within the scatter of stones, I scanned the landscape, watching below the mesas, valleys, an epic stretch of creosote-covered desert. I am still grateful to have found that place, that moment that had belonged previously to someone else.

But without touching even a stone, I walked away knowing that while I understood not a thing, I had in fact taken everything away.

Three months pregnant, I moved in with a cornflower blue-eyed man—the ex-boyfriend a state away who'd knocked me up when springtime urged us to couple, again and again and again. The night I arrived, he unlocked the door, looked at me through bleary eyes and returned to bed. I moved a couple of my bags into the foyer and went into the bathroom to shower. Watching the water navigate new paths down my burgeoning belly, I knew we didn't love one another. Two months later, I married him anyway.

Two years later, I am neither a stay-and-work-at-home mom nor a bitter wife. For the first time since pregnancy, I am spending a day alone—no family, no work obligations, no pressing guilt to spend time with neglected friends. I have plucked from a guidebook a trail in the Jemez Mountains, choosing this place precisely for its lack of familiarity. I don't care for the mountains the way I dream about the desert. But at this dull point in my marriage, it might crack my heart unbearably to crave the weight of a lover's body pushing mine into sand. In the desert, I'm like a snake coiled along the edge of the trail; the succulence of flesh is too great a temptation.

With the fat warm scent of ponderosa in the air, I follow a trail toward the east fork of the Jemez River. My center of gravity shifted during pregnancy and again following childbirth, and today, I cannot quite find it on the trail. Easing my way toward the river, I grab on to roots in the hillside.

Only physically off-balance, stumbling over stones popping from the springtime mud, does a realization finally shake loose within me: It had taken me years to familiarize myself with the woman I had become by my late twenties. Of course I mourn her.

How many walks in the desert, backpacking trips, nights spent under stars did it take for me to slough off the burdens and expectations of childhood? I'd spent years thirsty in the desert with the grit of red sand in my mouth, poking fingers into the chinks of walls someone else appeared to have left inside my heart. The desert has shaped my body; the sun permanently tinted my chest and the small of my back and tucked crow's feet into the corners of my eyes. This transformation—this excavation—had taken a very long time.

I love my daughter—more than everything else in the world put together, I tell her each night when lying with her before bed—but finally, my rage at domesticity makes sense.

Born in the "free to be me, free to be you" 70s and goaded by a father who made no distinction, in duties nor abilities, between his son and daughter, I'd then spent my twenties stomping about the Southwest self-consciously imagining myself a prettier, long-legged version of Ed Abbey—curmudgeonly, if not as literarily gifted.

I felt my best when I was drinking, backpacking, swearing, arguing about politics, running for miles through the desert for no apparent reason, driving aimlessly down back roads and walking into bars full of strange old men who were confused—aroused? comforted?—by the sight of a woman bellying up to the bar for a shot and some conversation.

After working at a regional newspaper for a few years, I negotiated a plan to return to the desert and open a field office in Albuquerque. I planned to write and take advantage of freedom from office life to travel, delve into complex and heartbreaking issues with sources and hoof it once again around the Southwest. With only a month left on my employer's health insurance plan, I had my teeth cleaned and underwent a physical at the local doctor's office.

As the nurse walked out of the room holding my urine sample, I asked her, as an afterthought, to run a pregnancy test. My nipples felt like wounds; the past few nights I'd knelt facedown in the bathtub, submerging my breasts in the hot water to try and ease the pain. I meant the pregnancy test to stand as proof. It would reassure my mind and stop my body from irrationally hoarding its flow of blood. When the nurse returned, beaming, I became the closest I've ever been to hysterical. For the next few months, driving on back roads or highways, I would watch closely the on-coming traffic, feeling the pull of release.

Once claimed by motherhood, I no longer knew what to do. My role models no longer made sense. At a loss, I retreated within traits not truly mine. I became careful, worried, nurturing, selfless.

And quite insensibly, I showed up at the door that night; then, became a wife.

Before heading home to my husband and daughter, I pull the car off alongside the Jemez River as it slices between mesas and mountains. Looking up at Guadalupe Mesa, I recall once standing puzzled and frustrated with friends just below the lip of the edge, wondering how to scale the sandstone cliffs that flank the top of the mesa.

Atop that hulk stands Astialakwa, a 250-room village. After the Pueblo Revolt of 1680, the Spaniards retreated away from this land and the stubborn people who wanted to live the lives they had for centuries. But full of resolve and blood thirst, they returned just a few years later. Across the region, natives retreated to mesa-tops, building defensive walls, doing their best to till new fields high above river floodplains while awaiting new wars.

Two battles occurred at Astialakwa—one in July 1694 and the second that September—and the Spaniards finally had their victory. An archaeologist tells me that when the local Jemez were living in that village, the Spanish snuck up that sketchy little trail in full armor and leading their horses. "All without being detected," he says, "so that at dawn they were able to charge the village and overwhelm it."

I somehow found a way to the top those years ago, because I remember walking around the ruins atop the mesa, hoping no one would touch the manos left in grinding troughs along the edge of a tiny arroyo.

But for the life of me today, I don't remember how we scaled those cliffs.

It's been eight months since my marriage imploded in a yellow kitchen. Before a judge had even stamped approval of our divorce, I retreated from the desert. Trading roadrunners for magpies, grackles for red-winged blackbirds, I moved north toward the Rockies.

This land is beautiful, but I do not love it. I have never longed to lose myself within the rocky masses here. Best viewed from a distance, the mountains encourage me to stay home, to distract myself with motherhood and community. I ignore my aching heart by pouring love into our sweet little house, snuggling back into the warmth of old friendships and exchanging cookies and zucchini bread with my new neighbors.

Here, no voices call to me in the night, nothing startles from the corner of my eye. I focus for the first time in my life on the living and the present. My life becomes one of medians: No highs, no lows, just an easy contentedness.

This blissful ease is disrupted only whenever I anticipate greeting my ex-husband for a custody visit and parting from my daughter for the weekend: I'm giddy to escape the demands of single motherhood, but also filled with guilt. The dread that something terrible might happen while she's out of my care—the product, I'm convinced, of a Catholic childhood and a mother who passed to me her worry gene—consumes me late at night.

This weekend, my daughter will spend two nights with her dad. It's the longest the two have ever spent in one another's exclusive company. But the anxiety I'd whetted to a sharp point against my temple each night in the weeks leading up to the exchange—which culminated in the purchase of a life vest for her to wear in the motel swimming pool—disappears completely as I walk away from my ex-husband's truck.

With forty-four hours ahead of me, I am anxious to cover some ground.

I drive away from snow-capped mountains in search of scrubby public lands. It doesn't take long to find what I need. Parking the car, I head with my dog up a two-track road. We wander up a small arroyo, then follow a series of game trails. The dog dives into the long grass to run after rabbits; we weave in and out of yucca patches and chamisa.

For two days I scour this landscape for signs of life. I don't expect ancient pottery here or cobbles piled together to form a wall; but perhaps I'll find some flaked stone chips. I wander from point to point—an abandoned cattle tank, a lone juniper tree, a granite outcrop atop a knoll—but find nothing. I am joyful, I am free, I can breathe. There's no one here but me. Or at least, no one has left behind any signs; I leave none either. For the first time in years, I'm no longer wishing away pieces of my life, longing for something I think I've lost.

On Sunday morning, I retrieve my daughter. We head home through the mountains, and I promise myself this weekend is the beginning of something new.

Five days later, I drive with her and our dog to a spot just shy of the Utah border. We hike in the desert, running fingers along dinosaur bones and hanging out with collared lizards. As if to remind me of my promise, the afternoon we return home the winds whip us with sand; the Colorado sky turns a shade of coral.

The spring turns cold again that night; later, the sky pours down mud. Thick drops of red splatter the cars; the following morning, a film of red covers my driveway. I pretend this isn't a sign meant just for me. And yet, I see the red desert dust everywhere.

I attempt with morning runs to forge bonds with the landscape here: Loading the dog into my car, I drive to a nearby mesa along whose hip engineers strung an irrigation ditch. Red dust even coats a concrete section of this ditch. I pause, while the dog trundles ahead, and wonder how exactly those grains of red sand have lodged themselves inside my heart. This is not the life I had ever expected for myself. None of it: Not single motherhood nor this sedentary life—and certainly not this obsession that sets me apart from people who don't seem always to be seeking signs of past lives.

The first time I left the desert, it was to run from the pull of bones and all their many stories. The second time I left, it was because I couldn't afford to stay. For now, the bones must stay where they are. But the land still calls me.

Driving home from that morning run, I notice a rivulet of red mud that has dried at the edge of my windshield. Pulling off the road, I get out of the car, look for passing traffic. I lick the dried mud—just a taste—from the glass.

A Good Sentence

Non-Fiction by Steven Schwartz

E dward Abbey sat squeezed behind a small
student desk. It wasn't an elementary school
desk, but it looked like one with him sitting
behind it. "What do you want to talk about?" he asked
that first day of class in 1981. He'd been invited to join
the creative writing faculty at the University of Arizona
in Tucson, and we were to be the first class he'd ever
taught—a graduate seminar in writing nonfiction. He
wore a red bandana tucked under a plaid shirt and a jean
jacket. Making little eye contact, he smoked a pipe and
spoke mostly in one- or two-word pronouncements.

He wanted us to call him Mr. Abbey, although
he didn't state this explicitly. Just that he called us Mr.

Kessler, Miss Temple, Mr. Hepworth, Miss Young, and Mr. Schwartz. He told us to write every day. We wrote this down in our notebooks. Did he write every day? No, he said, and didn't elaborate, except to admit that he revised very little. "I never spend more than twenty-four hours on a piece," he said. He always regretted this a year later when he read over the work, he added. We wrote this down too. There didn't seem to be any contradiction between what he said and did. Sometimes one's persona can embrace contradictions that in others would be screamingly hypocritical.

At break, he wandered away and got lost. University of Arizona is not that big a campus, but he failed to return for forty-five minutes.

"I got lost," was all he said. I was outside smoking a cigarette when he came back. We were all wondering where he had gotten to—back to Ajo, his home in the mountains? Had we alienated him the first day of class? Didn't he like us? Was academia that bad? I rarely smoked and didn't look natural when I did. The cigarette had burned down to the filter and either I imagined or it really happened that he stared in disapproval at my hand—which threw the butt (suddenly the word was so ugly) on the ground. I picked it up and walked a block to the trashcan where I deposited it, contrite.

The second half of class continued much as the first, with Mr. Abbey nodding occasionally. I felt at once protective of and embarrassed for him. On the other hand, he seemed perfectly comfortable with the large and silent gaps in the discussion. Wasn't this teaching? What's the hurry?

"Anyone want to discuss anything else about writing?" he said.

Mr. Hepworth, an ambitious young man who was running his own small press even while in graduate school, thrust his hand into the air. "The thing that bothers me about writing is the potential for failure," he said, and looked at our instructor plaintively.

Mr. Abbey leaned over his elementary school desk, his knees above the edge. "That sounds more like a psychological problem than a literary one."

"Really?" Mr. Hepworth said, intrigued.

"Have you seen your shrink about it?"

"I don't have a shrink."

"Maybe you should get one," Mr. Abbey said.

I'd had a certain reputation, you might say, as a promising writer in the program. And although it was mostly based on my fiction, I'd also done humorous essays for a local weekly, witty and clever and filled with subtle resonances, or so I thought. The first piece I submitted to the class was one of these. Before I got the sketch back with a B, which would have been enough of a blow, having never seen one of these in graduate school, we "workshopped" it in class.

The discussion was mostly uninspired and meticulous: "You've got a comma splice on page six, the fourth paragraph," Mr. Hepworth pointed out, having returned undaunted to class despite his psychological problem.

"I like how you start with the fire," said Miss Young.

"I think it might work better in present tense," offered Mr. Kessler.

"You make the neighbors very real to us," said Miss Temple.

Finally, impatient, because He wasn't saying anything, I asked Him what He thought. He was still behind the elementary school desk, puffing on his pipe—no one had told him he couldn't smoke in class, and would it have mattered anyhow to an anarchist? "What do you think of it?" His silence perturbed me. After all, he was the teacher, wasn't he?

"You really want to know?"

He was smiling.

"Yes, I do," I said. "What *do* you think?"

Thereupon he pulverized the small (oh, how much smaller it got in those ten minutes he expounded!) vignette.

"What's it about?" Abbey finally asked me in front of the class.

"Well, there was this fire—"

"What's it about?"

"Well, all the neighbors came out this night because of the fire, and we've never really talked to each other before—"

"What's it about?"

He kept pounding away and every time I tried to explain he'd ask me again to tell him what it was about until he humbled me into silence. He was right, of course: it wasn't about much, not at any level that mattered, and I don't think he considered social commentary on the planet going to hell the only worthy subject matter. He just wanted something truthful, something that *cut*.

I should have rebounded, but I caved and decided to drop the course. I needed to get his signature, however, since it was already weeks into the class. So I went to his office. It was on the third floor of the Modern Language building. Rather than use the fluorescent light in the ceiling he had brought in his own lamp with its single incandescent bulb that cast a jaundiced haze over his desk—a completely bare desk, interestingly enough. Even though it was larger than the one he sat behind in class, he was still hunched over, his long arms leaned across it as if waiting for someone to come in and rap his knuckles. He appeared misshapen and misbegotten behind the desk, and his beard, roughened skin, and deep-set eyes in the dim yellowish light made him look like a seafaring captain stripped of his commission.

"I just wanted to let you know that I'm dropping the course," I said.

"Why?" He seemed genuinely surprised, which caught me off guard. I didn't expect him to have any reaction at all, much less question me about my decision. My impression had been that he wasted little time on soothing anybody's hurt feelings.

"I don't think it's working for me. I'm not sure what you're looking for," I said, a statement that would make me cringe years later when I became a teacher and would hear it from my own students. "You don't seem to like anything I write."

"You're one of best writers in the class," he said.

I stood there surprised and pleased that he cared enough to try to persuade me to stay and just when I thought we would negotiate my decision, and I'd tell him more of what I needed from him as a teacher, I saw him go completely blank and withdraw, and he would say no more. He'd lost interest in my predicament or perhaps he was just being a hands-off Westerner and respectful of my rights. The message, however, was clear: it was up to me whether I persisted. After an awkward moment of silence, awkward for me if not him, I slid the form across the desk, he signed it, and I left, feeling relieved and cowardly all at once.

I saw him one more time. Invited by the Cultural Affairs Board, he came to Colorado State University to give a reading during my first year as a faculty member. I went up to him at the reception. It had been more than four years. I wasn't sure he would recognize me.

"Mr. Schwartz," he said. He seemed pleased to see me. He had heard I was teaching here. I complimented him on his reading, and we talked about Arizona.

"Are you still teaching there?" I asked.

"No," he said, "I don't have it in me to be a teacher."

I felt sad. I always felt sad when people made blunt and honest self-assessments and all you could do was nod. We were surrounded by people watching us talk. The lecture had sold out—twelve hundred people. There were another four hundred who had come down from the mountains around Fort Collins or from Boulder, from all over Colorado and Wyoming actually to hear him, many who couldn't get in the packed auditorium. Some folks from the radical environmental group Earth First! had broken the doors trying to do so. There are mortal and immortal writers and he was clearly on his way, at least in the West, to being deified as one of the gods, much to his discomfort it seemed. He had said once in class that he cared more about a good sentence than anyone could ever imagine.

Other people waited in a long line to speak with him, to listen, to hear anything he would say. We shook hands and wished each other well. Four years later I would learn of his death from internal bleeding. It was said that he'd been buried in his blue sleeping bag and without a casket in the Tucson desert—the same desert I'd seen him walk toward that day he got lost on campus.

Tabitha Dial

From Doc and Bonnie Go Shopping

i.
Thirty sons loaded the back of Doc's Buick station wagon.
Ten cases, new-waxed, business-sealed and stamped.
Straight Style. Red Cross Extra.

ii.
blaster out there, signing the last of the Federal forms.

iii.
We have this class.
G. B. Hartung blasting caps,
youngest wire, crimping boy,
fuse pliers over there
and the dramatic-looking safety stick.

iv.
a mining claim, the boy says, in your mouth.

v.
Now I mean your pocket.

vi.
You're your claims.

vii.
all this engineering
gonna develop
nothing into the boy.

It is up to
the young man.

"Oh," the boy says in Europe.

I hear gold
on the ranch

ANOTHER

GODDAMNED

COWBOY

Fiction by Ned Mudd

Frank opened the Crazy Eagle at exactly 10 am. He did it every morning except Sunday and was proud of his punctuality. It was the only facet of his life that ran on time. He'd been open for twenty minutes when a man walked in, took a seat at the bar. The man was lean as a flag pole, wore a tan hat pushed back on his head.

Frank smiled, said "Morning," and waited. He saw a horse tethered to the hitching post. Not many people rode up on horseback anymore. Mainly pickup trucks and BMWs.

The man looked around the room and said good morning.

Frank said, "That's a nice looking horse. Kinda small for a fella your size, I'd say."

The man swung his head back around. "Big enough," he said.

Frank nodded. "That a mustang?" he said. "Haven't seen one of those with a saddle on it for some time."

"Yeah."

"You break her yourself?"

"That'd be correct," the cowboy said.

Frank smiled. He figured the man to be in his fifties, tried to envision him breaking a wild mustang. "Damn," he said, looking back out the window at the horse. "Didn't get hurt?"

The man shook his head. "Wadn't much to it. Just had to convince her to figure it out."

Frank noticed the man had a scar across his neck. The thing was raised a little, a shade of purple. He wondered how somebody got a scar like that. Maybe a knife fight. Not unheard of in these parts.

"You looking for a drink? Kind of early for most folks," Frank said.

The man nodded and said, "I'll take a bottle of your best tequila."

Frank moved back a little. "You want something special?"

"Smoothest stuff in the house," the man said.

Frank smiled. "I got a friend in Nogales brings me tequila every now and then. His uncle makes the stuff in some village down in Mexico. But it ain't cheap."

The man nodded, said "That'd be good. I'll need a lime."

Frank walked off toward the end of the bar. He opened a hinged panel and pulled out a bottle. On his way back, he stopped at the juke box, reached around the back and turned it on.

"Music okay with you?" he said.

The man nodded. "Yeah," he said.

Frank made a selection and walked to the bar as Merle Travis warbled out of the speakers. The bottle had a home-made label that said *Salvador de Vida!* There was a crude drawing of a donkey carrying an agave on its back.

Frank put a shot glass down in front of the customer. "I tell you what," he said, "you try it and see if it's what you're after. You don't like it, no problem. This stuff ain't for everybody."

The man nodded and watched Frank pour his glass half full.

Frank rested his arms on the bar and watched as the man took a taste. There was a small amount left in the glass as it came back to the bar.

"Your friend's uncle makes good tequila," the man said.

Frank leaned closer. "The bottle's gonna set you back a hundred bucks," he told the man. "But I'll throw in a couple of greasy eggs and some toast if you want; might help the stomach."

The man nodded and said, "Good deal." He

picked up the bottle and the shot glass and walked over to a booth by a window. He stood a moment, looking at the iron bars in the window.

"Used to be a jail," Frank said over the music. "I'll be over with some limes in a second. Lemme put your breakfast order in. Consuela's gonna be excited; nobody much comes around for breakfast anymore."

The man slid into the booth. He held the bottle up to a shaft of light filtering in through the bars, then set it back down and removed his hat, placed it on the seat beside him. The room smelled stale, cigarette smoke lingered on the wall paper.

Frank returned carrying a bowl of limes and a small paring knife.

"Here you go," Frank said, "figured you might want to cut it up yourself." He set a napkin on the table, laid the knife down. "Breakfast'll be out in a few minutes. Eggs are sunny side up if that's good with you."

The man nodded. He took the knife and sliced a lime in quarters. "Much obliged," he said.

Frank wandered back behind the bar. The day was young and he'd already turned a hundred dollars. As far as he could tell, the future was one big mystery. He watched the man out the corner of his eye, noticed the guy being careful about how he drank, not shooting the tequila but sipping it, using the lime as a buffer against the alcohol.

"You want some water with that?" Frank asked the man.

"No, but my horse is gonna need some," the man said. "You got a bucket I could use?"

Frank walked to a small closet and came back with a plastic pail.

"This do?" he said.

The man nodded and said, "Should do fine."

"There's a spigot around the east side of the building," Frank said.

The man finished his drink and took the pail outside. Frank watched through the front door as the man watered the mustang. The man was meticulous, not in a hurry. Frank could swear that not a drop was spilled.

The man came back in the bar and went to his bottle. Frank took out a leather attaché and removed a sheaf of papers and receipts. He always made sure the paperwork was done before the place filled up with the lunch crowd. Not that he expected much of a crowd on a Monday, but it paid to be prepared.

Frank noticed the man ritually tend to his lime and pour a measured amount of tequila into his glass. The idea of drinking tequila in the middle of the morning made him quiver. The guy was drinking the best tequila Frank had ever tasted, but it still had the potential to cause trouble, regardless of its fine pedigree.

A woman's voice came from the kitchen with the words "Order up." Frank walked over to a window and picked up a tray, carried it to the man in the booth. He thought the eggs resembled a pair of rubbery tits. The idea turned his stomach.

The man said "thanks" as the plate was set before him. Frank made sure the customer had a fork and indicated a jar of preserves beside the wall. He looked the situation over and decided everything was in order. "Holler if you need anything," he said and walked back to the bar.

A pickup truck pulled up outside, its engine rattling as it shut down. A woman in a loud red shirt stepped out of the truck and looked a long time at the mustang tied to the hitching post. Then she walked up the steps and came inside.

"Who belongs to that horse?" she said, pointing over her shoulder.

The man looked up from his breakfast, watched the woman at the bar. Frank smiled, said "Morning Pico," and wiped the bar in front of her.

"That animal ain't yours, Frank," she said. "His?" She turned and nodded at the man in the booth.

"Yeah, but I'm not sure he wants company."

The woman walked over to the man. As she neared his table she turned to Frank and said "Might as well bring me a beer, Frank."

Frank nodded, shaking his head, rattling the few hairs he had left on top.

"I'm Pico," she told the man. "That your mustang?"

The man nodded, wiped egg off his mouth. "Yeah," he said.

"Mind if I have a seat?" Pico said.

The man pointed at the other side of the booth. "Suit yourself," he said.

Pico slid into the booth and watched the man tear up a piece of toast. She noticed a jar of preserves open beside the man's plate.

"Bottle of tequila before lunch, that's pretty crazy," she said. "That must be a tolerant animal you got out there."

The man looked at Pico and nodded. "I reckon so."

Pico smiled as Frank set a long-neck down in front of her. "You need anything else, Pico?" he said. "Consuela's got some stew brewing back there. Be ready in a minute."

Pico took a swig from the bottle. "Had something to eat already. Thanks."

Frank sauntered back to the bar and resumed his

paperwork. Buck Owens came out of the jukebox.

"I live over the hill by the river," Pico said. "Not much of a ranch, but it brings in enough to live on. Called *The Suzy Q.*"

The man put his fork down and looked hard at Pico. She could feel him sizing her up. She wondered if he was as wild as he looked.

"Old pop song," he said.

"If it ain't in that jukebox over there, I probably never heard it," she laughed.

The man nodded. Pico suddenly felt like her world was smaller than it used to be. The last thing she expected out of this guy was music appreciation.

"Where the hell you ride in from?" she asked. "You working round here?"

The man picked up his fork again and punctured the yolk on the remaining egg.

"Mexico," he said.

Pico sat back in the booth, let out a burst of air.

"Jesus," she said, "you just ride over and plop down wherever you want?" She scratched a spot on her head. "Border Patrol didn't mess with you?"

The man shook his head. Pico thought he might be handsome under the right light.

"Didn't see any Border Patrol."

Pico smiled. "Ain't that something. There's a war going on out there and some fool cowboy just rides across the border like it was fun." She paused, let her words settle. "Those federal bastards wouldn't know what to do with the likes of you."

Frank called across the room, "Everybody doing okay over there?"

Pico waved him off. She felt like there was a cloud floating over the table that was capable of snowing. She

looked out the window, through the bars. It was going to be another sweltering day.

The man finished his eggs and pushed his plate to the side of the table. He wiped his mouth again and slid the tequila bottle between him and Pico.

"Is that Frank's special poison?" she asked. "Mind if I have a taste? Always did want to see what the fuss was about."

The man nodded. "Be my guest."

Pico walked over to the bar and asked Frank for a shot glass, walked back and took her seat. The man pointed at a wedge of lime.

"Reckon I'll take it neat," she told him. "Lime makes my teeth squeak."

He filled her glass and she carefully tasted the tequila.

"Lord, God, that shit's strong enough to clean a stall with," she said.

The man sipped his glass and leaned back against the booth.

George Jones wafted from the jukebox. Pico thought the singer sounded like brushed velvet. She tapped her toes and dared another swig.

"You ain't scared of coyotes out there across the border?" she said.

The man looked at her, his eyes boring holes into her skull.

"Got a Winchester," he said.

Pico smiled. "I meant alien runners, you know, they call them coyotes."

The man nodded, took a sip of his drink.

"Got no problems with those folks," he said. "Showed a few where to find water, probably cemented my reputation."

Pico felt a small jolt. This guy was definitely crazy.

"You got a name?"

The man took another sip and said, "Cal."

"Cal," Pico said. "That it – Cal?"

"Burns."

"Well, Cal Burns, good to meet you." She held a hand out for him to shake. "You ride around on a mustang for the hell of it, or does the combustion engine bug you?"

Burns smiled. Pico noticed his lips were chapped and there were wrinkles across his face from too much exposure to the weather. She thought he might be younger than he looked but cowboys were hard to peg.

"I do odd jobs, requires a horse."

Pico nodded. *Odd* seemed like the proper word to come out of his mouth.

Frank came over and checked on the table. He pointed at a blackboard behind the bar. "Got fresh pie," he told them. "Peach."

"You want me to lose my figure, Frank?" Pico said.

Frank looked at Burns, said "How about you? Just out of the oven."

Burns nodded, said he'd take a piece.

"That's good," Frank said. "Consuela will be happy," he added and walked off to the kitchen carrying Burns' empty plate.

"Hey, Cal," Pico said, "you good with heifers?"

Burns looked at her, then through the bars of the window. A wisp of cloud was trying to get something going without much luck.

"Not interested," he said.

"I didn't offer anything yet."

"Just the same."

Burns poured them both another drink. Frank reappeared with the pie, ice cream melting across its surface. Frank set it on the table, laid a spoon down beside it.

Pico wiggled her nose, caught the scent of the pie, and made a little motion like a rabbit had just run over her grave.

"Jesus, Frank. To hell with my figure," she said.

Frank wandered off again and Pico suddenly felt like Fate was playing with her.

"Talking isn't your forte, is it?" she asked Burns.

Burns put a spoonful of peach pie in his mouth, chewed slowly.

Pico waited for Frank to arrive and started in on her piece of pie. The peaches had a faint tartness, not overwhelmed by sugar. Lots of butter in the crust.

There were only the three of them in the bar. Frank motioned for Pico to slide over and took a seat next to her, happy to be off his feet.

"Well?" he said.

Pico chewed, held up a thumb, bobbed her head.

Frank looked at Burns, watched him enjoy the pie.

"Make you a deal," he said, "I'll throw in the pie for a shot of that tequila. Don't know when I'll get anymore of that stuff."

Burns nodded and pushed the bottle across the table. Frank walked to the bar and rooted up a shot glass. When he got back to the table, Pico had almost devoured her slice of pie.

"Damn, Frank, that was delicious," she said.

Frank smiled, poured tequila into his shot glass. He held the glass up to his nose, smelled the darkness lurking within.

"This stuff was blessed by some kind of neighborhood shaman down in Mexico," he said. Frank thought tequila might be the weirdest spirit he'd ever encountered.

Pico allowed a moment of confusion to pass over her. She wasn't sure she wanted to drink anything that was hexed.

"What in the world does *blessed by a shaman* mean, Frank?" she asked. "You talking about voodoo?"

Frank laughed. "No, honey, the shaman talks to the brew before they bottle it, wishes those who drink it safe passage to wherever it is the tequila takes them. It's an ancient tradition."

Burns looked up at Frank. "Ain't that ancient," he said. "Conquistadors taught the Indians how to distill."

"Well aren't you the wise one," Pico said. "First music, now ancient history."

Burns set his glass down and looked at the two across the table. "Y'all want another taste?" he said.

Frank thought Burns might be a shaman himself. "Sure," he said, sliding his glass towards the bottle.

"If this is a community drunk, count me in," Pico giggled.

She and Frank clinked glasses and shot back the tequila.

"Whoo!" Pico hollered.

The bottle had less than an inch left. Frank had his head down on the table, bouncing his foot to the sounds of Pico's voice as she sang a tune she'd learned as a child back in Las Cruces. Several customers had come in for lunch and were told to get it from Consuela. Frank's customers were good for a tab. Always had been.

Burns watched the other two. He looked through the window and saw a vapor trail in the distance. "Gotta take a leak," he said and slid out of the booth.

Pico waved without missing a beat, her voice a screechy falsetto. "I like that guy, Frank," she said. "I think he's crazy as a March hare, but I've got a good feeling about him."

Frank raised his head off the table and said "The man has good taste in tequila, that's for sure." Frank was drunk and decided that was okay.

Pico smiled. She'd sat in this booth so many times it seemed like an extension of her own skin. The jukebox had decided to play a Waylon Jennings number. "Any more of that shit and I'll start seeing things," she said. She waved a hand in the air, looking for tracers.

"As long as you don't puke on my table," Frank told her.

Pico started singing again, finding a harmony to Waylon's lead vocal. She liked the song about the good hearted woman in love with a good timing man. She wondered if Burns was that kind of man. He was hard to read.

"Hey, Frank," she said, "you figure Burns is okay? He's been gone for two whole songs."

"Might have the runs," Frank said. "Tequila does that sometimes."

Pico winced. She didn't like to think about getting the runs.

"You reckon you ought to check on him?"

Frank looked up at her. "He's a grown man."

Pico caught the song as it hit the last refrain, added her own dissonant harmonics.   After the next song, Pico felt a strange urge to get up and walk around. She wasn't sure, but she thought one of her legs might be asleep.

Frank let her out and fell back in the booth.

Pico wiggled her leg, trying to shake some blood into it. The thing felt like a bag of bees that were crashing into each other. She looked out the bar's front door, noticed an afternoon slant to the sun.

"Frank!" she said. "Where the hell's that mustang?"

She hobbled over to the door and swept the gravel parking lot with her eyes. There was one old truck parked in front, which she figured out belonged to her.

"It's gone, Frank," she said. "You better get Burns. He ain't gonna like this!"

Frank felt heavy, weighted by inertia from a place he couldn't identify. The idea of walking to the restroom seemed out of the question.

Pico hollered at the kitchen. "Consuela, how's bout seeing if that dude in the head can get his ass out here. We got us a problem."

The jukebox played Patsy Cline.

Consuela appeared and said, "There's nobody in the restroom. Sorry."

Frank lifted his head.

Pico walked to the booth, looked at the place Burns had sat.

"What the hell, Frank?"

"His hat over there?"

Pico leaned forward. "Hell no."

Frank got up and looked for himself. His feet felt miles away. He saw what looked like amoebas floating in his vision. "The son of a bitch skipped out on us," he said. "Must've gone out the back door."

Pico drifted backwards, off her balance.

Patsy Cline was singing *Crazy*.

"Just another goddamned cowboy, Frank," Pico said.

INDUSTRi

SOCi

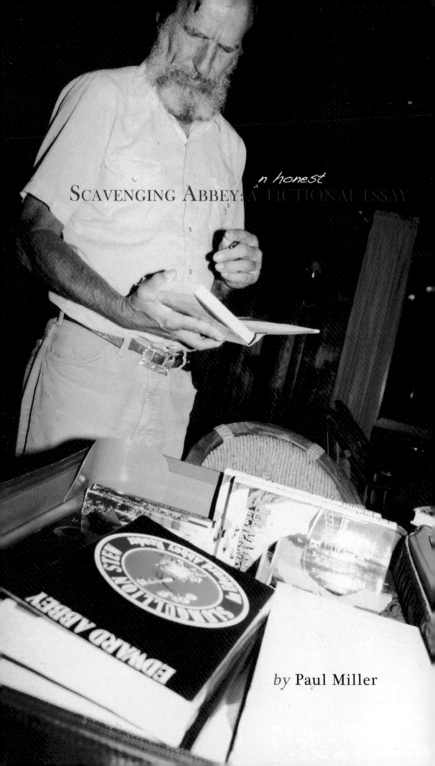

SCAVENGING ABBEY: A̸ͫ FICTIONAL ESSAY

by Paul Miller

P ull an Edward Abbey off the book shelf, let it fall open, and remember the dirty dog was one of the few who saw Glen Canyon before it was desecrated. He saw the canyon from a flimsy raft floating down the Colorado River, accompanied by a crew of attitude-packing hooligans. The canyon, "a portion of the Earth's original paradise" as Abbey said, is now decades buried under the muck of a reservoir. I'm jealous to this day that he saw the canyon before it became Lake Powell, but its loss is all our loss. We can't even let John Wesley rest in peace, his name buried in the cold, turbid depths along with a chunk of Abbey's spirit.

Abbey, decades dead, is now wandering rimrock in places the rest of us mortals can't imagine. Or we hope he's still wandering, in peace. Who knows. Maybe he's mad about what heaven or hell have become, whichever he inhabits. Used to be such nice places, before all the riff-raff started showing up. His arguments would probably be more vitriolic.

Another book falls open, and there's Abbey in Arches, officially nicknamed a "Government Wilderness Repository We Can't Stop Screwing Up," in southeast Utah near Moab, designed for industrial tourism, a concept that really frosted his hide. He was a seasonal ranger among those holy sandstone arches in the 1960s, before the place was paved and dressed up for Easterners to blow through in an hour. But now I'm hurrying too much, trying to cram all of Abbey into a few fragments. I can feel him over my shoulder, sharp eyes looking through sun-scarred face, talking softly and slowly in his clench-jawed, rural Pennsylvania patois, suggesting I get the hell out there and bloody my shins on some desert escarpment instead of sitting at a desk trying to be erudite. He knocks out pipe dottle and wanders off, once more unto the breech of the true wild places where he spent his life.

If he seems like an unpleasant, ill-tempered, petulant varmint, that's because he was. But he also championed landscape that couldn't speak for itself, and helped move green consciousness forward in increments that never seem to be enough. I admire his effort, but hate the way he just vanished into the wild for however long it suited him, to hell with jobs or marriage or commitments or any of that stuff.

As a married, full-time desk lackey, I pay attention to that stuff. Blame it on a stout upbringing, or some such debility. Although I don't have kids or pets to fawn over, I still stare out an office window, caught like a dung beetle in a specimen jar, and wonder how Abbey pulled it off, impulsively disappearing from polite company most of his life.

I guess he sometimes didn't pull it off, and that cost him. He wanted us to believe he spent all his time alone in Arches, a one-man soiree in the park, picking Kleenex flowers off bushes, pulling up survey stakes, bantering with chucklehead tourists, and rhapsodizing under the twinkling stars while listening to coyote. But he wasn't alone. He shared a flimsy ranger trailer with his wife and child, who never appeared anywhere in *Desert Solitaire,* a book he wrote about his experience. (He wanted to call it *Desert Solipsism,* the story goes, but somebody, maybe an editor, thought the public would be terribly confused if not scared off by 'solipsism,' a word that could cause widespread malaise and economic ruin if printed in a book title.)

So no, he didn't always get away with it. His solipsistic and gleefully misanthropic habits were not entirely bereft of human contact. Which proves absolutely nothing. My own wife will not appear anywhere over the next few pages, even if I go off on a lark to pick abandoned twisty ties off some lonesome trail, then become famous when I write about it.

I met the desert rat just once, at a now-defunct bookstore in Fort Collins. He was signing books. He looked drawn but not yet quartered, a tall guy in a worn, long-sleeved shirt, beetle brows regarding us legions of admirers with comfortable, detached amusement. He was out of his element, but he had a job to do, shilling his latest screed. Which of his books did he sign for me? I can't remember. I can't remember what I said, either, but here's the faithful rendering, the fictional truth of what happened:

Admirer: "How are you enjoying Fort Collins?"

Abbey: "Very well, thank you."

Admirer: "Had a chance to go hiking at all?"

Abbey (scribbling *Keep on wrenchin'* in a book): "No, not really."

Admirer (retrieving book): "Oh. Well, Thanks."

Abbey: "You're very welcome."

But then Abbey sees some spark, some longing in Admirer, and calls him back. Abbey stands up, announces he'll return in a few minutes, then vanishes for two months with his new friend on an excursion into high desert places uninhabited since Paleoindians mucked around building irrigation canals and storing corn in sun-baked, mud-brick granaries tucked at the bottom of 900-foot sweeps of sandstone.

I just hauled out all my Abbeys until I found the right one. The book he signed was *The Fool's Progress: An Honest Novel*, and he included the date below his name, November 3, 1988—mere months before he died. His script is perfectly legible. That means a lot to me. Illegible scrawl belongs to wazoos with big egos.

I guess I'm having trouble revisiting Abbey because his life cuffs me upside the head with proclivities I wished I'd had when I was young. Can't call it "free spirit" because I hate that fucking cliché, but he had the chutzpah to spirit himself out of town and through baking sands of missile test ranges, off limits to any living creature great or small. There he was, trudging along, hiding behind hoodoos while jets swooped past, dropping ordnance. Then he wrote about it, dismissing what well-mannered society requires of our lives, making us believe how 110-degree heat can be divine, how a creosote bush can tell you the truth if only you agree to lay your bones down to nourish its roots.

He was always looking for revelations in the desert. A favorite story is about a man and woman just married, out on a pleasant honeymoon drive. The man is distracted, though, by something only he can see, so he turns off the pavement onto a cow path, an abandoned mining track, a divot in the land, and keeps going, mile after mile, assuaging his increasingly unhappy wife that he just has to see what's across the next wash, that's all. Time after time the overheated car becomes buried up to its axles in sand. When they finally emerge back onto the asphalt, his wife makes him stop at the nearest town. She hops on a bus and never looks back, leaving him with the smoking ruin of a car he didn't even own.

I've come close to that same kind of indulgence, a self-centered flight to unreason—or reason of a different kind—but remain a neophyte compared to Abbey. It takes a certain panache, a honed confidence that borders on arrogance, to step into the wild for weeks or months on end and think you can come back out in one piece and pick up where you left off, making designer coffee in the morning before pulling on your clown suit and settling into a cubicle, wondering why the boss—we have a new boss?—is looking at you with a stink-eye fierce enough to wither the façade right off your plywood desk.

The longest I've managed to rattle around the Southwest at one stretch is not quite a week, six pitiful days, which isn't nearly enough time to lose your sense of self and replace it with some ephemeral Zen lightness of being, whatever the hell that means. But for years I fussed and stewed about reaching such a state, thinking I was missing some life-changing epiphany because I could never get Out There long enough.

Years ago I read an account of a man who, while hiking in the Southwest desert, found a moment of salvation in the form of an intact Anasazi pot hundreds of years old. The man—this wasn't Abbey, but could well have been—sat staring at the pot until he almost hallucinated. The exquisite, simple patterns and harmonious shape and antiquity of the piece spoke to him in a new language.

At least, that's how I remember the story. The man may have simply experienced a hefty adrenaline spike when he saw the pot, but still I wanted to be him. I wanted to struggle for miles through prickly pear and lost canyons until, dehydrated and bleeding, I'd stumble across a relic, maybe a whole village of relics, so intact, so perfectly preserved it would look like the inhabitants just left for dinner at a neighbor's. I wanted to stand in front of stone houses a thousand years old and experience the sensory overload of discovering cultural remnants lost to humanity until the moment I arrived. Then die and let buzzards recycle my body.

Not long after I read about the man and his pot, a friend asked me to join him for a week-long trip into Grand Gulch in southeast Utah, where the Anasazi, or Ancestral Puebloans, once flourished. I signed on instantly. Woo-hoo. Epiphanies, here I come.

Grand Gulch, a Primitive Area administered by the Bureau of Land Manglement, is pretty typical for canyon country: sandy, convoluted, wind-whipped, deep and towering, bathed in pastel lights of rose, red, orange, tan, and gray. Erotic, curved sandstone walls rise hundreds of feet from the canyon floor, exposing millions of years of erosion. Around 1,000 square miles of Southwestern high desert drains into Grand Gulch, creating, during flash floods, a wall of liquid sandpaper that rolls fifty-three miles from the canyon's beginning to its final pour-off into the San Juan River. After a flood, logs, cow bones, branches, mud, hikers, and boulders are left behind, stuck in trees and sandstone creases fifty feet or more above the floor of the canyon.

We descended into this labyrinth during a cold, dry Thanksgiving week. It was no mystery that some of the ancient dwellings still stood, and a depressing truth that lots and lots of modern lug-soled pilgrims visited the area, in spite of the relatively thuggish hike to get down into the canyon.

But it was exhilarating to hike through a jewel like that. Our boots scratched over frozen snow while trickling water chimed through hidden rivulets. I kept a close eye on horizontal fractures in the cliffs, looking for stone dwellings that, maybe, hadn't yet been found. In some ways, the ancient people formed complex cultures and practiced the kind of craftsmanship that's long been lost to our twittering, oblivious society, and I wanted to see clues of the loss for myself.

Excavations at the turn of the century had uncovered two distinct periods of occupation in Grand Gulch. The earliest were the Basketmakers, who inhabited the area from 200 to 600 A.D., building pit

houses with mud plastered over stick walls and roofs. The exquisite baskets of ash, willow, and fibrous grasses were woven so tightly they could hold water.

The Basketmakers were driven away from the area, possibly by drought (in the summer, this place can cook like a furnace), but their descendants, the Pueblo, returned and kept house between 1050 A.D. and the late 1300s, eventually abandoning the gulch for reasons that aren't clearly understood.

The Pueblo brought back to Grand Gulch influences from other surrounding cultures, including the Mesa Verde and Kayenta. Instead of baskets, the Pueblo made decorative pottery and cultivated corn, beans, squash, and cotton. Irrigation provided water directly to fields, and with higher levels of agricultural development came surplus crops. Those crops were kept in small storage rooms constructed with stone and mud daub to keep out rodents and moisture. The storage rooms represented a key movement from hunting and gathering to an agrarian society, which led to another important change in Anasazi culture, the development of the kiva.

Kivas, a term anglicized from the Hopi by John Wesley Powell, were round chambers built below ground and used for religious and secular ceremonies. Initially gathering places for small villages or extended families, the kivas became crucial to Anasazi culture as farming methods improved. The healthier the crops, the more people thrived in the area, which in turn created the need for ceremonies to cheer up the gods of rain and good weather so the next season of crops would be plentiful.

The first kiva we saw was at Junction Ruins, where Kane and Grand gulches met. We decided to stay there for the night beneath tall cottonwoods on a hard-packed site with an old fire ring in the middle. Another site twenty feet away was littered with empty water coolers, plastic pails, and heavy tent poles, most of the mess covered haphazardly with blue plastic tarps. Swell. A modern midden made of chemicals that may fragment over time but never completely decompose.

Not a full day into the canyon, and already the love-it-to-death syndrome was ramping up. I almost expected neon signs to flicker to life in the shadows, advertising souvenir gift shop emporiums. The sign I never saw: This Is Abbey's Country. All You Industrial Tourists Stay the Hell Out.

After setting up our tent, I stood in the weak winter sun and gazed across the wash at the ruins. From a distance they looked perfect, the stone walls puttied into the cliff as adroitly and securely as swallow nests. The ruins were on two levels, the lowest just thirty feet up a slope from the valley floor. The second level was perched higher on the cliff wall, tucked on a long, narrow ledge beneath a mammoth overhang. Kivas, living quarters, and granaries all were at the site. I gingerly walked up one of a half-dozen paths that led to the lower ruins, as if church service had begun and I was late.

But there was no need for caution because the spirit had been pretty much pummeled out of the area. Footprints were everywhere, all over the loose dirt of the hill leading up to the ruins and inside the dwellings. The three dwellings at the site had all lost their roofs and had been climbed over so much by visitors that stones were pulling away from the structures or scattered all over the area, making it hard to see where the bottom of walls emerged from piles of rubble. As a last resort, somebody had cemented portions of the ruins in an attempt to stabilize them, but it looked like amateurs had done the work.

Most flat rocks in the area had dozens of pot shards arranged on top of them along with small corn cobs, pieces of wood, small mammal bones, and ordinary flakes of sandstone that some hikers thought were artifacts. At least something was left—hard to know how many artifacts disappear every year. One BLM ranger later told me that, in the early 1970s, you could find sandals at Junction Ruins. Now you're lucky to find pot shards bigger than a quarter.

And so it went, footprints all the way down the gulch and up side canyons and down any surface that wasn't vertical. One evening while we were cooking dinner, a group of eight or nine backpackers set up camp around the corner from us, then decided to take a close look at nearby ruins. One tourist was determined to check out a higher level, but found herself stuck on a nearly vertical sandstone wall. She clung there, fifty feet above broken, sharp boulders, black spandex legs splayed, pink parka arms waving around for purchase. She kept insisting she was okay. A member of her group shouted, "You're going to run out of haaand hooolds!"

She finally scrabbled down, thwarted for the moment from finding her epiphany.

I kept fighting depression. Couldn't stop thinking about how our idiot species overruns the planet, sticking our runny noses everywhere, can't leave anything alone. And it only got worse the farther down the gulch we went, one small microcosmic example of what continues to happen all over the Southwest.

A few days later at another set of ruins, the same woman who tried climbing the wall strolled up to one of the kivas, exclaiming how beautiful it was. She set her camera case on the roof of the ruin, one of the few intact roofs left in the entire Southwest. She scampered around the structure, touching it here and there and everywhere, until something on a vertical stretch of rock caught her eye. Gilly golly! Is that graffiti scratched into the wall? She picked up a piece of sandstone and rubbed it vigorously on the rock. Genuine pictographs, exquisite works of art painted on the rock, were very close to the area she was earnestly scrubbing. Many of the once perfectly legible pictographs in the gulch have been worn away from constant touching, if not vandalized or removed altogether.

"I just don't know why people do things like this," she said, powdered sandstone falling from her fingers like sawdust, not having any fucking idea what she was doing.

"What is it?" somebody asked.

"Oh, a 'W' I think, I don't know, but it doesn't belong here."

On the way out of the site I passed another man standing in the middle of a kiva, shuffling around setting up a tripod, knocking dirt away from the base of a wall with his boot.

Later I asked the BLM ranger if there were

any areas that hadn't been touched since they were abandoned.

"Yeah," he said after a long pause, "but I would never tell you where they are."

"I know that," I said. "But they do exist? They haven't been touched?"

Another long pause.

"Yeah," he said.

"Have you seen them?"

"Yeah," he said, sounding far away, like he'd forgotten he was talking to anyone.

Toward the end of our trip, I wandered alone up a broad side canyon and discovered a remnant of Edward Abbey's spirit, that wily curmudgeon who should have been born an Anasazi, an Aztec prophet, a Comanche on the high plains. I should have been born his brother. Or a cousin. I'd wake him up and haul him out into the wild, alive or dead. The hell with epiphanies. Better to just find places worth getting lost in.

The canyon was nameless, not even big enough to rate a tweak on the topographic map. I don't know why I was drawn to the canyon, but our short trip was almost over, and the dreaded re-entry to civilization was just around the corner. I had only a few hours more to pretend there was no car exhaust at the end of the trail because the trail had no end.

The sun was brilliant on the overhanging stone walls, layer upon layer of compacted sand painted vertically with long strokes of desert varnish. Shadows created by the tilted winter sun were so deep my eyes hurt focusing from dark to light.

I ranged two hundred feet sideways for every fifty feet I climbed in elevation. Loose pieces of stone crunched under my boot, crumbled to powder, and ran like an hourglass down a seam in the slickrock. For long moments the silence was just how I liked it, so complete it was like something tangible, something to be held and admired.

The canyon steepened until I could find no way to go higher. A narrow bench cut through a wall to the right, and I followed its curving pathway until I had to stop.

A pinyon pine—a gnarled, stunted, sharp-needled, patchwork-barked master of the desert grew out of the scant soil where the flat bench met the dizzying sweep of sandstone. On the ground around the pinyon, a blanket of microbiotic crust, living layers of filaments holding the sandy soil in place, formed a rich carpet of dark nutrients, miniature towers of compact activity. Unlike so many other areas, the crust hadn't been cut with a dozen trails, hadn't been disturbed at all. No vandals had climbed up the cliff to deface it, no hikers had taken chunks of the landscape home in their pockets.

Shadows moved across the wall, enveloping the pine and its carpet. The sharp edge of wind smelled like snow, and the solo melody of a canyon wren fluted down from above like an aria. The Anasazi heard canyon wrens while they were firing their pots and building stone dwellings and grinding corn in their metates, and long after nobody is around to hear, long after the last stone buildings return to the sand of the river bottom, long after our own meager dwellings sag and fall and disappear, the wrens will still be singing.

A perfectly shaped clay pot caught my eye, but when I turned I discovered only the wink of a full moon, a relic of the deep desert sky, rising over the rimrock far across the canyon.

Drum Hadley

Hello Ed

hello Ed,
how the hell are you?
I'm sure you have stirred up something down there.
I know you think it's for the greater good,
and maybe it is.

Ed was an old friend of mine.
just before he died, he put me into one of his books.
I said "what are you trying to do Ed, ruin my credibility
with the ranching community?
Oh, well, you were thinking to simply stir the pot
dedicating your books to a few people who ask 'why.'

I got a call from you.
our relationship was made mostly of calls
all of those times
we spoke
together
telephones in Tucson
we usually talked about cows, horses, cattle, and gates left open.
you were against all of them.

you told of making love on the back of a pickup truck in June.
I would say 'making love,' I know you would say "the more corre
usage today would be fucking or fuck you."
by chance I happened to sit by your wife
on an airplane
going from somewhere to somewhere else.
you were blessed I guess by pretty women.

your old friend Doug Peacock came to Guadalupe Ranch
the other day many years ago. I liked his book a lot.
something about Vietnam

I heard that you were keeping up a post office box in Oracle
so that people would not be able to find who you are and
where you were.
you went down to the Pinacate desert country—
the stretching of the plains to the west...
always seeking selective solitude...

Keith Wilson said he used to eat lunch with you and
talk about philosophy.
poets dine on words.

You were not young Ed and
you were not nice.
you probably were not feeling very well either.
you came back from the dentist and he had told you
"you won't need to floss anymore Ed"
a dark humor.
you were tough and alive even as you were dying.

the power of a piece comes from the irreverence.
this life as you know, isn't a goddamn garden party.

you were a raven
cawing and calling out
across the desert.
you were a crusader of landscapes.
irascible.

I guess your friends came to bury you out west of Tucson,
I really don't know
I wasn't there.

now here we are
and here we are not
ever changing forms
one who has died
or is dying
and lives on
and so it is safe to say
everything and
nothing.

what and who will fill the gaps now?
in that sandy soil
carried by winds
away.

Heidi Blankenship

Finding Everett

Even if they were his bones
would it hurt
to leave them
tucked between dust
and stone,
his aching body
stretched out in the shade
of the only place
he ever loved?
All the lonely desert miles
pounded into
marrow's memory,
sorted into calcified fibers
rotting in a canyon's shadow.
There is a solitary place
for every individual,
in the moment before birth,
or the second of death.
Our bodies fade,
but the spirit?
What good would it do to shake
the ash of his energy
into the Pacific?
Let him be,
Everett or not—
let him disintegrate,
scattered by the wind
across the arid sea.

Jerrod Bohn

Parch / Dust

cactus spike under bloom-
thistle thirsts a needle-full
                    of water

thimble trickle scant enough
not to douse but root-soak
                    root out

        arid tangle
        leaching mud
        from crust

        lapping wren
        spit from stamen

spilt coyote urine stagnant
pools last spring wrung out
                    sipped

        most up again

Susie Martinez

Epistolary III.

(Deserts)

Foothill

rocks fast waterfall the foothill and those two behind the sage
bush drunk and dosed on reckless.
the girl, a flammable cherub. the boy's laugh lights her up. it
lights her all up when he shouts
at the prickles in his back.
grow a thicker skin she says him.
I am a desert creature. coming
home with twigs in their hair and chameleons
on their faces. exhausted every morning from walking that
dry sea into the light behind the hill. she speaks of it epic.
light nesting in sand.

Yucca

crimson road shelves gutter moans
byways rife with yucca spike spokes
and her father does not remember when her brother fell in
the memory sutured in her mother's fingers
pulling every thready splinter from his body wailing.

Mountain

she has been saving up she knows for here.
gowned in sand she sees an adolescence shrouded
in pearl but waves do not calm her furl. sand water only washes
ripples what dirt makes. she hovers
a mountain around a teenage bonfire. seen
in lichen light they watch her in reluctance
of cactus.

Rico Moore

Memory of a Birdsong
—*after Dan Beachy-Quick*

I'm thinking of Abbey's line—
a *blue-eyed Navajo bedouin* watches
water spill over a dam, centuries from now
& wondering—I'm wondering what
has caused me to inadvertently imagine a world

without the song of birds
                    our breath
a human breath
                    a birdsong

a beating heart which lulls our dreams
to sleep—a beating which does not always
peacefully cease, but many times, by the force
of another, or by the force of many others
who are the same one, erased

& there is a cadence through death
a flickering pulse   planets   stars & suns—

flickering hearts   birdsong
a wind for wings   we sing

in a language of birds. A bird sings
in a language born of breath and bird.
A song in breath which could fail a song

Silenced. A silenced world—

The Consolation of Birds

Non-Fiction by Jeana Steele Burton

Sitting on a rotting log on the bank of the slough, on the morning of my Grandpa's funeral, I looked up to see eleven pelicans wheel overhead. From where I sat, they were only W-shaped flashes of white with black-fringed wings, but I knew them. On the way to the church, I had seen a breeding pair cruise in tandem over the pond across from Grandma Maughan's house. The pair was so synchronized, so close, that at times they appeared as one bird. Now there were eleven of them, circling the slough. They looked like giant versions of the common terns that dove relentlessly into its waters.

Common terns weren't that common in Benson, Utah. Though Grandpa and I had been birders, his funeral was the first time I'd seen a tern—a sleeker, more graceful version of the ubiquitous seagull—outside of our dog-eared Sibley's Guide. Now, I watched two of them above the slough, winging in hard, hungry circles, yelping to each other, more like bird-dogs than birds. At an underwater sign, I could only guess at from the shore, the terns folded their wings close to their bodies and plummeted. Letting velocity and gravity spin their bullet-shaped bodies, they hit the water like crashing jets. I watched them come up empty-beaked after each stunning failure.

The sun came in and out of the clouds and I let the waters of the slough carry my mind further away from the church and what awaited me there. Staring into the distance, at a rookery of Canada geese, I could almost forget the reason for my being here. Two adult geese swam patiently with eight homely goslings, the sleek adults book-ending the wooly babies. The call of a redwing blackbird, that distinctive *konk-konk-LA-REE*, brought my attention back to the inlet. A yellow-headed blackbird harassed his redwing cousin from tree to tree, shore to shore, never satisfied with a perch once he'd taken it.

I had never seen this many different birds all at once, all in one place, not even in Benson where birds were plentiful. Was I hallucinating from grief? I rubbed my eyes, opened them to the feel and the sound of something whipping the air above my head—*whump-whump-whump*—like a small helicopter. I looked up to see the sun shining around the bodies of twin Icaruses. Human-sized beings, wings spanning seven feet, awesome and terrible, like angels in the Old Testament. They passed over me and descended to the island on the other side of the inlet. Now I could see – pewter bodies, crimson heads – they were sandhill cranes, close to six feet tall; their long-leg, short-runway landing a dance of near disaster. They made it through the cattails without upending themselves, then began to dance in earnest, leaping from the packed dirt bank, plié-ing like feathered Baryshnikovs, two beautiful males rending the chill air with their trumpet songs.

"Grandpa?" I asked, feeling foolish but feeling something. Every hair on my body stood on end and I had a sense he was there. A sense. Or a wish. I'm not sure which.

Silence, except for the sound of water and the cries of birds, which is not silence at all.

"Grandpa?" I said again, just to give whatever this was a chance to show itself.

"What are you doing down there?" boomed an accusing voice. The sandhills hid in a grove of trees on their island. I turned to see Mom standing at the top of the rise where the slough bank met the road.

"It's starting," she said, and turned to walk back to the church.

This is how this dream always starts. I am walking to my Grandma's house in Benson, Utah. I have to get to Grandma's right now. The sense of urgency is acute though without reason. Sometimes I get to Grandma's house but she's gone. Other times, I lose my way from Logan out to Benson and wander in sad circles. In this one, I am walking on the road that runs from my Great Grandma Maughan's house to my Grandma Steele's. On my left, Great Uncle Calvin's dairy farm. The black and white Holsteins chew their cud and watch me pass. Everything is as it should be until I see a condominium tower where my Grandma's white farmhouse used to stand.

"Oh, my desert," I say, stealing Edward Abbey's words, "Yours is the only death I cannot bear." It doesn't matter that Benson isn't the desert, I dream-think as I crumple and wail. Abbey would understand.

I awoke from the dream, looked around my bedroom in Fort Collins, Colorado, and laughed it off. High-rise condos in Benson. Right.

Later, talking to my mom on the phone I'd told her about this crazy dream of mine. I was doing the dishes while talking, looking over my little plastic Buddha on the windowsill to the field across the street. Buddha came with a houseplant I bought years before we moved to Fort Collins. I keep him to remind myself of what he knows. He's one of those fat Buddhas. In one hand, he holds a walking stick, in the other, a bird's nest. The nest contains a lone, precious egg. Buddha is smiling. I know little of Buddhist cosmology but I believe his happiness originates from and returns to the egg. When I do dishes and look out the window, over Buddha on his sill, to the fields and skies beyond him, when I see the blackbirds, falcons, ospreys, magpies, kingfishers and herons that are my neighbors, the birds my Grandpa Steele taught me as a child to know and love, I feel infused with the same happiness.

In the summer, when pterodactyl-like pelicans glide over the house on their way to Richard's Lake, I am suddenly eight years old again, crouching next to my four year old brother on the bank of the Benson marina, Grandma standing behind us blocking the wind, Grandpa crouching beside us holding his binoculars —the ones now sitting on the sill next to Buddha— first to my eyes then to Randy's. We didn't really need binoculars to see the pelicans, though. There were so many big white birds riding the small waves, like slow motion whitecaps, I had wondered how there was any water left, how they hadn't slopped it all out like when my cousins and I took play-baths.

Every year after, I made my Grandpa take me back to the marina, but it was never like that again; the pelicans' numbers dwindled, maybe from the delayed effects of DDT banned in 1972, so during some years of the 1980s, there were no pelicans at all. In the 1990s, when my Grandpa could no longer drive me to the marina, or even remember who I was, they'd made a kind of comeback. It was a comfort to see them gliding over the fields of Benson again, on their way to the marina; to feel that some things could change back to what they'd been, that not everything was inevitably declining, decaying, dying.

"That's funny you'd dreamt that," Mom said. "Grandma just told me they'd started to build an apartment complex on the field across the street from her house."

Funny? Tears came on hard and sudden.

"Oh no," I said. "No."

"I don't want to live another twenty years if that happens," Grandma told me, her voice breaking a little.

"Frankly," I said, patting her on the un-bandaged arm, "neither do I."

I was visiting Grandma in a nursing home in Logan, Utah. She was eighty-three years old but only a visitor herself, a temporary resident while she recovered from a heart-valve transplant.

Her surgeon had replaced her valves with the valves of a specially bred pig from Australia. "I don't usually do this surgery on old ladies," he told her, "but you're otherwise so healthy you could live to one-hundred-and-three!" This is what she would tell me, anyway, when I finally found the nursing home and made myself go in.

She would also tell me the apartment complex was scrapped. Now, there was talk of putting 1000 houses on the 500 acres. Benson residents—most of them, not including the old ranchers' grandkids who just wanted to sell out from under the tax burden—weren't happy about that and they'd put a stop to it in the courts, somehow. Logan was trying to annex Benson so the city could push the deal through, somehow. She wasn't sure of the legal details. But it was just a matter of time before the fields went under the yellow earthmovers' blades.

When I left the nursing home, I was reassured to see that downtown Logan looked the same. But once I passed the bowling alley, what used to mark the boundary between town and country, I was lost. Where there used to be fields and the occasional farm-related business, like the tractor lot, there was now a solid wall of strip malls. PetsMart, WalMart, Best Buy, Costco.

I was so disoriented I drove past the turn-off for rural Benson, and got half way into the next town, Smithfield, before I realized it. I flipped a U and headed back. Where the tractor lot used to mark the turn-off, bladed dirt awaited the next chain store.

Finally, on the right road, I hoped, I made my way out to Benson. There'd been a few businesses clustered around the airport but now there was an industrial park. That miniature strobing lighthouse that I, with a child's narcissism, used to think existed just to cheer me with its green red green was still there. But made obsolete by a modern control tower, it had fallen into disrepair.

Past the airport, the land opened up on either side of the road.

At last. I felt I could really breathe. There was the falling down barn that had been falling down as long as I could remember. The fields still looked the same behind their barbed-wire fences, bunched with sage, dotted with black and red steers. A magpie flew from fence post to fence post ahead of my approaching car. I looked to my left for my caterpillar—a stand of trees that on moonlit nights came to squirming life. This fabulous creature, created by a windbreak's shape, a car's velocity, and my child's imagination, had inch-wormed its giant way across the valley for years. The trees—I couldn't tell you what kind because they stood smack in the middle of this 500-acre spread—were still there, though one in the middle had died, cleaving my caterpillar in two.

The little grove of trees that marked the halfway point between the airport and Grandma Maughan's house had had its casualties too. One lone cottonwood clung to life in the dry streambed, which had once been lush with watercress and moss. The steep, shady bridge, which used to fling the car up and down so it gave you a carnival thrill, had been replaced with a regular stretch of road. There was no longer anything to bridge.

Just when it was that I burned the bridge between myself and the church, between my agnostic self and my large, religious, extended family, it's hard to say.

It was more disintegration than conflagration. Like a rope bridge where a slat fell out here and there, here and there, over the years, over the chasm between my desire to belong and my ability to believe, until it hung slack and useless.

But the land. This land awaiting the earthmovers' blades, I never stopped loving it, never stopped believing in its holy powers. They say you can't go back home but this land is my bridge back home to Benson, to its birds, to my family, to my earliest and most essential self.

These fields and the road running between them were the meridians I used to navigate my way back and forth between the poles of my known world: between my Grandma Steele's and Great Grandma Maughan's, between Benson and Logan.

I remember the thrill of walking to Great Grandma's all by myself when I turned five; feeling so brave, so big, not knowing until years later that I was being watched anxiously from opposing kitchen windows.

I remember driving between these fences on the morning of my Grandpa's funeral, back from Logan Cemetery to the supper the Relief Society ladies put up for us in the church gymnasium. I was twenty-five and it had been three long years since the last time I'd had the money to fly home from Arizona. Three long years living with a boyfriend who couldn't quite decide if I was worth his love. I felt the weight of those years lift from me as I watched my cousins, my first friends, Tracy, Trudy and Teresa, drive past Grandma Maughan's old house in Tracy's black jeep. We'd stood shoulder to shoulder at the family plot, brushing aside the spring snow that had fallen during Grandpa's eulogy, to read the headstones of our ancestors. Tracing the dates with my fingers, I felt the power of each eroding year.

On the drive back to the church, I looked at the fields, at the soil reemerging in brown shining patches on either side of the wet blacktop, all of it glinting in the comeback sun. I looked at the fields and at the road between them—the way that has always brought me back home—and I remembered where I came from, who I was, and what that was worth. For three long years, I had held myself hostage in that apartment, meeting the madman's demands, and then suddenly I was free.

As I drove farther in to Benson, I saw metal realtors signs jammed into the ground next to the wooden cattle chutes that jutted from the fence line about every mile. I steeled myself for what was coming. The subdivision on the parcel across from my Great Grandma Maughan's house. But it wasn't there. Not yet. I exhaled in relief that I knew was temporary. There were more realtors' signs than anywhere on the previous stretch. The red and black steers were gone. No spring calves would ever take their place.

I drove past Great Grandma Maughan's house past where ducks and geese used to sail over a ditch, on their flights to and from the swampy pond that lay beyond. Now there's a big dun-colored building where the pond used to be; it's made to look like a barn but it's full of brand new appliances instead of cows.

I drove to what used to be the old church but is now a grass lawn in front of the new church. I turned my back on the new, yellow-brick church and walked to the center of the field next to it, to what used to be the old redbrick church's gymnasium. For Mormons, whose temples are reserved for only the most solemn rituals, and only the most devout practitioners, the church gymnasium is the true axis mundi, the place for wedding receptions, family reunions, fund-raising carnivals, anniversary parties and, of course, church basketball games. Some Mormons have never set foot in a temple. Some Mormons joke that basketball is their true religion. And wouldn't you love the game too, if its court was the stage on which your memories played?

The church gymnasium, back before I grew up and grew my own ideas about God, was where I ran across the basketball court—my Sunday shoes clop-clopping over the lacquered planks in the most satisfyingly horsy way—to reunite with Grandma after our respective time in Sunday school and Sacrament Meeting.

I stared through the ghost walls of the old church to the parking lot where, on Sunday afternoons, my lapsed Baptist grandfather, smelling like the baked beans he made for Sunday dinner, parked the car and waited for Grandma, my little brother and me. We ran, yelling "Grandpa! Grandpa!" I had liked going to church with Grandma when I was little, but still, Grandpa had been our liberator, delivering us unto play clothes and Play-doh.

I walked across the road and down to the slough bank, to the spot I had seen all those birds on the morning of his funeral, to the spot where he and the other old men had taught their grandkids to fish. It was the place we'd seen the kingfisher sitting on a telephone wire. Now, I couldn't see a single bird. I could hear the distant call of a redwing blackbird but no bird answered in reply.

I turned away from the empty slough to stare at the new church, peering through all my memories and prejudices, trying to really see it.

Someone in an undergrad class at Arizona State once asked me what it was like growing up non-Mormon in

Utah and I blurted, "Like growing up in a POW camp." I think I stole that from comedian Roseanne Barr, who grew up Jewish in Salt Lake City, and who called the Mormons "the Nazi Amish." It came out before I could think, before I could explain I was more of an ex-Mormon, before I would realize that Benson, with perhaps the most Mormons per capita of any place in Utah, had been my refuge. It was Pocatello, Idaho, I was really thinking of, the place I lived from age eight to fifteen, a place, coincidentally, thirty miles from Camp Minidoka, where Japanese Americans were imprisoned during World War II.

At least once a month after we moved to Pocatello, my parents would drive my brother and me back to Logan to spend a weekend with the grandparents. From the backseat of our orange Blazer, I would see the "Welcome to Utah" sign on the border between Preston, Idaho and Richmond, Utah and happiness would hiccup out of me. "Yay, Utah!" I would cheer. I was eight years old. I could cheer without irony, without ambivalence. Because Utah was still my home. It didn't matter that I had a room, a bed, some toys and books in a basement apartment in Pocatello. Logan, where I was born, Benson, where my Grandma and Grandpa Steele lived, that was home.

The Blazer would pull into the parking lot of Sambo's café in Logan where Grandpa had his afternoon coffee. And the five of us would sit in the orange vinyl barstools at the long counter facing the kitchen, the Friday afternoon sun at our backs. Swiveling back and forth on our stools, savoring the soda pop we rarely got at home, Randy and I let the grownups talk while we read the Little Black Sambo mural, which spanned the half-wall half-hiding the short order cooks, like a giant comic strip.

Now I know the Sambo story is racist. But back then, all I knew was Sambo and the tigers chasing him around and around a palm tree were beautiful. They were luminescent; a word I didn't know then but didn't need to know to see how the millions of tiny "crystals" glued onto the mural magnified the colors. Little Black Sambo wasn't really black at all, I saw, sipping on my Shirley Temple, but Burnt Sienna, Raw Umber, and Indian Red, some of my favorite crayon colors. And the tigers weren't just orange but also Maize and Salmon and Goldenrod and black and striped in their relentless pursuit of the little boy who ran so fast for so long.

Around and around the palm tree he ran. Looking at the climactic panel, I could feel Sambo's terror tightening in my own chest. Sambo had his tigers. I had, in my new neighborhood, bullies, who rode their bikes around me on my walks to and from school; the bullies knocked the hat off my head, swatted the books out of my hand, and told me I was going to hell because I didn't go to church, like they did, every Sunday. My parents didn't go to church anymore; the only time I could go to church was with Grandma, in Benson. I tried to explain this to the boys but they didn't care. Every school day, every morning and afternoon, I faced the dreaded gauntlet. The soda straw slipped from my lips as I gasped for breath. Would Sambo escape? Would I?

While Randy and I were contemplating Sambo's fate, Mom would transfer our PJs from the backseat of the Blazer to the bed of Grandpa's truck, a big blue Ford with a white camper shell. Then she'd come back in and stand between Randy's and my barstools. Putting a hand on our seatbacks to stop us from swiveling, she said "Listen now, be good."

"Go," Grandpa said, waving Mom and Dad out

the door. "I've got 'em." Yes, go, I thought. Go now so Grandpa has time to give us a quarter for the jawbreaker machine before we go get Grandma from work.

Before Grandma got in the truck, Randy and I climbed out of the cab and crawled inside the camper shell that was open in the back. From where Randy and I sat with our backs against the cab, the arched white opening was a covered wagon's, just like the cutout our Benson ward Sunday school teacher patted onto the flannel board every Sunday. The white canvas cover ballooning up and out like bread dough rising in a pan, the single red ox a synecdoche for a team of four or six, through the miracle of static electricity, they stuck to the flannel all the while the teacher she told us how our ancestors had crossed the Great Plains, starving, thirsting, into northern Utah to found a new Zion.

Watching Logan speeding away from us, it was easy to imagine how those pioneer children must have felt watching the towns on the Mormon Trail—Nauvoo, Council Bluffs—get swallowed up by prairie. The pang of saying goodbye, again, to just-made friends and store-bought sweets, then the green, damp smell of the twilit Earth wrapping around you, prairie grass whispering consolations, prairie birds calling you on.

Redwings and yellow-headed blackbirds singing their sunset songs, flying back to their cattail nests, guiding me home.

I knew the way out to Benson as well as I knew the prayer Grandma Steele would say over our dinner that night of pan fried burgers and home fries.

Bless us oh Heavenly Father for this thy bounty we are about to receive may it strengthen and nourish our bodies this we ask in the name of your son Jesus Christ amen… flashing red and green airport beacon, falling-down-barn place, where the white horse died place, where I picked milkweed for my kindergarten caterpillar jar, thick ditch grass place where pheasants hide, far field where the windbreak caterpillar creeps, butterflies-in-stomach bridge, big cottonwood hawk's-nest, field, field, cows, cows, Grandpa Maughan's field, Grandpa Maughan's cows, Grandma and Grandpa Maughan's house, Benson ward. Home. Sweet. Safe. Free. Breathe. Birds. Home.

The morning after visiting my Grandma Steele in the nursing home, I drove out to Benson again. I pulled into the lot of the Appliance Barn across from my great Aunt Chris's house, which I still think of as Great Grandma Maughan's, though she willed it to Chris a decade ago. It was just after dawn, my car the only one in the lot. I walked past it, past the realtors' signs and out into the field to say goodbye.

I grab the metal "No Trespassing" sign for balance and limbo under the barbed wire threshold. I have driven and been driven past this field a thousand-thousand times and now I am standing in it. From here, I can see how the fields of Cache Valley are a green bowl in the blue mountains. This field is the bowl's flat bottom. The irrigation ditches are dry and the ground is dry and cracked beneath my feet. The feed grass has died away and weeds have taken over. But even this field's weeds are beautiful to me. They are Spring Green and Burnt Sienna, Raw Umber, Indian Red, Maize and Salmon and Goldenrod, they are thin, bushy, or nubby; some have pink and purple flowers. I crouch down and press my palm to the warm ground. I want to lay face down, spread eagle. I want to break the hard ground with my fingernails, my toenails, my teeth. I want to cry. I want to make mud from my tears and the land. I want to smear it on my face. I want to scoop it in my mouth. I want to eat it up, the whole field: dirt, weeds and all, as if that would let me keep it the way it is. Instead, I look up, wonder who might be watching me from distant kitchen windows, peering through binoculars, asking themselves, "Who is this stranger?" No one, not even my Aunt Chris, would recognize me as the church-going girl I once was. I stand up. I close my eyes and imagine the field's past, all those who loved it before me: the Paleolithic people and the Native Americans; and my people, my great-great-great-great-great grandparents, who were the first Caucasians and first Mormons to settle in this valley and who took it for their church; the first ranchers who bought it from the church; their great-great-great-great grandkids who're selling out because they can't make ranching pay what the developers will. I open my eyes and try to make my peace with the field's future. I vow never to slit my eyes at it as I drive by it on the way to the slough. I vow to love it, no matter what, through the houses. And then I get back in my car and drive.

Back in Fort Collins, I'm doing dishes again. But there is the consolation of Buddha, of looking past him to the field and canal beyond; there is the consolation of birds. I have seen pelicans, magpies, herons, and hawks. I have seen osprey kamikaze into the shallow water and fly over the house with their catch. I have grabbed Grandpa's binoculars and shouted, to him, to myself, "Did you see that!?" The carp's gills were still pulsing. You could see the spots on its smooth belly, the grain of the osprey's rough feet.

Today a kingfisher perches on the telephone line, a scissor-beaked, big-headed, short-bodied, blue and black and white bird. Before we moved to Colorado, I had seen only that one, perched on the telephone line above Grandpa's fishing spot on the slough. Grandpa

and I had had to look it up in the Sibley Guide. Maybe they too, like the pelicans, had been decimated by DDT or the nitrogen run-off from Benson's farms. I remember how that lone bird looked upon us, how it let us behold it, with a stillness and a solemnity that made it seem something more than real, like it had punched a hole through the flimsy curtain of illusion just to show us real.

I hear the *beep-beep-beeping* of the yellow earthmovers clearing another field, one upstream on the canal that runs behind my house. I hate them. Not the people, as Seldom Seen Smith, the Mormon river guide, emphasizes in Edward Abbey's novel, *The Monkey Wrench Gang*. Not the people who buy and sell the land, or the people who build the houses and the strip malls, not the people who drive the machines but the machines themselves. They are scooping up soil, grass, and milkweed; they are sawing down cottonwoods, elms, and willows. They are "mitigating" the wetland, allegedly preserving it, but only making it a fishbowl with an asphalt rim. They are scraping and gouging. They are killing everything in their path. Everything that hasn't already fled. Of course, I grieve for the birds first, but also for the bees, bats, deer, fox, mice.

And they are doing all this to make way for a new grocery store—the largest in all of Colorado!—across the street from an older grocery store. They are doing this to "revitalize" our cross-the-tracks neighborhood. For this, I hate the machines. I hate them although I agree the neighborhood could use some revitalizing. I hate them although I'm sure I'll find myself, months from now, standing in the condiment aisle, standing on what used to be a shaggy , lovely little field, bordered by trailer parks.

This wasn't "virgin" land, not majestic land worthy of a conservation easement. The field's grasses, weeds and trees had grown over the ruins of a demolished motor-court motel. Before the motel, the land had been farmed and homesteaded. Before that, it had been, coincidentally, the site of one of the earliest grocery stores in Fort Collins. I found a photo of this one-room country store in the Fort Collins archives. Only back in the 1860s this wasn't yet Fort Collins; the city wouldn't annex the land for about a hundred more years.

What had already been lost was easy enough to find in my research. What I was really looking for, what I couldn't find online, in the library, or talking to my biologist friends, was what would be lost. What, exactly, were we losing by paving over this suburban wilderness the city had declared a "blight"? I couldn't find a definitive answer. The answer is we don't know. We don't know just how much oxygen the plants exuded, or how much carbon and other toxins they absorbed. We don't know exactly how many creatures they fed and sheltered. We don't know how many pollinators, seed carriers, insectivores, scavengers, and decomposers we subtracted from our ecology. But we do know — I and my neighbors who mourn the passing of this field — we know it was a living thing and now it is being entombed in a concrete shroud.

I hear the *beep-beep-beeping* of the yellow machines and I hate them.

I feel them shaking the ground as they move it, scrape it, blade it flat. So does the kingfisher. It flies off, beak and belly empty of fish. When they've finished building the grocery store and the strip mall it "anchors," where once there was a field, will the birds come back? Will I still need Grandpa's binoculars on the sill?

As a little girl, I had loved the story of Joseph Smith's first revelation as a prophet. I loved looking at the illustration the Sunday school teacher showed us of him kneeling in a grove, every leaf on every tree illuminated by the pure gold light of God.

But I never did feel what the Young Women's teacher told us we should feel when we prayed to God to help us choose the right, "a burning in the bosom." I couldn't stop laughing at the image of my bra bursting into flames. Even my devout friend Karen cracked up over that one. But Karen clearly felt something I didn't.

By the time I turned twelve, I was having a hard time believing that God and Jesus had actually appeared to a guy in the woods of upstate New York in 1820.

By the time I turned thirteen, I was having a hard time believing that God and Jesus actually existed. Maybe it had something to do with learning about the Holocaust in the seventh grade. Maybe there's a "faith gene," something you have or don't have that makes you look at a history book, those Rorschach blots of humanity, and say "God," or "No god."

Whatever it was, I stopped going to church.

I started going to the Pocatello library, stalking its dim aisles for my spiritual path. And when we moved to Arizona, I stalked the aisles of the Mesa library, the Barnes and Noble, metaphysical bookstores that smelled of strange incense and dusty Persian rugs. I studied and considered many 'isms: Catholicism, Protestantism, Deism, Judaism, Hinduism, the Celtic paganism of my pre-Mormon, pre-Christian ancestors.

The only 'ism that rang true for me, was the only one I wished was false: Buddhism, the revelations of a guy who sat in the woods of upstate India in 528 B.C. Nothing lasts. Everything changes. Attachment leads to suffering.

My husband, Matthew, and I moved from Arizona to Fort Collins in 2006. It was 110° F in Phoenix when we left. The drive through northeastern Arizona and New Mexico made us even thirstier for the green we knew awaited us in the Rockies. And the mountains did not disappoint. They were cool, pine-scented, majestic, all of that. But when we drove out of the mountains and onto US 287, past Denver, past Boulder, Berthoud, Mead, out to the rolling green fields of the northern Front Range, that's what really took my breath away. I beheld a vast quilt of fields tilting up to the mountains, and I said, "It looks just like home! Just like Benson!"

If we need to go far from Fort Collins, our home now, we take I-25 because it's faster. I love I-25 because it runs parallel to 287 but on a raised roadbed so you get a panoramic view of the yellow plains, the blue mountains, the patchwork of fields. I hate I-25 because it takes you by all those signs. All those realtors' signs —AVAILABLE 340 ACRES—their posts pounded deep into prairie or farm land, land so beautiful that to contemplate losing another acre to yet another strip mall, yet another housing development, is, literally, sickening. I get so upset, so sick in my stomach, that I have to remind myself to breathe. I have to remind myself that I don't own this land. I have no control over it. It's not yours to worry about, I tell myself. But I don't believe me.

In my desperation to assuage this feeling of dread, of sin, really, this feeling of standing idly by and watching the murder of a loved one, I need something transcendent. I try to remember something from the books I've read on Buddhism. But reading about Buddhism and being a Buddhist is not the same thing.

Buddha, meditating under his tree for forty-nine days, found nirvana, the absence of greed, hate and delusion.

Sambo found peace by climbing his tree, by looking down on the tigers chasing nothing, chasing nothing, chasing nothing until they churned themselves to butter.

What I've found are words in books. Signs and signifiers attached to nothing but empty sounds.

I say them to myself: nothing lasts, everything changes, attachment leads to suffering.

It doesn't help.

I hate the big, yellow machines and I, now, understand Abbey's anger toward them so much more than I did when I was fifteen, when I heard him rail against them at a reading he did at Idaho State University. This was only a few months before my parents would move me, against my teenage will, to Arizona, to the desert that I learned to love by reading the flaking, paperback copy of *The Monkey Wrench Gang* that Abbey signed for me.

Learning to love the desert is signing on for heartache. Learning to love any piece of land is signing on for heartache. I didn't know this at fifteen and that's why I didn't understand how Abbey felt. I thought of Abbey often during the twenty years I lived in Arizona; I thought of him as I watched those inexorable, yellow machines devour farmland, orchards, and finally, the desert that used to separate city from city. I was glad Abbey died when he did, before Phoenix ate 400 square-miles of his beloved desert; witnessing that would have cleaved his tough old heart in two. The saguaros' supplications could not stop the machines. Nor could the cries of those people who, though they never owned the land, felt it belonged to them. Ground was broken. The federally protected saguaros were relocated. Asphalt and concrete were poured and then more workers came pouring in, framers, finish carpenters, plumbers, electricians. Then the realtors and the buyers and the strip mall developers. By the end, by the time I decided to move, I understood Abbey's anger and the deep sorrow it masked.

I remember what the machines did in Arizona, and I fear for the farmland and orchards and grasslands separating the cities of the Front Range.

I have learned to love this land and sometimes wish I had not—especially when coming back home to Fort Collins, cresting the northbound rise on I-25 between Johnstown and Loveland. It is a place, coincidentally, called Buda. I love this stretch of land because you can see for miles. The plains to the east furl out, each undulation a quarter-mile-long; and the plow-swaths have cut the wheat stubble this way and that, striping it like a giant flag. The grassland to the west plateaus then folds on itself, secreting little arroyos; only their treetops give them away.

To the north, a calico of farmland and vacant fields, pocked with realtors' signs. Farther north, farther east, yellow grasslands; a Canadian mining company owns the mineral rights, is slowly sawing through some legal red tape. It won't be long before they're boring for uranium.

I love this land.

But it's not mine.

I am sick of loving land and losing land and mourning land that isn't mine. I don't want to go through it all again. I have willed myself to hate this land so that losing it won't hurt.

It's not working.

What used to work was lying in bed at night, lulling myself to sleep with the thought: At least Benson is still the same. What used to help was walking that road in my mind, past the fields in my mind.

But when Logan annexes Benson, when the city gets its way in court, houses will sprout in the fields I used to think of as mine. And what will assuage my grief then?

Houses will cover the fields where, for now, birds hunt the weeds for bugs. Houses will sprout lawns; lawns fed by the ground water that, for now, flows into the Bear River watershed, water that, for now, flows into the Benson slough. The slough, in dry years, will end up as parched as the ditches that used to run alongside the road that used to run alongside the fields that used to take me to my Grandma and Grandpa. When my Grandma dies, which she will, she will, a year from now or twenty—when the birds have all flown away—where will I call home?

Jane Miller
—*from THUNDERBIRD*

CONSCIOUSNESS

There's lightning by firing of eyes

    thunder by flapping of wings

& a massive shadow of hubris

    having no feathers but smooth skin

& wingflaps of nearly transparent

    lugubrious membrane

crashes through a universe of thorns

    two cowboys fire rifles but the legend disappears

rumors persist

    of a big dead bird nailed to a barn

with a mighty span unfurled

    & several men posed under it for scale

Dorothy Burk

After the Hunt

In the low rushes where the grouse was caught
it has a name they do not know that speaks
to the sage and the juniper berries,
to the breeze and the mother of the wind;
un nom de guerre to suppress the sort of attention
that has gotten him taken.

To think that a whole long parade of breaths,
a seamless string of organic interactions has totally ceased
in these few moments is absolutely absurd
but it is well known in these parts
that invested effort can come to nothing
in the long-shot moment of fate.

In the low rushes where the grouse was caught
silence prevails in the evenings where once
names were chittered in the foliage with affection
between this and that mortal little bird;
someday things will swing back
to the unspoken language.

TO THE SECRETARY OF THE INTERIOR

Dear Secretary Salazar,

Here in your home
state Colorado
polls show the population
largely in favor of reintroducing
the Gray or Timber Wolf to our
mountains. I once wrote
that I hoped my children would live
to hear the wolf howl some day.
Word has it you are working to
remove the wolf from Federal protection
and hope shortly to delist it
from the Endangered Species Act.
This leaves as you know wolf
management in the hands
of ranching interests, and as a federal court
noted, does bypass proper scientific
study of whether the Northern
Rocky populations are viable.

I want to suggest
that should you remove
protection, and many of Idaho's wolves
disappear under the guns of mid-level bureaucrats,
we request the Teton Lakota rename
their winter month 'Moon when the
wolves used to run,'
and petition the Farmer's Almanac
to delist January as Full Wolf Moon—
they could rename it Moon of
Political Payback,
Aerial Gunning Moon
or Full Moon of the Rancher's Lobby.

Thank you.

Andrew Schelling

Helen Skiba

Sky Burial

> *I was neither*
> *Living nor dead, and I knew nothing*
> *Looking into the heart of light, the silence.*
>   - T.S. Eliot

I have thrown the horses out and watched them drown.
There is no wind. I throw everything out.
Where are you, my love?

I throw everything out! Tongue, teeth, eyes, out!
Witness the sharp stick of me, stripped spine of me.
I bare my body of this thinking. I eat of the dry pine,
plow the earth under with the dry pinyon pine.

I throw out the words and the pages. Purgatory
has no language but the sweeping breeze.
Ever do the dark shapes turn their unspeaking circles.

A storm of sunlight is set loose upon me.
I lay what is left in the shadow of the rock
where blue grama will graze my wrist
like another wrist:
I surrender
you are with me—

You are so mute and naked, bearing such broad black wings!

Matter 14 Animal

Seeking fiction, non-fiction, poetry, photography, collage, and other ephemera.

Fiction Contest: $5 reading fee/ $250 prize. 5,000 words or less.

All submissions due 15 October 2010.

Send to:
Wolverine Farm Publishing
PO BOX 814
Fort Collins, CO 80522
or:
mattersubmissions@gmail.com

More info: wolverinefarmpublishing.org

Kelsi Vanada

Beef Cut Diagram

mother on a ladder painting the barn in her bikini,
great-grandfather red, shaking his tongue (it isn't seemly, a scandal
for the cattle?) This rusted spoon a bone poking
the skin of the land, for other artifacts it's too soon to tell.
These fences were made for shorter cattle, today's steroidal beasts
engender hours of 'fixin fence,' an occupation for only
muscular of men—or WANTED, women with an extra upper limb,
if such exist. Little wonder my uncle is dead, his specialty
the old-fashioned pregnancy test; he never felt
the same about his arm. Our freezer forever stocked
with white-paper bundles of rock-meat
I closed my eyes to watery blood stains on the wrapping, and became
an expert on motherly love at twelve; my heifer laid on her calf—
an unfortunate loss of three hundred dollars, I was told.

Detritus

Fiction by David Gilbert

The visitor dipped the cup into the algae-bottomed cow tank, beneath the rusted windmill, and drank. The water was hot in the low August sun, clear, and tasting of green life; he felt the water fill his chest, and now some of the place was in him. The water in the soil, in the bodies of the cattle distant across the sagebrush, in the steel tank – he shared it with them. The slow repeated shriek of the windmill's rod scraping its housing was the only sound.

Over the cricket-loud grass the visitor opened the unlatched door of the abandoned house and stepped in. The floorboards groaned at his steps. Inside was frozen chaos, tempered by fragments of humility. A few of the kitchen cabinets were open; a few porcelain dishes remained intact, covered in mouse droppings. Others were shattered on the floor. Tumbleweed branches filled the sink, and the gleaming gas oven was wrenched from the wall. Yellow wallpaper peeled and curled. A small table sat in the corner with a single aluminum chair. The last person to sit at the table had made sure to push the chair in when they rose.

A black leather recliner, facing the tall window, was the sole furnishing of the living room, with its yellow carpet and once-white walls. A tall fireplace, with some of its bricks fallen to the floor, dominated the far corner. A swallow's nest was bunched above the front door.

From the living room could be seen what must have been the master bedroom. On the turf-green carpet sat a large porcelain sink, and a toilet – lifted heavily from their fittings, only to be dumped ten feet from the bathroom. Light filtered softly into the bedroom from the boarded-up window.

A sharp gust blew the front door crashing open, and the visitor stepped outside. A barn, two small sheds. Surrounded by high grass was a light blue station wagon with its roof split open by some improbable force. Breezes whished through the dry grass and creaked the sheet metal doors of the sheds. Nothing slowed the wind as it blew from the west toward a line of low, sandy bluffs to the east. To the south a dry gully was guarded by a dead cottonwood tree.

A line of cottonwoods stood in front of the house. How pleasant, to have stepped outside in the morning to this line of trees, quaking with leaves over a small lawn. Now they were broken and dead, with heaps of leafless limbs piled at the base of the trunks. Their remaining limbs clawed at the sky. Against the side of the house, a small concrete enclosure marked the descent into the crawlspace, now choked with wiry raspberry vines – bright and heavy with ripe berries.

The visitor stepped back inside and pulled one of the tin bowls from the kitchen cabinet, and with his shirt wiped the grime from it. He brought the bowl outside to the raspberry vines, and began gently plucking berries and placing the berries in the bowl.

The bowl was in the home to hold food, he thought. The berries had been planted to be eaten.

He picked most of the ripe berries, about half a cup. He stepped through the back door and into a small dining room. On the wallpaper, outlaws on galloping horses brandished rifles, stagecoaches pulled up to saloons, and cowboys lit cigarettes. Punctuating the scenes was the repeated smirk of Butch Cassidy, across a dozen posters announcing the five-thousand dollar bounty for the robber. Behind them all was a map of the Wild West, with favored outlaw hideouts highlighted.

He went to the kitchen, pulled the chair away from the table and sat.

This chair was for sitting in, he thought, the table for putting meals upon.

He stared into the wallpaper as he put the berries in his mouth, one by one, and puckered his lips. Looking into the dining room, the cowboys seemed to come to life in the warm glow of the setting sun.

The bowl was empty; he replaced it in the cabinet. He walked through the living room and out the front door. In his arms he gathered the fallen limbs and branches of the cottonwoods, and brought them inside, where he laid them in front of the fireplace. He cracked them one by one over his knee, and placed each forearm-length log into the fireplace. He lit a match, and blew it out. He held the smoking matchstick just outside the fireplace, and watched the wisp of smoke be pulled into the chimney. The flue was open.

Wadded in the corner of the room was a sheet of butcher paper, which he placed under the logs and set aflame. The dry wood crackled and sparked, and before long, was ablaze. He dragged and swiveled the recliner to face the fireplace.

The recliner was for lounging, he thought, and for watching the fire.

Flames danced, and as they died he occasionally rose to place more wood atop them. For hours he watched the flames, as their dim orange glow lit up the walls with prancing shadow figures. Cobwebs hanging from the ceiling swayed in the warm air. Occasionally the wind would blow the doors banging against their moldings, but otherwise the house was silent, save the crackling of the burning logs. Mice scurried back and forth along the walls. The room filled with a tender radiance.

Slowly the visitor drifted to sleep.

Glowing coals and small blue flames were not enough to keep the room heated, and he awoke. The darkness was encroaching, the small cocoon of warmth and light had shrunk to the few feet immediately in front of the fireplace. He stepped cautiously into the bedroom. Long slats of wooden lath dangled from the ceiling, and with loud cracks he broke several from the joists. He snapped them into arm-length pieces and placed them in the fireplace. The blue flames nipped at the strips of wood, and the fire consumed them.

He stood in the front door and pissed in the soft dirt. The cottonwoods stood silhouetted deep black against the night sky where blazed the whole of creation. Their high branches clasped the galaxy above. Chirps came from the cricket-grass, and the dirt road, across the cattle guard and the barbed-wire fence, scraped onto the prairie, lay silent.

The recliner and the fire beckoned him back. He fed the fire a few more strips of lath, and squatted to watch the flames eat them. He backed into the recliner, and slumped in its swaddling warmth. His mind drifted, and the crackling of the fire became hushed. Again sleep tugged at him.

Deep in the long night, bobbing along the dirt road, framed in the window, was a pair of lights in the distance. Silently, they slowed and turned gracefully across the cattle guard and came to a halt just outside the window. No car was attached to the lights, and they swam in midair with a rippled plasma glow.

One followed by the other, the lights elongated and undulated, and floated toward the window, brilliantly illuminating the trunks of the cottonwoods and the dry grass beneath them. They floated through the window, and between the visitor and the fireplace. The orbs swirled slowly through the room, as if examining their surroundings. He heard a dry crinkling, and turned his head to see the paint chips that littered the floor floating upward and replacing themselves on the wall, like jigsaw puzzle pieces, each in their place, until the wall was a uniform white. The lights swooped to the floor, and the fallen bricks of the fireplace wobbled upward through the air and back into place.

Rising to meet each other in the middle of the room, the lights coiled around one another like snakes, then drifted apart. Gliding through the air, they went separate ways. One floated into the kitchen, the other into the bedroom, and disappeared around their respective corners.

Sudden sunlight punched holes in the planks nailed over the windows before ripping them down. Pebbles in the carpet vibrated, and rolled up the walls and out the windows. The toilet and sink scraped across the floor and installed themselves in the bathroom floor, their bolts whirring into place. The cabinets in the kitchen swung open, welcoming to the dishes which were reassembling themselves in midair. Glass shards fused themselves into panes and filled the window frames.

In the fireplace, logs were flaming now and started to stir. They were toppled, and from underneath them a low table used its legs to struggle free. It crawled from the fireplace and walked across the room before halting in a corner. The components of a bookshelf inchwormed through a hole in the floor and assembled themselves upright against the wall. From unseen hiding places, dozens of books fluttered and flapped toward the shelf like pigeons coming home to roost, and aligned themselves side by side.

On the kitchen floor, the mouse droppings emanated from every nook, and rolled together in a heap on the linoleum. Familiar shapes began to form from their writhing mass: sticks of butter, bottles of milk, cartons of eggs. With millions of unseen flagella they crawled into the yawning refrigerator and settled in place.

The visitor turned to look into the bedroom, and his eyes followed a wide white sheet as it floated down onto a crisply made bed.

The sheet was guided by the hands of a short, pale woman in a flowered house dress. Over her face was a funeral veil.

She left the bed and walked into the living room. Through the veil, he detected her worry and fear. She paced to the stairs leading to the single upstairs bedroom, and opened her mouth to shout to the children the visitor knew were playing there. He couldn't understand what she was saying; though her lips moved as if she was speaking, what he heard was like the static between radio stations.

She moved now into the kitchen, hunched and sighing. She opened the cabinets and acted as if she was pulling cooking pots from them, and though her hands pantomimed the form of pots, her hands were empty. She placed the invisible pots on the stove and struck an invisible match to light the burners. The visitor watched her from behind, as her squat, stocky form moved about the kitchen, examining the labels of invisible cans.

The front door squeaked open, and in stepped a tall farmer. His age was hard to determine; his face was sun-worn and wrinkled. His mouth hung open. His eyes scanned the room worriedly. He panted as he stalked toward the kitchen. The farmer's flannel shirt was in tatters, and his back was lined with wounds. Some open and bleeding, others dirty and closing up. The lacerations continued down his arms, deep enough in places to expose bloody muscle. He shuffled into the kitchen, where he removed his baseball cap to kiss the woman smartly on the lips. She turned back from the brief chore of the kiss to her cooking, and opened the oven door to check the progress of an invisible loaf of bread. The smell of baking bread wafted from the oven. The farmer looked at the chair, and finding it already pulled away from the table, plopped his weary form down. He glanced back to check the progress of supper. The woman still shuffled about, stirring invisible soup.

The couple spoke in whispers, still sounding like radio static, and their eyes repeatedly scanned their surroundings, nervous and suspicious.

Just as the woman began to pantomime setting the table with invisible plates and silverware, the walls began to warp.

The farmer and the woman sighed, apparently resigned to this inevitability. In the recliner, the visitor glanced at the front door, and back to the kitchen, and the couple that only a moment ago had been preparing for supper had become a heap of bloody clothing, sticky with blown dust.

Outside, the yellow sun that had wrenched the boards from the windows now dove for the horizon, and impacted the plains with a colossal crash. The house shook, dishes fell from the cabinets, the paint chipped off the walls, bricks fell from the fireplace. Swooping in from the two side rooms came the two glowing orbs, which now spun in circles through the room with a mad fury, ascending to crash into the ceiling, where they were dashed into a splatter of tiny droplets, like mercury.

All around the visitor, furniture collapsed and broke to splinters. The toilet and sink were heaved angrily back onto the floor of the bedroom. Through this cacophony, he was gripped with the fear of intrusion. Soon the house was returned to its familiar devastation. The fireplace, which had fallen dormant, now sprang to life with chipper flames.

And again there was silence.

In the recliner, panting, his heart beating fast, the visitor took time to calm himself and still his shaking hands. The fire burned even and friendly, and outside the crickets chirped once more. Before long, mice cautiously sniffed the air, and tiptoed forth to resume their hunt for morsels.

Out the window he saw a smudge of gray on the dawn horizon, growing and warming. Slowly a layer of pink was added to the soft gray smear, and the stars faded one by one. Sounds became muffled, and his eyes shut. Sleep enveloped him once more.

Mid-morning. The visitor awoke curled in the chair. His eyes opened and returned to focus. The sun was high now, and the house was growing hot. The fire had long since gone out. He stood, stretched. He knelt before the fireplace, and blew on the white ash. Flecks of ash swirled around his head, and he sputtered and shut his eyes. Once more he blew into the dust, and stopped when he had exposed a layer of glowing red cinders. He pulled the front door shut on his way out.

Sergio Ortiz

Dead Willow

There is a straw mattress
full of bedbugs under the dead willow,
where the tears of every whore
in the city are as open as red hibiscus,
the only place left to wait.
We go our separate ways,
and when we reach the train tracks
we pick up a few rocks to throw
at the racemes of trouble hanging
in the meadow.
Our Feet,
undefined wanderings
of a bite,
pulse like the pupils
of a hundred virgins.
And we know
there is a mystic
in the ordinary,
the cut grass.

The Potter's Field

Fiction by Maximilian Werner

After the rain had quit, the boy left the aspens, under which he sat with a shotgun and a nearly headless rabbit, and he strode through a field of alfalfa that wet him to his belt. Slung with a length of twine, the rabbit swung side to side over his shoulder. In the cool air, barn swallows gave way to bats as the dark bloomed. All about him the grass was pocked with horse droppings. A coyote's howls crossed the matted weeds and tunneled through the rotted trunk of a long fallen tree to where the boy laid out the rabbit, and with his eyes and feet he hunted for wood in the outlying darkness.

On the edge of the field white box-hives stood together in the grass like the burial markers of many generations, and in the wind's interims the drone of sleepy bees came to the boy's ears and the ears of a dog that looked like it had been living hard. Drawn by the sweet and salty smell of blood, it sat rigidly in the flickering light of the boy's young fire. The boy then drew from a sheath on his hip a buck-knife that threw firelight into the leaves of a branch that hung overhead. He took up the rabbit by its hind legs. In the cool night he could feel the last hints of the rabbit's warmth on his wrist. He laid the rabbit in his lap like an unctuous scarf and it made a small pool by the toe of his boot.

As the dog looked on, the boy piled a load of damp wood on the fire, then sank the knife just below the rabbit's skin and ran its length. A sough of air from the rabbit's left lung where the knife pierced it rose like an anti-soul into the smoke of the fire. The boy then tore out the organs and flung them to the dog. Earlier the boy had walked through an orbweaver's web and now its silk glistened on his face and his clothes steamed.

He sat looking like some strange suborder of this world as the dog lay before him in the grass, filling his slender belly and growling even though the animal at the fire gave no sign that he would have it otherwise. In a low voice, the boy told the dog as much, and he pulled the rabbit from its damp integument. In the full glare of the fire, its pink and densely muscled body resembled a humanoid that had come into the world all wrong.

After the boy fed on the rabbit, he left the fire and the dog and trod toward the river to drink and wash. The sky had cleared and the moon's high and lowlands shone with equal brilliance, and its light ran on the water and on the painted backs of three Appaloosa horses that stood many hands high in the grass across the river. The boy drank long and deep. He could taste the silt and stones over which the river flowed. The piquant smell of wild mint, clover, and drying hay steeped the brume that lay upon the water and in each mouthful he could taste some of that, too. Even in that dark he could see a brightly banded caterpillar drifting down river like nothing else in this world. After it had passed, the boy turned his eyes upriver as if waiting on another and there, in a pool that whirled against the bank, the head of a drowned colt turned. He said shit and spat. Then he climbed the stony bank and walked back toward the glow of the fire.

The dog had not moved. He lay in the wet grass panting and watching the boy poke and build the fire into an ample light. The crickets made little of the night. The boy pulled up the collar of his slicker and bedded down beside the fire to wait on the arrival of his brother. Across the moon, a band of frayed and discolored clouds. The land still except for the long grass along the tree line that parted as if through it something were walking. But no eyes to happen on that place would find any reason to believe it.

Ursa slept and dreamed. From the knoll of soft ground upon which he stood, he saw three figures foot a cattle path that severed a grove of Russian olive trees. Their faces were ashen within their hoods and they moved clad in black gowns with such languor it seemed they were strangers to sleep. Above him both the moon and the sun. No wind through the trees. No sound but the sound of gowns being torn from the frail bodies of the walkers who, from out of the trees, emerged hairless and naked and wild-eyed. Before them sat an infant with a face so strangely composed that it could not be deciphered. The figures gathered around the infant in a wretched parody of the moon and in the amber light their bodies seemed to sweat a violet fog in which the infant was enshrouded like an obscene jewel.

Crows cawed, roosting in the trees like macabre fruit. The boy heard his own panicked voice calling his name from the din, and it was as though that voice had risen from deep under water. Toward it he walked the way mourners walk toward an open grave. The nudes looked upon him in expectation and they parted before him as if he were kin and they were mere attendants to the imbrued creature that sat in the dust. The boy looked into their vacant faces. Then he turned to the infant who had been watching him and he threatened to pick it up and take it who knows where. In a flurry of black snow, the crows quit the trees and drifted overhead. The infant tried to stand and run but could not, and he turned his back on the boy and went down on all fours like the animal that he was and crawled out of sight.

The boy looked to the figures as if for some instruction but they were gone. He followed the infant into a stand of ancient pines whose canopy was impaled with shafts of light.

In the dimness the infant crouched on hands and knees. The boy heard its catlike pants in the shadows long before he set eyes on the eyes looking back at him. "Ursa!" The boy turned and sought the body of the voice behind him, and he waited until it seemed the darkness alone could claim ownership. Nor could he hear the infant's breathing now; when he stepped to search it out the dank humus of the forest floor gave beneath his feet and his eyes fell on a figurine interred to its waist in the loam.

As the boy pulled the doll from the earth to better study it, the ground made a small sigh in which he could smell something old and not to be bothered. The doll was carved of wood and wore a top hat and its face was soft, white and sunken as if nothing were beneath it. When the boy looked on this visage he screamed, and as if wise to the boy's horror the doll's eyes widened and it opened its mouth and mocked him until it seemed the doll alone were the screamer.

II.

High on the mountains crowns of aspen burned in the dawn. As if autumn's currency, or messages sent to the still-green world below, red and yellow and orange leaves rode down the dark and sleeping river. In the sky a ghost moon and a few pale stars and spiderlings drifting by on their web balloons. Where Cider stood he could see a group of does drinking up-river, and though they were entrusted to the fog, the deer did not drink long, and one by one they returned to their covert of riparian growth. He reckoned they would stop and browse once hidden, but they did not. He listened to them go until they were gone and then made his way to where the river widened and was shallow enough for him to cross. There, fresh cow pies like smoldering fires and the river still turbid where cattle had walked.

Though four years Ursa's younger, Cider stood a full foot higher and was made of a heavier timber than his brother. The sun had done to his face what strong wind does to water. He made short work of the river even with his load. In the mud his tracks together with the tracks of many mammals and birds interlaced like vestiges of a saved world or afterlife where there was no fear and no blood to be lost. A few steers lingered and watched Cider cut up-river along the arterial path that led to his brother. Then the steers turned and lowed at the sun rising over the mountains.

Ursa's hair and the grass in which he slept were covered with hoarfrost. Judging by the color of the matter beneath the nails of one hand fallen out from under the blanket, Cider rightly reckoned his brother had not gone hungry. He shed his pack and with a stick stirred the ashes of the fire to articulate any coals that still burned there. Finding none, he pulled a folded sheet of paper from his pocket and he tore it into strips and piled them together with small sticks in the ashes. Cider then took a saw and a ball of twine from his pack and moved off through the field toward a ribbon of trees left alone for the sake of shade and demarcation.

There everything slept in rehearsal for the coming snows and in the stillness Cider could hear leaves falling and hitting the forest floor. Fallen about him were young trees a beaver had felled and from the breaches in many of their slender trunks the sap still flowed. He parted and bundled a tree that had been dead awhile and stuffed his pockets with wood chips fallen around the tree's stump. Through a clearing Cider saw that Ursa had awakened. He shouldered the bundle of wood and made his way back to his brother's camp. Before he was well within hearing, Cider called out and Ursa raised a closed hand and then opened it as if to say he had caught his brother's greeting and was now returning it.

The brothers spoke little as they prepared the fire and the morning meal. Cider spread the wood chips he had gathered over the coals and upon the chips he set a cast-iron pan. While the pan heated, the brothers ate goose-jerky and got warm sitting between the fire and the sun. Ursa rolled a cigarette and laid it on the toe of his boot to dry. "Damn I'm hungry. What all you brought to eat?" he asked. Cider winked at him and with one hand he gave Ursa his own last two cuts of jerky and with the other he pulled a cutthroat wrapped in paper from his pack. "This is what all," Cider said. He held the trout out with both hands and with his thumbs brushed away a few leaves and blades of grass that hid the fish's stippled markings. A string of roe coiled around his finger and he held it over the pan and slid his hand down the silky belly of the trout to empty its contents.

Cider told his brother where to find the bread as he gutted the trout and scooped the last beads of roe from its body. Deboned, the fish sizzled in the pan and turned from orange to pink, a splayed and smoking flower, and the boys lifted the sweet flesh from its skin and put it in their mouths. Ursa moved the pan to a cooling-stone between him and his brother and they finished off the trout and sopped their bread with tender beads of blackened roe. "You see a dog when you come up this morning, skinny lookin' mutt, yea big?" Ursa asked, lighting his cigarette with one hand, showing size with the other. "Nope," Cider said. "Thought about havin' Dime and Slowdee kick along with me though. Thought 'nah, dogs wouldn't be worth wakin' Rance.' You think he wake and he wake." "You done right Cide," Ursa said, nodding. "I's surprised he wasn't up before me, the way he been huntin' you lately and all that. Surprised I got out of the house without him beatin' me to it. He been goin' crazy. Won't sit with mama. Shit, Ursa, I know the man's sour as pipe-rot, but what in hell'd you do to get him seeing red?"

Ursa looked out across the field. "A dog sit up with me last night. He didn't fuss, didn't do nothin' but lie right over there the whole night. Shared a rabbit with him. Wonder where he's gone to. Fire's hungry. Toss on some a that wood," Ursa said. "Snows'll be comin, Urs. How long you expectin' to stay out here?" "I figured I'd go hole up at the autumn house when the weather make me. Place's still got the one good room there in back. Got a roof. Between you and the river, I'll eat alright. What'd you catch that cut on, anyway?" "Deputy. You want a couple?" Cider dragged his hands through the wet grass and dried them on his pants. He then rose and walked the few feet to the pack. Returning to the fire, he opened the pack wide and from it he took a box of shot-gun shells, four cans of beans, a tin of hashed beef and a tightly rolled blanket. And from his coat pocket he produced the two flies, which he placed into Ursa's hand.

"The beans and such oughta get you through til you can scare up some fish or somethin'. I seen a clutch-a turkey when I come through here the other day. They fast," Cider said, shaking his head, "real fast." "Yeah, they fast. But those fat bastards cain't outrun no shot," Ursa said, studying the flies. "Real trouble is's that they're smart. They know you're huntin' em even before you actually huntin' em. So there's that. Can't have no thoughts about em whatsoever until you're lookin at one in your sights," he said, pointing a shot-gun made of air. "Spose that sounds right. Well, I got to get on. Rance be expectin' me shortly. He knows I don't use no time fishing after the mornin' hatches. I'll see you out at the autumn house in a couple a days. . .let whatever this is settle down a bit," Cider said, rising from the fireside and stretching his long arms into the sky.

"Appreciate you comin' out, Cide. You get the mind to go moon-fishin' you let me know." "Alright, then. Couple nights from now we'll go. Me and them fish will give you an education," Cider said, raising his eyebrows. "You know I need it. But we'll see who learns who, specially if the moon's got anything to say about it. River's a different animal then. What you know of it in the day don't apply at night." "Yeah, well, moon ain't never said much to me. I'll take your word for it though." "Wish you wouldn't. Ceptin' these things here, words's all I got left." Cider looked as if he could not decide on what to say and he shook his head three small shakes as he grabbed and slung the pack over his shoulder. Ursa pressed his cigarette into the earth and put what remained on the cooling-stone. "You don't need to say nothin', Cide." Cider toed the dirt. "Yeah, well, I got to get on."

He took the path his brother had made through the field the night before. Ursa did not watch his brother go. He gathered up his things and rolled stones and stood over the fire, and he doused the last flames with a deep yellow rope of piss. Columns of stinking and ice-colored smoke billowed about him, and like some novice magician's failed act of teleportation, when the smoke had cleared Cider was all but two strides from disappearing into the trees.

III.

Spent from the full-summer sun, Ursa climbed down from the apple tree with his half-bag of fruit and he leaned both it and his back against the dark and worn hip of the tree's trunk. Over the whine of pomace flies swarming some rotting fruit Ursa could hear Cider humming and his ladder knocking in the branches of a tree farther down the small orchard. Fainter still he heard Rance's work-a-day curses. Dime and Slowdee were sprawled atop a mound of packed dirt on the edge of the orchard; so intent were they on watching some hidden thing across the field they did not rise when Ursa forgot himself and called to them.

If all that were sour in the world had a voice it was Rance's. Each time that voice made the sound of his name, Ursa felt sickened and certain that somehow he was being killed by it. Ursa rolled his head around the tree and looked down the orchard and he saw Rance's pale face framed by the leaves like a baleful lantern. "Whachu doin' sittin' there like these apples 'ready been picked?" When Ursa did not respond to his chiding,

Rance cussed, and as he climbed down the ladder several apples dropped from his bag and made small thuds on the earth below. "Damnit boy, I'm gonna knock you on your brain-pan fer makin' me come down there." Ursa felt weakened by the sun and the heavy smell of apples, and though he knew he should, he could not rise.

Cider watched Rance empty his apples into a crate and walk toward Ursa. He figured this meant he wasn't that angry, and he tested his theory by calling to him. "You seein' any rusty apples on your end?" Obscured by the leaves, only Rance's legs could be seen. "Well hell no, an' you better not seen none neither . . . trees've been sulfured three times in three month. Damn. Don't tell me you got rust up there." Rance took off his hat and beat it against his thigh. He walked beneath the tree to where he could see Cider. "Well, I don' know. Take a look at this one here." Cider leaned from the ladder and dropped the fruit into Rance's hand. Rance mumbled and studied the apple. "Ah shit, boy, this aint rust. Wipes right off. It's pollen." Rance looked up at Cider for an explanation. "Like I said, I didn't know. If it was rust, figured you'd wanna know about it," Cider said. Rance shook his head and smiled meanly. "Boy, your pa didn't learn you too well did he? If you can't tell the difference 'tween rust an pollen, maybe you'd better jus stick to loadin'. But I reckon youd fuck at up too." Rance took half the apple in his mouth and chucked what remained at Cider. The apple struck his calf and left a moon-shaped stain on his pant leg. "God damn." Cider was more surprised than injured, which he feigned by rubbing his calf. "God ain't got nothin' to do with it. He stay clear of this orchard. Like I told im to."

After Rance turned his back, Cider looked at Ursa, and when he saw that Ursa saw him he winked and made a contorted grimace. Ursa swallowed his laugh and looked up at Rance. "Look at chu. You look like a heap a dead weeds. Git yer ass on up to the house and get us somethin' to eat." Ursa pulled himself up using the tree and he slogged toward the house. Once he had cleared the orchard the dogs rose from their piling and followed him at a distance and he could hear them panting and Rance hollering, "An check on your mama."

Inside the house was cool and dark save where mid-day light shone through curtained, south facing windows. It smelled of molded wood, night-sweats and drying fever herbs, dust, dirty dishes and a week-old bouquet of elephant heads, bog-orchids and yellow monkey flowers that Cider had gathered for his bed-ridden mother. Ursa walked lightly to the icebox and from it he took a pail of lemonade. As he drank, silver threads fell from his mouth's corners. He could feel the liquid loosen his tongue and wash over his insides and down his neck like a penetrant rain. Having drank too fast, he was about to give it all back when he heard a muffled cry from his mother's end of the house. He listened for anything forthcoming. Then he swallowed hard to keep the rain in him, and he poured what remained into a cup and walked to his mother's room.

Ursa stood outside her door and listened to her breathe as if she were submerged in mud. When he opened the door he saw she had slipped half-way from the bed. Her gown was bunched to her waist and her stomach was gibbous with sunlight. He had been watching it rise and fall for what seemed like a long time when a bark came in through an open window and startled him

back into the room. He placed the cup of lemonade on
the bed stand and saw that her stomach shined with a
dew-like sweat. After he looked into her face and saw
that it slept, he ran his hand over her stomach as if
to dejewel it. He then wrapped his hands around her
nearly deer-sized ankles and lifted her legs back onto
the bed. As he pulled her gown down, he spoke to
her in a whisper. "Brought you somethin' cool to drink,
mama, right here," he said. "You ain got no business
trying to get up. Me and Cider will tend to you til you're
well again." He looked her over. "Your gown come up,
mama. Don't worry, I'll cover you. You thirsty? Want
some lemonade?" But she lay there as if between two
worlds and did not stir as Ursa covered her.

Over places where sweat lay, her nightgown sank and
darkened until her body looked lunar beneath it. Ursa
studied each dark patch. The contagion had wrought
nothing on her body, still brown and firm and soft as
packed dust. Outside a bank of clouds blotted out the
sun and when the room darkened Ursa rose from his
mother's bed and walked to the window. In the air the
smell of dust and rain and rain-laden sage. Hair-thin
needles of lightning striking hills to the south. Ursa
closed the window and latched it and returned to his
mother's side.

Her eyes had opened. When he moved over her to see
if those eyes saw he smelled the odor of shit. "Damn,
mama, you messed yourself," he whispered. He went
to the kitchen to get some water and rags. Sara felt the
warm mixture beneath her and a breathy wind chill her
damp places, and though she wanted to rise, she could
not, and she lay there like a soiled and goose-fleshed
effigy of the damned.

Ursa drowned the pail in an open cask his father built
the summer of his death, and he took rags made from
a pair of his father's pants and he walked back to his
mother's room. He lit a candle and its light faltered as if
it were not sure that it should be there. Once the flame
steadied, he placed the pail of water on the foot of the
bed. Again he spoke to her in a whisper and he told her
what he was going to do and not to be afraid and he
slipped the straps of her gown over her shoulders and
worked it off like a slough. Ursa dampened a rag and
rolled his mother on her stomach.

A dark rill had formed beneath her. He wiped it as
best he could from the sheets, and even in the dimness
he could see small gold hairs that shined like marigold
pollen on the small of her back. Her skin was smooth
and placid, yet the soles of her feet and hands looked
like they had lived much longer than thirty-four years,
and when Ursa poured the lemonade like some freakish
nostrum between her legs her toes curled and those
hands seized the sheets, and did not let go until the
pouring ceased.

He tore a large rag in half and with it he wiped away
feces and lemonade that had puddled in the creases
of her buttocks, and as he did so his mother made his
name. When he asked if she were awake she did not
respond. If that sound meant he was doing wrong he
could not tell, and he paid it no mind as he turned her
on her back and lifted her leg up by her ankle and rested
it on his shoulder where her pale and supple calf hung
as though it were filled with milk. The skin of her inner
thigh reddened where he had run the rag across it, and
thinking the cloth too coarse, he wet a corner of the
sheet and set to cleaning the rest of her.

157

So absorbed was he in the sound of his own and his mother's breathing he did not hear Rance enter the house nor open his mother's door. Rance was on him now. He took Ursa by the hair and yanked him off the bed. He would not let go. He kicked him in the face and stomach and shouted some maniacal obloquy and Ursa knew the man was going to kill him. He looked up long enough to see how Rance stood and when he saw that Rance faced him he punched him squarely in the groin. Rance made an animal sound and dropped to his knees and he held himself with one hand and Ursa's hair with the other. Ursa spun around and planted his hands on the floor behind him and he put his boot to Rance's head. When Rance reeled back from the blow, Ursa broke free and dove like a crazed and bloodied bird through the window-glass.

Cider sat whittling beneath a tree on the edge of the orchard. He heard the glass breaking and saw his brother pick himself up from the ground and move at a broken run across the field. The dogs saw him too. They did not recognize his gait and the hair on their shoulders rose and they bolted toward him through the knee-high grass. Cider called to them and Ursa cast a sidelong glance and saw the dogs coming for him. He yelled their names lest they keep mistaking and tear him asunder. The dogs began to trot but they were still growling. Seeing this, Ursa slowed to a walk and called to them as calmly as he could. When they had come within twenty feet, they raised their heads to smell him out, and recognizing him they turned and headed back toward Cider. Ursa whispered sweet Jesus and moved off toward the river.

The dogs approached Cider proudly. He took them

by the hispid scruffs of their necks and held them for fear they would bolt again. "Where you headin'?" Cider yelled. Ursa slowed and hollered. "One of two places. . .you know em both." Cider's brow furrowed and he turned and walked the dogs toward the house. He looked at the window through which his brother had flown and there, framed by the broken glass, was Rance. He was breathing heavy and blood from a cut above his eye curtained half his face. Then he slumped like some miscreant deity who had just made himself a world he was now too weak to live in.

IV.

A horizon of pines stretched like a saw-blade in the gloaming. Beyond them, a meadow and a house sullied with bullet holes and fire and time. Ursa moved toward it and on either side of him the wind fussed in the blue-black grass. Shaggy mice sat watching on their haunches in their autumn coats. A pair of red finches broke from their bower and flittered overhead in the moribund light. Though the door was unlocked, it would not open, and Ursa followed a well-worn path until he came to a wall in which there was a man-sized hole. He passed into the house, and while it seemed he had been there before, he could not remember when, and he walked into a large room whose plaster walls were wavy and yellowed from soot and water.

Glass from the room's only window was gone, and in its corner there was a web in which hung the twilight husks of many insects and small copper leaves and a young bird that by its colors seemed the offspring of the kind he had seen outside. The bird's bright wings were wrapped thickly to its sides, and like a knife-blade, its beak was folded into its breast feathers where it could do no harm. As Ursa studied the gray art that enshrouded its head, one of the bird's dark eyes opened and looked at him. He took a step back and heard someone walking the floor of the room above him. He saw that he had no shoes and that his teeth were falling into places where he could not reach them.

The room in which he heard the walking was lit by a fire that could not be seen, and where the roof had once been there was now night sky that wheeled overhead. Ursa looked about the room for some sign of the walker and high on a charred ladder that leaned against the wall he saw his mother climbing. Her hair was white and frail as ash and her skin shined like sulfur-rich coal. When she neared the place where the ladder vanished against the night she turned and looked down at Ursa. "Come with," she said. He looked at the ladder and back at her. That ladder won't hold me, mama."

V.

The full moon rose with the setting of the sun. It had been up for some time as Cider quietly packed his things and climbed out his window by its light. Behind him he could hear the house settle in the cold. He walked to the far edge of the yard where the dogs were tethered to an old spring-tooth harrow that was bushy with long dead grass. As he neared them, the dogs let out a low whine from somewhere under the harrow and, trailing their ropes behind them, they crawled out with ears flat and tails between their legs. They each licked his hands as he reached to untie them.

Cider held Slowdee by the loose skin above his neck
and he ran his hand over the top of his head to check it.
The dog winced and broke from his grasp. He spoke to
the dog in soft tones and got him to come round again,
and he got down on his knees and held the dog's head
with both hands and turned it to the light. As he studied
the mouse-sized welt above the dog's right eye, he said
damn. That Rance had beat him good. Cider whispered
to Dime and the dog walked cautiously toward him. In
the clear crisp light he saw that the dog's jowls were
still crusted with blood from the pig he'd killed hours
before.

Rance had won a duroc hog on a bet, and when she
farrowed for the first time it was like she was dying.
The dogs heard the ruckus and they broke from their
pen and charged the farrow stall that Rance had thrown
together with old two-bys and chicken wire. Bristling,
the duroc rose to meet them with a piglet hung half-way
out her backside that made a small, dark grammar to the
world and the get that lay below. While Slowdee barked
at the sow, Dime snuck round and he broke through the
slats of the stall and snatched a piglet that had already
dropped and began to devour it. The duroc heard its
squeals and then nothing. She turned and looked at
the dog finishing one of her young, and lest the dogs
kill them all, she began to cannibalize her litter and had
eaten two before Rance could come and do anything to
stop her.

Cider let Dime loose and rose from the cold earth that
wet his knees. He looked back at the house for some
sign of Rance's waking. There was none. He turned
and lead the dogs toward the tree line to get them out
of the moon's light. There he bucked off his pack and

fished a stone from inside his boot. The dogs paced and whined a little ways off. Cider softly told them to hush as he urinated on a hoof-beaten patch of scrub oak. He then shouldered his pack and walked the seam that ran between wood and field toward the autumn house. Slowdee and Dime trotted around to the scrub oak and pissed where Cider had, and when they caught up with him, they slowed then bolted ahead. He called to them in a strong whisper, but they paid him no mind and soon they were gone from his sight.

The air was cold and sharp and the few clouds overhead drifted east. When he reached the head of the woodland path, Cider stopped and listened for the dogs. He heard the flutelike sounds of bog toads and heard stones rolling in the river that flowed farther off. He moved quickly through the dark band of pines and crossed a small field of cattle-cropped grass on whose far corner the autumn house was built. For the fifteen years Cider had been in the world the house had been abandoned, and except for the north wall where in daytime the sun did not show, it hosted vines that hid and heavied its rotted timbers. On the roof a mulch of leaves from as many autumns rustled, and where a branch had fallen there was a hole through which moonlight and leaves and weather fell.

Within a few yards of the house, Cider called to Ursa. When no answer came, he called to the dogs. He scanned the tree line. When he saw that they were not forthcoming, he climbed the front steps whose soft planks sagged beneath his weight. Mud nests hung like hives in the nooks above, and from them steel-blue swallows darted as Cider lifted away the door and walked into the house. Again he called to Ursa and heard nothing but the tick-ticking of mice and a small wind sounding through the house's many breaches and glassless windows. The house grew darker as Cider made his way to the back room. By what light ran thinly across the floor, he could not see, and he lit a candle and followed it into the room.

In the corner a pile of sticks and an upturned wheel-well of a tractor filled with ash. Cider eased the pack from his shoulders and held his hand just above the coals and felt no warmth. He walked with his candle to the other side of the room where Ursa had spread his blanket. There he lit three candles that Ursa had placed on the floor and he squinted at their flames then looked away while his eyes adjusted to the light. On the wall Cider saw distorted forms and pieces of words scribed in coal. He could not even guess at their meaning. Outside the moon was directly overhead and its light erased the stars and deepened the shadows of trees. Figuring Ursa had gone to the river without him, Cider left the house and took the path that lead there.

He passed a woodshed on whose door hung a bovine skull and farther down what may have been a pen or familial necropolis made with aspens that looked silver and swollen in the light. The path ran into a band of trees that stood between him and the river. In there he heard the muffled growls of dogs. Cider stopped at the top of a knoll down which the path descended, and below where that knoll ended was an ax-hewn clearing whose shore was lined with a rotted cord of wood. Against it he saw Ursa's slumped and silent form and a dog Cider did not recognize stood over him and its hair was raised high and it growled at Dime and Slowdee as they circled around him. Cider yelled at the dog that guarded his brother. It turned to him and its teeth flared in the light and he saw that its face was damp with blood. He continued to yell and clap his hands but the dog would not scare. He picked up a stone and hurled it.

When it struck the dog's backside, he whirled around to meet his attacker. He saw that nothing was there and he backed over Ursa's body and watched Cider and the other dogs. Cider searched the trees and he found a heavy pine branch, and with it he walked toward the dog, shouting and striking trees and bushes. Distracted by the noise, the dog did not see Dime and Slowdee coming, and when Cider was within a few yards, Slowdee nipped the dog's spine and together they drove him off.

Ursa sat on the ground with his shotgun resting longwise and upward between his legs and his head was savaged in the back and had fallen to one side. Where blood did not chart it, Ursa's down-turned face was stone-gray, and it glowed with earthshine. Cider crouched down in front of him and he repeated the Maker's name. Ursa's mouth was filled with congealed blood that flowed out like some strange libation for a defunct god, and it dried into an orb as if Ursa wore a small dark apple around his neck.

The dogs had returned from chasing the stray and Cider looked at them and saw that their faces were also bloody. He screamed half-crazed curses and took the shotgun from his brother's lap and fired. Both barrels of the gun were empty and Cider threw it at the dogs like an ax. The gun did not strike them, but they ran back into the trees and they did not try to approach him again. Cider returned to Ursa and he asked him what he should do and he pleaded with the corpse as if he knew the language of the dead. Said there was little chance their mother would recover, but that it was still a chance, and whether his death would destroy it, Cider did not know, and could they wait on telling her until she grew stronger, and would that be alright, brother?

The moon was now low in the western sky and Cider took Ursa by the wrists and pulled him up onto his shoulders. He carried him through the trees and across the river toward the plot of ground where their father's body was buried. There Cider used his knife to hack away a grave and he worked the night to get it done by dawn. Cider tended to his brother's clothing and he spat on the cuff of his shirt sleeve and wiped the dirt and blood from his face that the river had not washed away. He eased Ursa into the grave and lay the shotgun carefully down on him and covered his face. When he was interred, Cider did not pack the earth. As if one day his brother would wake from this sleep.

VI.

Westerlies had turned late autumn rains into snow, and if not for the burrow holes of pot-guts and black weeds the snow could not cover, it would have seemed as though no autumn or other world had ever been. As if the snow were the warmer blanket, Sara rose from her bed late in the night and walked barefoot out into the yard and lay down beneath the stars. Rance found her the next morning before the sun had risen, and where her body was not covered, her skin was frost-blue and her eyes were open and glassed with ice. He walked back to the house and jarred Cider from his sleep. "Yer ma quit us in the night. Get up," Rance said. "What in hell. . .mama what?" "Get yer boots on and meet me in the yard."

Cider did not weep as they worked. When Sara was freed from the earth, Rance insisted they carry her to the barn where her body would stay cold until they could get it buried. Cider looked back at the house and then at Rance. He bent down and slipped his arms beneath his mother's knees. Rance raised the latch and pushed the door open with his shoulder, and they muddled through the dark toward a packing table at the rear of the barn. They laid her down the table's length and Rance lit a lantern that hung overhead. In its light she looked wall-eyed and wore a strange grin. "Shut her eyes," Rance said, and he walked out of the lantern's light.

Cider did as he was told and he listened to Rance fumbling and cussing in the dark. When he returned carrying an apple crate, his face was red and shining with sweat. Cider looked at the crate and wondered out loud if his mother would fit in it. Rance stared at him as though he had asked if the moon would fit in the sky. "Hell yes she'll fitn it. Now git up to the house and git her some clothes." The dogs sat outside the barn door, watching, and when Cider approached them on his way back from the house they slunk off.

To his chest he held a linen dress and a pair of deerskin shoes his mother was wont to wear in spring. He walked into the barn and placed them on the crate. Her body had begun to thaw and from it wisps of steam rose and disappeared. Rance eyed the clothing and gestured to

Cider to come to the body and together they got her dressed. Sunlight fell on them now through the open door, and when he saw that she would not fit, Rance said damn and that he wasn't buyin' no coffin and he shoved Cider toward her feet and told him to lift. They walked her over the mouth of the crate and lowered her in. Lengthwise the crate was too short and Rance rolled her on her side and bent her knees and he lifted the crate's lid into place and held it there.

"There anything you wanna say," Rance asked, 'cause me, I said everything already." Cider watched his mother's face in the shallow light. He made a small prayer. But like some newfangled apparatus found in a dream, he could find no way to use it. Rance nailed the crate shut and from the barn wall he took down a pick-ax and shovel and leaned them on the crate. He looked at Cider. "Going into town. Got to tell someone should anyone come wondering." Cider stared at the crate. "You got any sense at all you'll get started on that hole while the weather's with ya," Rance said, banging the mud from his boots. Cider took up the tools and bore them on his shoulder. He walked out of the barn toward the nameless bone-yard where his brother and father lay.

"Where you goin with them tools?" Rance barked. "I'm going to our plot," Cider replied, "like mama wanted." Rance's face reddened. "Not by my account," he said. "She's my wife. Where she bury is my decision and no one else's." "That's shit and you know it," Cider said. He let the tools fall into the snow. "You can dig your own damn hole to hell or anyplace you see fit but she ain't goin in it." "Damn you, boy." Rance rushed out to where Cider stood and he picked up the tools with one hand and took Cider by the arm with the other and he walked him hard across the yard to the end of the orchard. There Rance dropped the tools and pushed Cider down. "Boy, if you've a mind to stay in the world you'll have that hole dug by morning."

VII.

Piles of clouds had blown in from the north and settled in the basin, and by their and night's cover Cider snuck out to the barn. Inside he closed the door and lit a candle. He heard pigeons cooing in the rafters as he walked to the barn's far corner where old boards and fence-posts were stacked. He spied two posts and slipped them from the pile and carried them to the packing table. From his pack he took a wool blanket and spread it out across the table in the candle's light. He took up the posts and laid them on either side of the blanket, into which he rolled them and then wrapped them with baling wire. Earlier that evening, Rance had returned from town drunk on hell's blood and he'd slogged off to bed. Still, Cider worked quickly because he knew that Rance was all foul darkness now.

A cold rain had begun to fall and it made a wooden music as it struck the roof and walls. Above him the pigeons were spooking and he told them to settle as he set to prying the lid from the apple crate. Cider tipped the crate and rolled his mother out on the barn floor. Her body was stiff and heavy. He straightened her as much as she would allow. Then he filled the crate with sacks of mulch-apples and compost to take her place. When the crate felt like she was in it, he replaced the lid and he then carried his mother to the barn door and left her in the dust while he gathered his things and erased all signs that he had been there. His ear to the door, Cider heard only the rain. He put his head out and looked for anything his ears could not tell him. Nothing stirred except a barn cat whose belly dragged in the snow as he drifted across the yard.

Cider appeared in the door with his mother over his shoulder and he held her there with one arm and the tools and stretcher beneath the other, and should Rance see drag marks when he finally awoke from his drunken slumber, Cider bore these things across the yard to where the field began. The waning moon wavered like an eye under water, and beneath it Cider pulled his pale load across the field. At its edge, impresses left by bedding deer. He stopped to get his breath and figure the night's age, and he judged there was no time for standing there.

Tracks of the rogue dog crisscrossed Ursa's grave, and at the grave's head the faint tailing of a hole the dog had been digging. Cider looked around to see if he was still about. He cleared away the snow from his mother's would-be grave. The ground did not give beneath his feet, and so he dropped the shovel in the snow and took up the pick-ax and brought it down hard on the earth. The pick stuttered and cleaved its width in dirt. He studied the chunk to see if it got softer but it did not, and he chucked it and circled to the head of his brother's grave. The dog's hole was a dark reminder in the snow. Cider sunk his bare hand down in it and the earth there felt crisp and grainy but it had not clotted. He looked at his mother and then at the moon, which had moved the space of twice its size. There would not be time.

He set to exhuming his brother's grave and when it lay open he brushed the dirt from his brother's face. Ursa's eyes were open and while they made his death seem a benign thing, Cider shut them quickly as if they were the eyes of a Judas horse. He climbed from the grave and readied his mother's body and from the stretcher he took the wool blanket and wrapped her in it. Cider lashed its ends with baling wire then lowered her and the two posts into the hole. He looked down at the amalgam he had made and he spoke to the corpses in a low voice. Told them why he'd done what he'd done and gave his word he'd do otherwise come spring. To the east the sky was paling. Cider refilled the hole and packed the grave with his feet. And he left no marker so that no one would find them out. So that nothing could take away their right to darkness.

David Spiering

big city driving

in the north country heat vapor hangs
over the farmland; as I drive I make eye
contact with people I pass as if to take
their picture with my sight to create my own
north country upper Midwest gothic—once
every six months I have to go to the big city
to meet with bankers holding my loans—I feel
out of place in the city with its many urban
abhorrences, circling shark-eyed gang-bangers,
angry people feeling put out wolfing other
people for status, satisfaction and blood—
I stare at the city people in their
slim mink cars—the drivers roar their engines
at me; I see anger on their faces
because I turned my eyes at them as if my stare
insulted their cars or them—I can't help it if
all I have to watch are the farm
animals and the moon—I stop at the liquor
store to get some bourbon and beer
for the ride home—I drive off in my
mud-caked truck to the north country where
the only growling I hear comes
from stray dogs and large mosquitoes

Faith Walker

Incantation of the Vehicular Operator

Let me insert my bumper into your lungs
Let my wheel scrape the ear from your head
Let my left headlight bounce gracefully into your eye
Let me open your veins
Let blood spray
Let your sculpted face be crushed
Let you bloat by the roadside
Let me transform you so the next human calls you
reviling disgusting sick
Let me mash your heart into pavement
Let me not pause so as not to disturb myself
Let my music be loud so as not to hear you
Let me part your eyebrows

Let feathers fly
Let my only concern be the dent
Let your hoof be grated, let your hand lay limp
Let you be an inconvenience
Let my speed and size be your judge
Let my paint be untouched
Let ribs snap
Let there be a beautiful sunset while I dissect you
Let my hood screen you from sight
Let there be many of you so your death seems insignificant
Or let you be non-native so your death is for the greater good
Let me transform the mystery that is you into nothing
Lay your skin behind me
Decorate it with glistening scales.

INTO THE MAZE

Non-Fiction by Robert Fillmore

I read about the Maze in *Desert Solitaire* long before I had the opportunity to go there. Abbey described it precisely—*terra incognita*—one of the most remote and isolated places in canyon country. My first foray into the Maze area was a spontaneous affair—an impulsive effort to see this immense canyonscape—and it failed. It was spring, 1980, and two days into a fine road trip with Jill. We were in her Datsun hatchback of some sort—it was old, but it carried us and all our gear. She didn't care much for White Canyon, where I had originally chosen to go. I'd checked it out the previous spring on my way to the Escalante, during another flight from snow. *I* thought it was amazing—a deep, shadowy sand-floored labyrinth, miles long, with towering cottonwoods and huge bouquets of purple lupines. I had briefly picked my way to the bottom, to see if it could be done, discovering abundant water-filled potholes and several narrow, shadowed side canyons with that alluring "come hither" look about them. In short, paradise. But Jill didn't like it. "Too close to the road," she complained. "OK," I said, trying valiantly to be agreeable, "then where?"

I pulled out my piecemeal gas station road map and we immediately focused on the Maze. It wasn't that far from where we sat, but there were several ways in. We immediately chose the most likely one. It was only sixty miles of dirt road.

The country dirt roads where I grew up in Oklahoma were flat things scraped from red clay that you barely thought about—they were places to drive slowly with beer in hand, joint in mouth, watching for tarantulas with the stereo blaring. We had all the ingredients but the stereo.

Five long miles in, something under the car began to clatter. That's the problem with no stereo—you hear every little noise. Jill was concerned, but I waved my beer out the window, enthusiastically gesturing at the scattered piles of orange sandstone. This was nothing like the dirt roads in Oklahoma! We hit a series of sharp washboards, and the clatter beneath the car was immediately masked by louder rattles from within. After another mile the back windows began flapping spasmodically, like the wings of some deranged bird attempting flight. The screws had loosened and the latches were gone. Jill was alarmed, but I spoke reassuringly as I rifled through my pack for duct tape. A few minutes later, windows secured, we bounced toward the Maze. Jill wasn't talking. Twenty minutes and three miles later, as I gunned the lethargic Datsun through the deep sand, one of the windows fell off. That was it. At Jill's "request" we turned around and limped our way back to pavement and eventually, the land of snow.

A day after our return, I saw her at the bakery huddled in conversation with her old boyfriend. The worst part, however, was that I had nary a glimpse of the Maze. I had many questions, but most prominent in my mind were, When, and How?

Fifteen years later I attempted to enter the Maze again. I don't know why it took so long, but there were many other canyons to explore, and college to complete. One year before I earned my "terminal degree" in geology at the University of Kansas, all I had to do was write my dissertation. That spring the geology department awarded me a fat scholarship check to ensure that I completed this final step. After the awards ceremony I gingerly approached my adviser and asked him if I was required to live in Kansas for that year. He squinted at me questioningly. "I don't think so," he replied cautiously, "but I'm not sure."

A week later I was packing. I'd called an old friend who lived in Castle Valley, at the foot of the La Sal Mountains near Moab, Utah. Yes, she told me, there is a place you can live – house-sitting with cheap rent, while the crazy seventy-year-old physicist-owner runs rivers in Alaska for the summer. Three days later I was there, unpacking. I was coming off a painful break-up with a girlfriend, so I planned to keep busy to avoid thinking about it. Writing a dissertation was *not* part of that plan. It was spring and I needed canyons…and aridity, cactus, sand…. I had thought long and hard about the Maze during my exile.

The approach drive was long and bumpy—just as I had remembered it, but more beautiful. I was entranced with the fins and loaves of red rock, and the sparse lime-green vegetation. I sucked it all in, taking an entire day to reach the trailhead at the end of the road. I ended up on a narrow forested neck of land, at the head of the appropriately named Happy Canyon.

That evening I explored the west side of the plateau. Gazing down from the steep rim I spied a vague trace of a path that rose from the floor of Happy Canyon— likely an old uranium prospector's trail. It seemed to intersect with the rim on which I sat. I wandered over to the apparent top of the path and there, hidden in brush, was a trail blasted into the rock, occasionally obliterated by gargantuan blocks, the product of rock fall. These 1950s era paths are familiar features across southeast Utah, cutting through thick vertical cliffs of Wingate Sandstone that rim the plateaus in an effort to get to the uranium-saturated (in the crazed prospectors' minds) Chinle Formation beneath.

Early the next morning, in a rush of anticipation, I quickly brewed coffee and packed. It was already hot, so two gallons of water went into the pack. They were heavy, but the heat and uncertainty of springs and waterholes below made me cautious. I shouldered my pack with a grunt and started down the Flint Trail, a four-wheel drive road apparently dynamited into the cliffs by obviously unhinged prospectors. It said "road" on the map, but it looked passable only to jacked-up monster trucks; whatever it had been, *something* with oil and rubber passed this way. The three-foot-high vertical sandstone steps blasted into the cliffs were plastered with a thick exfoliating patch of black rubber, and dark fetid oil smears outlined the path. I don't know how they did it, but I was glad to be walking. I had to downclimb some of the steps.

I eventually descended to a flat bench, pulled out a water jug, and drank heavily. The short descent through the Orange Cliffs was a sun-baked furnace, and I was sweating heavily. The calendar said spring, but the temperature screamed summer. I continued a couple miles across the undulating mesa top, pained by the water-laden pack, and eventually reached another cliff band at the edge. After dropping down the Golden Stairs—another unbelievable four-wheel drive section, I finally reached the floor that led to the edge of the Maze.

I shed my pack in the cool shade of a room-sized boulder and again dug for the water jug. I took a deep pull when I heard a horrid grinding sound—metal against metal, and metal against rock. Peering up, back the way I had just come, I spied a cloud of blue haze emanating from the rim.

After another few minutes of hearing scraping and screeching, a small squat jeep lurched into view. I sat down, both amazed and appalled, to watch the spectacle. Twenty minutes later the driver stood before me, hand extended. I wanted to inquire about his kidneys.

"Damn, that was fun," he bellowed, "Got any oil?"

I reached into my pockets. "Nope," I said, "All out." I pulled my empty hands from my pockets as if to convince him.

"Oh well," he said, "I'll be OK… got a little leak under there." I squatted to look under the jeep at the constant drip of oil soaking into the porous sandstone. It's returning home, I thought. "How do you get outta here?" he asked. I looked at him in disbelief, but he was serious. Keeping my eyes on him the entire time, I slowly reached for my map, unfolded it, and laid it on a flat slab of sandstone.

We looked at it together. "You have two choices. Back up the way you came…."

"Oh no," he shook his head violently, "Not back up."

How could anybody come down something like that, not even considering how to get out?

I pointed him south. "That way then, if you follow this road and you'll end up at Lake Powell."

He brightened considerably. "Thanks a lot." He climbed back into the jeep, waved, and took off in a noisy cloud of exhaust.

What I had yet to understand, however, was that although I had finally reached the floor far below the forested rim, the Maze remained at the end of a six-mile hike. I again inspected the opened map, and sighed. The hot trudge continued.

When I reached the edge of the Maze late that afternoon, I dropped my pack in the dusty shadow of a wide butte and sank heavily into the red dirt. This was it—the most surreal and remote rockscape in which I had ever been immersed. Isolated clusters of striated brown-red buttes and uncertain ribbed pinnacles were scattered across the vista. It was a bizarre landscape of clashing horizontal and vertical lines. A single slender column stood sentinel over this particular rim. It vaulted into the pale blue sky in the same pool of shade that I occupied. Other towers rose haphazardly around the rim or straddled impossibly narrow necks and islands, all on a foundation of striped slickrock. It was only upon focusing on the nearby horizon that I realized that everything fell away abruptly into a bewildering puzzle of deep vertical-walled chasms—the Maze. From that vantage the shadowed canyons were bottomless. On the topographical map it resembled the convoluted furrows of a brain. In real life it was scary. The vertical stacks of stratified brown rock were balanced precariously on the brink of these 400-foot-deep canyons. Trying to trace a single canyon from that vantage made me dizzy. I needed to get down there and follow the meandering floor and folded walls. But therein was the problem.

Only two quarts of warm water remained as I set camp up in the late afternoon shade. I had seen no potholes or puddles on the hike—it was too late in the season for that. Springs were clearly marked on my map, but all were nestled in the canyons below me. I had to find a route down. Later that evening as I skirted the rims of two box-headed canyons, seeking a way down, I caught glimpses into several shadowed alcoves tangled with green, a sure sign of a reliable seep. But no way down.

Early the next morning, after a savored cup of coffee, I set off in search of a route down. After a long morning of dead-ends at slickrock pourovers and yawning overhangs, I was desperate. Finally I found an abrasive, ten-foot skid down a steep, water-polished furrow. I thought I could get back up it.

I reached the canyon floor with only a minor loss

of skin. Parched, I trudged through the soft sand to the spring marked on the map. The dry canyon bottom looped through the entrenched meanders—giant horseshoes where the ghost stream arced back onto itself. Thick cottonwoods, trunks scarred by eons of flood debris, lined the ephemeral channel as their shiny lime-green leaves fluttered in the canyon-funneled

breeze. Naked roots of juniper and piñon reached into
the desiccated stream bed like thick snakes.

An hour later I stood in a glen where the damp air
was at least twenty degrees cooler. The tinkling sound
of water dripping into a shallow pool resonated loudly.
Water trickled from a thick beard of moss, columbine,
and monkeyflower. I raised bottle after bottle to catch

the water until my arms were exhausted. I downed a liter while standing there, straining the blackened plant bits through my teeth. I watched the buzzing insects and traced the wet sand downcanyon until it became dry sand. The water was the best I had ever tasted.

The climb out was tedious—head down, straining against the load on my back. My adrenaline had dissolved after finding the water, but I was well-supplied and relieved.

The next day was spent exploring for alternate routes into the canyons, but to no avail. Finally, I returned to descend the slickrock furrow, for more water and a long hike to the "Harvest Scene," a fantastic panel of ghostly Barrier Canyon-style pictographs. The large unearthly figures had been applied to a smooth, slightly concave wall only barely protected from the elements. Five hundred feet above loomed Chocolate Drops, a great serrated blade of brown-red siltstone carved into a series of spires and fins—all capped by a dollop of stark white sandstone. The entire place was surreal and hallucinatory, especially as my gaze shifted between the skyline pinnacles and glowering figures. After an uneasy break in the shade beneath the pictographs, I headed back up the canyon, focusing on the scalloped rim, trying to recognize my escape route. Glancing down, I realized it was clearly marked by my lone footprints.

Joshua Marie Wilkinson

Breaker, Breaker

Spirit thief, your angle is thin—
the jackdaws, the lightning insects

its path into your own. Stand down
to suffer fools rocked with a current

amidships. The haunted blunder off
to the night owl's lit offices.

Notice given, a dead clearing
in which to clumsy around.

White eyes turn to position us
in the storm, keeling forth.

Here, little storm, is how
to get into the grass awhile.

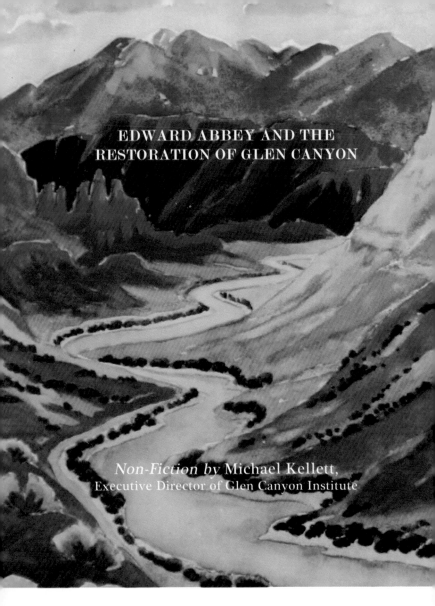

EDWARD ABBEY AND THE RESTORATION OF GLEN CANYON

Non-Fiction by Michael Kellett,
Executive Director of Glen Canyon Institute

E dward Abbey was outraged by many aspects of modern industrial development. However, there was nothing he despised more than Glen Canyon Dam and its reservoir, Lake Powell. As he writes in his classic, *Desert Solitaire,*

The beavers had to go and build another god-damned dam on the Colorado. Not satisfied with the enormous silt trap and evaporation tank called Lake Mead (back of Boulder Dam) [now known as Hoover Dam] they have created another, even bigger, even more destructive, in Glen Canyon. This reservoir of stagnant water will not irrigate a single square foot of land or supply water for a single village; its only justification is the generation of cash through electricity for the indirect subsidy of various real estate speculators, cottongrowers and sugarbeet magnates in Arizona, Utah and Colorado; also, of course, to keep the engineers and managers of the Reclamation Bureau off the streets and out of trouble.

The impounded waters form an artificial lake named Powell, supposedly to honor but actually to dishonor the memory, spirit and vision of Major John Wesley Powell, first American to make a systematic exploration of the Colorado River and its environs. Where he and his brave men once lined the rapids and glided through silent canyons two thousand feet deep the motorboats now smoke and whine, scumming the water with cigarette butts, beer cans and oil, dragging the water skiers on their endless rounds, clockwise.[1]

Abbey had floated the Colorado River through Glen Canyon in 1959, while the dam was under construction, and wrote that

I was one of the lucky few (there could have been thousands more) who saw Glen Canyon before it was drowned. In fact I saw only a part of it but enough to realize that here was an Eden, a portion of the earth's original paradise. To grasp the nature of the crime that was committed imagine the Taj Mahal or Chartres Cathedral buried in mud until only the spires remain visible.[2]

Abbey would go on to write books, essays, and articles expressing his contempt for Glen Canyon Dam and his lament for the apparent permanent loss of Glen Canyon. He even imagined the destruction of the dam. In his novel, *The Monkey Wrench Gang*, he follows the exploits of a group of people who dream of blowing up the dam. One of the main characters, Seldom Seen Smith, prays to God for "a little old *pre*-cision-type earthquake right under this dam."[3] In 1981, Earth First! (whose founding was inspired in no small part by Abbey's novel) unfurled a giant, simulated crack over the front of the dam. Abbey was at the demonstration, and from the back of a pickup truck, he declared, "No man-made structure in all of American history has been hated so much, by so many, for so long, with such good reason!"[4]

Abbey never actually advocated destroying Glen Canyon Dam. However, his writings introduced countless people to the drowned wonders of Glen Canyon and made them wish the dam had never been built. As a result, along with David Brower and a few other conservation visionaries, Abbey became a primary catalyst for a growing citizen's movement that has sought to undo the massive mistake represented by Glen Canyon Dam.

In 1996, Glen Canyon Institute (GCI) was founded—with the help of Brower—to restore Glen Canyon and a free-flowing Colorado River. Back then, the idea was still considered "radical." GCI set out to show that it was not radical at all, but actually the most ecologically, economically, and socially reasonable alternative. Over the next few years, GCI conducted a number of scientific studies, published peer-reviewed articles, presented at conferences, and issued reports to educate the public. This reasoned, well-documented approach built significant credibility for the organization's vision. However, it was not enough alone to prompt action by decision makers.

The trends of the last decade have dramatically changed the situation. Rising public water demand, relentless drought, and climate change have significantly reduced the flow of the Colorado River from that of the past century. Scientific studies have predicted that this situation will continue. Lake Powell reservoir, and Lake Mead reservoir downstream, are half empty. Most scientists believe that there will never again be enough water to fill both reservoirs.

GCI believes that this unprecedented convergence of factors provides the opportunity to change Colorado River management to address today's new realities. This is the goal of GCI's Fill Lake Mead First project. The goal of water managers has been to keep both Lake Powell and Lake Mead full. Now, with two half-empty reservoirs, this policy no longer makes sense. GCI is advocating an alternative approach that consolidates most of the water from both reservoirs in Lake Mead, with Lake Powell used as backup in flood years.

This Fill Lake Mead First strategy would benefit the people and ecosystems of the Colorado River Basin and beyond. This approach would help to maintain a reliable water supply for millions of people in Arizona, California, and Nevada who depend on Lake Mead. Water would be permitted to flow more naturally through Glen Canyon Dam, helping to heal the damage done by the dam to the Grand Canyon. A lowered Lake Powell would expose many more portions of Glen Canyon that have been flooded under the reservoir, allowing them to recover their natural beauty and integrity. This could all be done without infringing on any existing water rights and needs.

In his later years, Edward Abbey dared to hope that Glen Canyon could someday be restored. Although he died seven years before the founding of Glen Canyon Institute, he seemed to anticipate the group's optimistic vision in his forward to the 1986 book, *Ghosts of Glen Canyon*:

> I do not hold with those who say that Glen Canyon has been lost to us forever. Romantic dreamer that I am, I really believe that sometime soon—say, within the next fifty years—a more enlightened less power-greedy generation will assume the management of our society. And when it does, the gates of Glen Canyon Dam will be opened, Lake Powell will be drained like dirty water from a tub, and a living river and the sandstone canyon will again be revealed to our eyes, accessible once again to sunlight and life. The restoration process will require a few years... but it can be done. And then the trees will return to

the river's shore, and the birds, and the columbines will bloom once again in those seep-fed hanging gardens that once adorned the high red walls of Glen Canyon.

It can be done. It will be done.[5]

1 "Down the River," in Edward Abbey, *Desert Solitaire*, Ballantine Books (1968) p. 73-74.

2 Ibid, p. 74.

3 Origins III: Seldom Seen Smith, in Edward Abbey, *The Monkey Wrench Gang*, Avon Books (1975), p. 33

4 The Cracking of Glen Canyon Damn. Summer 1982. Distribution: Earth First! Roadshow, Produced by Christopher (Toby) McLeod, Glenn Switkes and Randy Hayes. http://www.sacredland.org/glen-canyon-damn/

5 Edward Abbey, Forward: Glen Canyon Remembered, Pack Creek Ranch, September 1986 in Crampton, C. Gregory; Forward by Edward Abbey; Color Photographs by Philip Hyde and W.L. Rusho. 1986 (2009). *Ghosts of Glen Canyon: History Beneath Lake Powell.*

RESIST MUCH
OBEY LITTLE

Hey, Randy Ol' Desert Rat:

I gotta hand it to ya, man, asking to be buried
in the desert. No service, no saccharine
speeches, no veins full of chemicals, just
illegal placement of your earthly body after
surgery, in a sleeping bag, in the desert. I
used to be pissed off at you! I guess I
took for a fact your "image" as a macho
wildman having fun and riding around in an
orange fuckmobile while, I imagined, the

women in the gang, in the bus, cooked, did the dishes, kept clothes clean, and watched the babies that came along. But you cooked, too, didn't ya, and you wanted the ones who'd bury you to get fed and booze it up, play music, and dance. I'm with you on that one, man! "If I can't dance, I don't wanna be part of the revolution!"

How ya scoffed at "too much time wasted in library conversation-clogged seminars." Ha, listen, ya didn't exactly brag on being a Stegner Fellow at Stanford! Hey, a question for ya. Isn't the point of learning this: To call out the government when it does rotten shit in our names? You'd be so pissed off today, Ed. Here it is, twenty years later, and what they've done to Nevada, especially Las Vegas, why you'd want to blow the whole place up. Parts of Utah and Arizona, too. You'd hate it all. Because of you, though, I gotta admit, we haven't given up. We haven't given up on any of it! We ain't afraid to be mean and feisty. To break the law where it counts. Go to prison if we must.

Ed, I gotta tell ya, I was gonna haul off and call you and your friends a bunch of macho drunkards blowing smoke out your asses, but I gotta hand it to ya. Having fun and writing beautiful stuff and being angry at the dams and all that nuke waste in the desert—and specially angry at the agencies that say we need them—you were right on, my man. Right on.

Your words stand. And, even if you hate it, you're an icon. You made a difference and not many of us do. Some are out there right now letting the fury of their care be heard. Man, you were right: " In the Soviet Union [sic], government controls industry. In the United States, industry controls government." (You wouldn't believe what just went down here, with the greedy big-ass banks getting bailed out by the government for being stupid!) But my favorite thing you said is: " A patriot must always be ready to defend his (or her) country against his (or her) government." Yeah! As I always said, " If voting changed anything, they'd make it illegal." Don't forget the rage of the ladies!

So, Ed darling, here's some whiskey on your grave and love to ya.

" Red Emma" Goldman

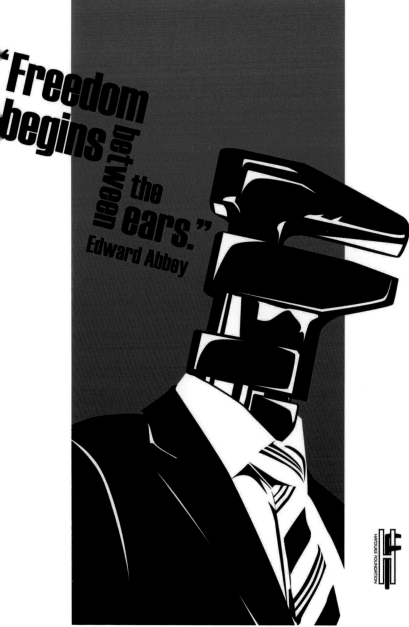

"Freedom begins between the ears."
Edward Abbey

Jeff Poniewaz

Shining City on a Hill

George W. Bush
lops off mountaintops
to keep Reagan's
"City on a Hill" shining
and sends the utility bill
to future generations.
Lopped-off mountaintops
in West Virginia melt
snowcaps on mountains
around the world.

Is Survived By

Non-Fiction by **Denis E. Foley**

Jesus, of Nazareth in Galilee, passed away on Friday, April 10, Anno Domini 33, near Jerusalem. He was a respected teacher, evangelist, desert wilderness explorer and raft guide on the Lake of Galilee. He is survived by 210 million human beings.

William the Conqueror, Duke of Normandy and King of the Coastal Islands (also known as William the Bastard) departed this earthly life on Sept 9, AD 1087, near Paris. He was noted for habitat preservation subsidized by government funding and use of imminent domain to create the New Forest across 36 parishes of the island of England. He is survived by 315 million human beings.

Thomas Malthus, of Bath, England, has gone to be with the Lord, on Dec 23, in the year of our Lord Jesus Christ 1834. He was a noted Anglican clergyman and the author of "An Essay on the Principle of Population" (1743-1st Edition of six). He is survived by 1,062 million human beings.

Theodore Roosevelt passed away January 6, AD 1919, in Oyster Bay, NY. He will be best remembered as 26th President of the United States under whose leadership more than 160 million acres were protected as public lands and as explorer of the River of Doubt in South America. He is survived by 5 new national parks and 1,980 million human beings.

Sir Alexander Fleming, Scottish biologist and pharmacologist, died on March 11, AD 1955, in London, England. Fleming shared the Nobel Prize for Medicine in 1945 for his research leading to development of antibiotics. He is survived by 2,756 million human beings.

Margaret Sanger left this Mortal Realm on Sat, Sept 6, AD 1966, in Tucson, Az. She is best known for her controversial promotion of contraception to preempt dangerous and illegal abortions, and for founding the American Birth Control League (now Planned Parenthood) in 1921. More recently she was a champion of the 1965 Griswold v Connecticut Supreme Court decision, which legalized the use of birth control for married couples in the U.S. She is survived by 3,340 million human beings.

Edward Abbey died March 14, 1989 CE, at Fort Llatikcuf, Az. Abbey was a seasonal employee of the federal government, a writer, a river drifter and a connoisseur of women's thighs. Mr. Abbey's writings as a proponent of wilderness often called attention to increasing human population pressure on National Parks and other public lands. He is survived by "a dozen pretty damn good books" and 5,177 million human beings.

Pope John Paul II (Charles Wojtyla) passed into Eternal Reward April 2, AD 2005, in Vatican City. As Pope he traveled extensively to visit rapidly growing Roman Catholic populations in Central America, South America and Africa while emphasizing humankind's universal call to holiness. He was criticized for his opposition to birth control as an interruption to the sanctity of human life. He is survived by 6,454 million human beings.

Dr. Norman Borlaug died Sept 12, AD 2009, at his home in Dallas, Tx. Borlaug's research and "in country" work contributed to doubling crop yields in Mexico, India, Pakistan and other countries in which rapidly expanding populations faced starvation. The Distinguished Professor at Texas A&M University was considered father of the "green revolution" in agriculture and won the 1970 Nobel Peace Prize for "providing bread for a hungry world." He is survived by 6,784 million human beings, as many as 1,000 million of whom may owe their lives to agricultural innovations. ⌐

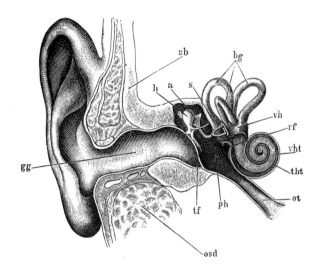

THE ABBEY INTERVIEWS
ILLUSTRATIONS BY SUE RING deROSSET

1. JACK LOEFFLER

2. JIM STILES

3. DOUGLAS PEACOCK

4. CHARLES BOWDEN

5. KEN SANDERS

6. KATIE LEE

7. GARY BURDEN & ED PRESSMAN

Ed Abbey, Hero Activist:
A Conversation with Jack Loeffler

Interviewed by Todd Simmons

Everyone kept pointing to Jack Loeffler when I mentioned that we were doing a special issue of Matter *about Edward Abbey. From things that I had read, I knew Jack and Ed had been close friends for decades, he'd helped bury Abbey in the desert, and had gone on to write a memoir of his late friend,* (Adventures with Ed: A Portrait of Abbey). *I sought out the still-busy aural historian, writer, radio producer and sound collage artist, and he readily agreed to an interview.*

Jack Loeffler has a radio voice—smooth, consistent, and engaging. His memories of Abbey came pouring out during our phone conversation. His breadth of knowledge concerning our human plight impressed me more than anything else, and it's easy to see why he and Abbey got along so well. Listening to Jack, it's fairly straightforward which path leads us away from our short-sighted, destructive relationship to the earth. His vision stems from his curiosity about indigenous and traditional cultures, and his work to record and preserve their music and lore. He has conducted field research among the Navajo, Hopi, Ute, Tewa, Keresan, Zuni, Chiricahua Apache, Tohono O'odham, Nez Perce, Yaqui, Seri, Huichol, Tarahumara, Mayan, and California Indians; and Hispano, Basque, and Anglo-ranch cultures. His traditional music library contains over 3,500 songs that he recorded on location.

Todd Simmons: When did you first meet Edward Abbey, and did you know his work before you met him?

Jack Loeffler: I knew the man before the myth, but we first met—although we didn't start hanging out then—back in '62 in a place called Claude's Bar in Santa Fe. Somewhere along the line I got a job as a fire lookout for several seasons, beginning in 1965. Every now and then I'd go into Durango for supplies. My fire lookout was up in the Jicarilla Ranger District to the Carson National Forest. It's in the San Juan River watershed. And I picked up a book called *Desert Solitaire*, hard back, $4.95 or something. I looked at the picture in the book and recognized Ed. I read the book, and thought, boy, that's a really good book.

We have a mutual friend, John DePuy, an artist who lives in northern New Mexico, whom we'd both known for a long time. I think Ed and John met back in the '50s, when they were both somehow associated with UNM. I was doing a job with a museum in New Mexico and realized that the skies were getting pretty funky. The Four Corners power plant really bugged me.

In the meantime, a Park Service friend of mine, Bill Brown, had become aware of the debacle that was about to take place out on Black Mesa in Navajo and Hopi country, land that's sacred to both tribes. So in 1970 we started the Black Mesa Defense Fund. I hooked up with Ed again and we both hated what was going on up there. We spent a lot of time up there thinking dire thoughts; that was some of the field research that happened for the book *The Monkey Wrench Gang*. We discovered that we were simpatico, and we started camping together. We'd go camping a lot over the years. We camped several times a year, a week or two at a crack. At Christmastime, we'd take our respective families to some place like Cabeza Prieta or Mexico and camp. Basically it was this endless conversation that went on between the two of us for, really, about twenty years. Sometimes he'd call me or I'd call him on the phone and we'd carry on. We were truly buddies, right down the line, and camped as much as we could because that's when we had a chance to talk. And that's what we enjoyed.

TS: What prompted you to write a memoir (*Adventures with Ed: A Portrait of Abbey*) of your late friend?
JL: On two different occasions Ed asked me to be his chronicler. That's the word he used, but after he died that didn't even enter my mind. Then a publisher back in New York asked me if I'd do a book and I said no. It was too...too soon. They tried again and I finally said yes. Then I wrote the book, and that publisher was bought by another company from Germany, I guess, and all the environmental writers who were there— including Dave Foreman—got bounced. Eventually the book was published by UNM Press. But what happened was, I was able to get a copy of Ed's journals from the University of Arizona's archive, and I also had my own notebooks and all the books Ed had ever written except *Jonathan Troy*, which I later got a copy of. Ed had never wanted me to read that book; he thought it was a terrible book. He gave it a D+ or something.

When I decided to do it, I started by rereading all of his books and reading all of his journals—the ones that remained, I think one through four or maybe one through three were lost. At one point I went back to Home, Pennsylvania, and talked to his dad, Paul Revere Abbey. He gave me some stuff that was stashed in their basement, which I still have, that's never been published. It was just some letters and things. I think I put some of that in my book. I had recorded Ed a couple of times. I have always taken good notes and I have a good memory, so when I got into that book it started writing itself. Every morning I'd write a minimum of 1500 words. They weren't all good words, but I wrote everyday until that book was done, until the first draft was done. Then I'd go play with it and mess with it until it finally turned into what it is. UNM Press published it, and now it's in its third or fourth printing, I guess. It's all in paperback anymore; the hardbacks are all gone.

TS: Was it hard for you to write about your good friend? What was it like?

JL: To write the original draft was really far out, because I was reliving experiences with Ed and actually going out and rehiking a lot of our old trails all over the American Southwest and even down into Mexico. It was like Ed and I were walking together, and the conversation continued (chuckle). So I told the ghost of Ed what I was writing about and I made it as honest as I could, because he had two mottos. One was *resolve*—with his finger pointed toward the sky (chuckle)—and his other was *follow the truth no matter where it leads*. And that's what I tried to do with this book. I remember when the *New York Times* review guy T.C. Boyle got it and reviewed it, he couldn't understand how I could remember all those conversations. I wrote him a letter back and told him how I could remember all those conversations, because we had them, and I always took notes and know that Ed did too, because our conversations ended up in his books, in his novels. That was always kind of weird (laughter)—to be reading one of his books and suddenly there was this familiar conversation going down. So, anyway, it probably took a good year to write that first draft adequately. Then I played with it for several years, off and on.

TS: What about Edward Abbey surprised you, or would surprise his readers?

JL: One of the things that would probably be surprising to people who didn't know Ed very well was just how deeply spiritual a person he was. But it was within the context of the flow of nature. At one point he considered himself either a naturist or an earthiest, bearing in mind that he had a masters degree in philosophy from the University of New Mexico. He was deeply into the flow of nature on some sort of an almost—I hate to call it a mystical level because that connotes something that he really wasn't—but it certainly got past any kind of organized religious point of view, and it was deeply spiritual. A lot of our discussion revolved around that kind of thing.

A few things almost surprised me that I found revealed in his papers. One was from a lecture that he delivered at UNM, when he was still an undergraduate. He called himself, "A barefoot eco-freak anarchist." And he was consistent with that same point of view with regard to himself, or at least that was his guiding light throughout the whole span of his lifetime. That didn't change a bit. I have all of these journals and papers of his written in his own hand—and his penmanship stayed just about the same through his entire adult life.

Also, at one point, Ed considered a double career, one as a composer and the other as a writer. I have a few scribbles of some of his compositions. My wife and I had given him a copy of the 1911 *Britannica* for his birthday one year, and my wife had rebound the whole thing. She's a book binder. As a gift he sent her a cassette of one of his own compositions played by himself on the piano. And I said (chuckle), "You know, Ed, I'm glad you gave up being a composer (laughter), and opted to be just a writer." It's really something, though, to listen to his head musically. He had a hugely wonderful ear. One of our favorite games was a guessing game, as to what the piece of music would be. If we couldn't get that, we would try to guess the name of the composer. I remember one time sitting in his living room and he said, "I want you to listen to this and tell me who it is." It was incredibly difficult and incredibly out there. But I recognized the piece and said, "That's Charles Ives." He said, "Good for you!" and told me the name of the symphony—I think it was either the second or the fourth—and he later dedicated *The Fool's Progress* to the memory of Charles Ives, who was an anarchist, composer and insurance salesman in Hartford, Connecticut.

TS: Increasingly it seems the environmental movement is too heavily dependent on science, in the sense that if we just present the facts, then of course people will listen and act accordingly. Ed certainly questioned science in his writing—what are your thoughts?

JL: We won't be able to pull ourselves out of this dilemma

without a high ratio of applied—well-applied—science. The word "well-applied" is key. I have a lot of questions about what is regarded as the proper application of science, but I think for environmentalists to turn the tide it will take a much bigger point of view—a total shift in cultural paradigm. Our cultural paradigm right now is an economically dominated paradigm, which is fundamentally turning habitat into money, and that needs to be shifted.

One of the things that I really love—and am working on diligently and have for many years—is trying to understand myriad Native American points of view with regard to living successfully within the context of homeland. The traditional indigenous peoples I've worked with, throughout the American West and Mexico, have without fail regarded the planet as sacred. Truly sacred. Our culture has utterly secularized landscape. We need a huge sense of that sacred which Ed certainly felt, and a deep abiding understanding that we are spawned by the earth itself. Subsequently, we have to perceive that almost within a kind of mythic context. The mythic process has to be revitalized in a way that does not crystallize into some form of a religion—to really understand ourselves on some deeper level than just in terms of cold, hard science. I think those two elements—the mythic and the sacred—have to be factored into the way we look at all of this. Plus, I think we're going to have to redefine a whole philosophical system that does away with our current sense of economics. That has to be understood. Wendell Berry certainly understands that economics is indeed the great enemy. But it also occurs concurrently with human overpopulation, so we have to reduce our numbers. One of the things Ed talked about and Garrett Harden talked about and lots of us have talked about is, we have to really concentrate on reducing human population. If we make it to nine billion or ten billion by 2050, it's all over as far as I'm concerned. It may be all over anyway. That's the hard part. But we have to so completely reinvent our sense of scope as we pursue this problem—and indeed it must involve a huge amount of science—but it involves a lot more than just science.

I recently worked on a project where I interviewed a bunch of Los Alamos scientists—I live about forty miles from Los Alamos—and I heard some extremely interesting cases for the use of nuclear energy from them. One guy said there was no way that wind and solar and all the rest of it can even touch the energy needs that we're going to have by the year 2050. I asked him if he could imagine using less energy by 2050. That was not a part of his paradigm. My favorite of Ed's apothems is, "Growth for the sake of growth is the ideology of the cancer cell," because that is what drives our economically dominated paradigm. In a sense it is like a state of metastasis; it's not just our species, it's what our species brings with it that is metastasizing.

TS: Why is Edward Abbey still important?
JL: I think it's because he was recognized as a hero activist. He did his fair share of night work. And he had the courage to say precisely what he thought and he behaved absolutely fearlessly. I don't think anybody has touched him with that kind of power subsequently. There is a lot of really good writing going on and a lot of really good thinking going on, but I think Ed was one of the very first true environmental activists. You know, cutting down billboards or whatever. There's this whole array of deeds that he did that—he's beyond the statute of limitations—that caused him to be regarded

as he is. But what's so interesting to me, knowing him as well as I did, was that he was a very shy fellow (chuckle). He could deliver a mighty speech, but when there was a social occasion, he was really very shy.

I remember one time, for *The Fool's Progress*, he'd wanted to include a cabrito roast. I told him we could do one at my house, because I'd done a bunch of them in the past. So we did a cabrito roast, which is roasting a goat in a pit underground. It's something you invite a lot people to because there's a lot of meat (chuckle)—boy it was good, too, we put a pork roast inside the chest cavity of the goat and marinated the whole thing in beer, red chili, garlic, and oregano for twenty-four hours, and it was so good, it was just outrageous (chuckle). But anyway, there were a few other writers there, and Ed admired Godfrey Reggio enormously—the guy who did the *Quatsi* trilogy. Ed regarded Godfrey as probably the best filmmaker of his time. And Godfrey was there, and Ed was too shy to actually engage Godfrey in conversation. It was interesting to watch all of that go down. But one on one, after Ed got to know you, or at least after he and I got to know each other really well, the conversation just went on and on and on about everything.

His brother "Hoots" told me that at one point back in Home, Pennsylvania, the two of them were walking down the street, and a car stopped at a stoplight, but the front of the car was in the crosswalk area for pedestrians, and rather than walk around the car, Ed stepped up on the fender, walked across the hood, stepped down on the other fender and hopped off the car. He walked over the car rather than around it. That was the way he was. He was absolutely fearless.

Another time, this is when he was not well and knew he could hemorrhage to death at any minute, he and I were taking a hike down a sandy arroyo out in the Sonoran Desert and a guy came cruising up on a four-wheeler. Ed grabbed the handlebars and dragged him right out of the arroyo and told him to get out of there immediately. It was just interesting to see how Ed did this. He had great courage, and he had the courage of his convictions. And in a time when few people display that would lead me to think that's why Ed is still highly regarded. Not only that, his writing is extremely compelling. He said it the way he saw it, and he saw it as correctly as anybody has.

TS: The comedic aspects of Abbey—his playfulness with language, the puns, the goosing of nearly every sacred cow—sets Abbey apart from his contemporaries. Even today few writers approach similar subjects with as much humor and wit. Any thoughts?

JL: He had a really good sense of humor. There were times when we cracked each other up so hard that we could barely breathe. Sometimes it was in (chuckle) weird circumstances, but his sense of humor was really evolved, and at the same time some people have thought of him as being morose. You know, he had his ups and downs. But he had a sense of humor that wouldn't quit.

TS: Who inspired Ed, who did he read that we might not know about?

JL: Some writers that he appreciated included Thoreau, Tolstoy, Mark Twain and Kurt Vonnegut. He regarded Shakespeare as a toady, a sycophant. No real heroes like Spartacus. One of the people he read was an anarchist thinker named Benjamin Tucker. It seems to me that Tucker may have been the first guy to say something to the effect that, "A true patriot must be willing to defend his country against his government." Ed took ideas like that and made them his own, perfected them in his own way. It's really great to read who Ed read. Ed was also interested in Peter Kropotkin, but I think that his real anarchist hero was Mikhail Bakunin.

In his masters thesis, he wrote about Bakunin who fought at the barricades and he was actually a bomb thrower; whereas Kropotkin believed in revolution, but I don't think he ever engaged in battle. He was exiled early on and lived in Britain. But his writing—he was the most intelligent of that coterie of anarchist writers who were born in the 19th century and he wrote into the 20th century. He sort of took over the mantel of anarchist philosophic spokesman after Bakunin died. Ed's dream early on would have been to die fighting. In the '50s, in one of his journals, his idea of a good way to die would have been in a gunfight with the FBI out on some remote corner of Baboquivari somewhere. I understood that very well. In fact we had matching .357 Magnums. That way if we were ever really (chuckle) put up to it, we'd at least have the same kind of ammo (laughter).

TS: How do we best avoid the shoot-out?

JL: If we cease to think within the context of current geopolitical-organizational framework, and revert back to John Wesley Powell's notion of looking at the watersheds of the arid West—if we decentralize, that is key. We have to decentralize political power—that's been understood for a long time—then reintegrate within the context of home watershed. We have to see the watershed as a commons so that the people at the top of the watershed are just as aware of the needs of the people at the bottom of the watershed, and vice versa. And we have to work within the context of mutual cooperation, and use the commons as a model, recognizing that the commons is the entire biotic community and not just the human species. Then we need to get out in it to learn how to restore it in order to live in a healthy fashion—that to me would also be key. I've been thinking about this for a long, long time. We have to redefine the way we look at watersheds. And it's not just the water; it's the entire biotic community. It's the geophysical cradle. It's the atmosphere. And it's human culture, human consciousness.

TS: What is Edward Abbey's greatest legacy?

JL: Well, to me personally, it's having had a best friend (chuckle). Ed rearranged a lot of the environmental point of view and spearheaded the radical environmental movement, which then split into a whole array of other ways of looking at environmental stuff. Ed, with *Desert Solitaire*, sort of threw gasoline on an ember. And it took off. His great legacy is having melded anarchist thought with environmentalist thought, which turned into what it's growing into now. That to me is an enormous legacy.

TS: You were with him as he was dying those last few years. How did it start?

JL: He keeled over in our living room—in 1982. They misdiagnosed him, saying he had pancreatic cancer. It was revealed within the month that he had esophageal varices, but none of us knew what that meant. He had his first bleed right around Christmastime that year. We were supposed to be camping down in Baja for six weeks with our families. And he had his first hemorrhage. So we ended up just going into the Superstitions—just him and me—for a couple of weeks.

TS: Any last thoughts?

JL: The one thing that strikes me now is that Ed was older than I when he died, but I have now outlived him by over eleven years. My mind has had a chance to go through all sorts of wonderful permutations, and I just wonder what Ed would have been like at the age of 73, which is my age now. The last ten years has been the most productive span of time that I've ever had. Ed's last ten years were really productive for him. Boy oh boy, what would have come out if he could have had another ten years? It could have been really far out. He died at the age of 62 years and 45 days. It's a big thought: What could he have done?

Some Goddamned Liberal or Something:
A Conversation with Jim Stiles

Interviewed by Joshua Zaffos

Jim Stiles abandoned his home in Kentucky for the Golden West after first reading Edward Abbey's Desert Solitaire. *In 1976, Stiles headed to Wolf Hole, Arizona, where Abbey claimed to reside, only to find no sign of the author, or any sort of town. Instead, Stiles moved to Moab, Utah, to work as a volunteer at Arches National Park, following in Abbey's footsteps.*

Stiles soon learned that Abbey still lived in Moab and met his hero at a poker game. Stiles showed off a drawing of Glen Canyon Dam blown to pieces; Abbey responded by asking him to illustrate his next book, The Journey Home, *published in 1977.*

More than a decade later, Stiles decided to launch the Canyon Country Zephyr, *an independent bimonthly newspaper in Moab. The paper debuted in print on the day that Abbey died, March 14, 1989, and ever since it has served as a torchbearing record, published in his spirit. For 20 years, the* Zephyr *combined Stiles' quirky illustrations and his own contemplative tirades against environmental destruction with fond remembrances of wilderness adventures and the good ol' days.*

Stiles' 2007 book, Brave New West, *offers a harsh critique of the development around Moab and the sagging moral compass of the environmental movement. In late 2008, the* Zephyr *went out of print and moved online because of the financial challenges of publishing.*

Stiles—and the Zephyr—*remain devoted to a brand of uncompromising environmental writing that would make Abbey proud. And, as I learned when we talked during the Western Literature Association annual meeting in Spearfish,*

South Dakota, in October 2008, Stiles can do a spot-on Abbey
imitation, too. (All quotation marks that appear below within
Stiles' recollections mean he was doing his Abbey impersonation
as he spoke.)

Joshua Zaffos: When we were introduced the other
night, you told me to make sure I ask you about the
dead dog story.

Jim Stiles: Oh, this isn't some environmental story. This
is more of a story about Ed Abbey's humanity.

I had a dog named Mukluk that I probably loved
more than any other. My old dog Mukluk was fighting
a losing battle and she finally died. I was really upset. I
was just devastated that my dog was dead.

Well, Ed came by about a week after Mukluk died.
I was moping around and talking about Mukluk, and,
finally, Ed said, "For chrissakes, Stiles, get over it. It's
only a goddamn dog." I looked at him and I said, Hey, I
really loved that dog, Ed, and it meant a lot to me and I
just feel really bad about it, ok? And he kind of looked
at me, and he nodded.

Well, a couple times that winter—this was in
October—I would get these famous Ed Abbey
postcards, the blank postcards that Ed sent out to
everyone all the time. Instead of picture postcards, you
know you can go to the post office and fill out these
blank white postcards? That's how Ed communicated
with most people. But you'd always hear from him.
Sometimes it would be, "Stiles, what's the latest on the
Exxon drilling rig, and when you gonna send some
monkey wrenchers up there to take care of it?" "Or it
might be, Can you mail some letters for me from my
Moab address?"

But a couple times that winter I got these postcards,

"Stiles, I haven't heard from you in awhile. What's going on? I hope you're doing alright. Come and visit us." I didn't. I've always been a bad person that unless they practically beg me to come visit I don't do it because I always feel like I'm imposing and I never know.

Anyway, I never thought anything else about it. Then after Ed died, I was talking to Clarke [his wife] one day, and she said he felt really bad about what he said to you about your dog. This was years later, and I said I don't remember what you're talking about, and she said, Well, apparently you said something about your dog had died, and he made some wisecrack about it's only a dead dog. She said he worried about that, not like he spent every waking moment worrying that he had insulted me, but he had sent me those two cards that winter because he was afraid he'd hurt my feelings and he wanted to make sure that I knew that he still cared and that he wanted me to come down and visit.

It was just the kind of thing that people who read Abbey's books, who think he's this brash, arrogant, you know, shoot-from-the-hip kind of guy, don't understand: that he was a man of real humanity who really cherished his friends.

JZ: Among people who knew Abbey personally it seems like he's a very strong force in your lives. At the same time, there's this culture around his books and people really love his work. So what are the differences between Ed personally and the literary character and the figure that we see? What other distinctions are there for people who get turned on to him today?

JS: For starters, what worries me more than anything is that young people of today are not being turned onto Abbey, not in the way that my generation was. That scares me most.

Some people have even accused me of exploiting my friendship with Ed, and only putting his name in there [the *Zephyr*] like I have a personal thing with Edward Abbey…which is bullshit, you know. I do it simply because I want Ed Abbey's thinking to be put down somewhere on a regular basis, to remind people that this man lived and stopped here and made a difference. I do it out of honor and respect.

But I always thought that the difference between Abbey and somebody like Thoreau or Muir or any of these guys: Ed struck me as the first workingman's blue-collar environmentalist. He was a guy with this lusty desire for women and an incredible sense of humor – a self-deprecating sense of humor – and a willingness to laugh at the absurdity of life.

I mean, Ed could become so deadly serious. But he may be in a very lyrical mode, and he's describing some extraordinary scene and suddenly he writes, I once sat on the rim of a mesa [above the Rio Grande] for three days [and nights], trying to have a vision. I got hungry and saw God in the form of a beef pie. [The lines are from "How It Was," an essay in his collection, *Beyond the Wall*.] That's Abbey, taking the edge off of it, so you don't get to the point where you go, Oh, come on, I can't take one more paragraph. Which is what drew me to him: his compassion and his humor and his eloquence, all wrapped into one man. And his anger, too.

JZ: Today Abbey takes criticism for being sexist, but it seems like there's a very damaged emotional psyche to Ed Abbey, and that he was also really kind of hurting with the land.

JS: Hurting with the land and hurting with his own life. Everyone makes all these jokes about Ed and his women and all his sexual conquests, but Ed did keep falling in love. It's hard to explain.

People who think Ed got a divorce and he just moved onto the next woman, and it was, like, just one more woman to fuck…. Ed went through times when he was just destroyed by the breakup of his relationships.

There's always been this debate about whether Ed was an alcoholic or not. Dave Petersen [who edited Abbey's journals in *Confessions of a Barbarian*] has written a 3,000-word-essay in *Mountain Gazette* proving, medically, that Ed was not an alcoholic, and I think in the clinical definition of the word Ed was not. But when Ed was really down, he really did drink a massive amount of alcohol.

When his wife Judy Pepper died of cancer [in 1970], he wasn't there at the end, and then he ended up leaving Susie [his daughter] with her grandparents. He was wracked with guilt over that. So there were a lot of personal things in his life, as well as just his grief over what was happening to the planet.

JZ: You first headed out to Moab to basically go and meet Abbey, and then you did and showed him your illustration [of Glen Canyon Dam, destroyed]. What did he do? When you finally crossed paths and got to know him, did he live up to the legendary figure?

JS: That's the most amazing thing to me about Ed Abbey. I've known three or four writers in my life who I've considered authors of natural talent, and as I got to know them I became disillusioned. Except for Ed.

The odd thing about Ed was that the more I learned of his flaws, the higher he seemed to climb on the totem pole. I can't explain it. But knowing him – and knowing him and all his flaws and knowing that he didn't try and hide them, and that he was: This is who I am – made him grow in stature for me, instead of the other way around. Part of it is because not only did he stay true to his beliefs, he wrote from the heart, he wrote from the soul, but he never took himself too seriously.

One of his best buddies was this guy that just died a couple of years ago, in Moab, named Tom Arnold, who was Ed's Volkswagen mechanic. Tom's shop – Tom worked exclusively on Volkswagens – was just about a half a mile from Ed's home on Spanish Valley Drive. For awhile, Ed refused to get a phone, so every time he had to call his editor or whatever he'd go down to Tom's shop, which was the most filthy, oily, miserable, just a hovel of junk. And Tom – you've seen *The Wizard of Oz*? Frank Morgan was the actor who plays the wizard; that is Tom Arnold with this white hair, this jolly cherubic face, always had a laugh. He was also a good pilot. Believe it or not, he used to fly Ed around for some of his book readings.

Those were the kind of people who Ed revered. Those were the people who were his friends, and he never forgot them. They never ever ended up taking a backseat to some literary giant.

JZ: Here you were doing a sort of pilgrimage [to meet Abbey], and it seems like you were able to show up and be a part of this person's life. And, then, next thing you know, your illustrations are in his book?

JS: Well, for starters, it was just the right place at the right time. It was the early '70s, and *Desert Solitaire* had been out since '68, and it hadn't really started to catch on. But there was this little cadre of us who had discovered Ed, and he was just so accessible. You know, Ed was going to play poker at Treadway's house [Doug Treadway was a wilderness ranger and another friend of Abbey's] that week, that Wednesday night, and a buddy of mine came by and said, You want to give him that drawing? And I went out and I met him, and that was it.

I have to tell you I was absolutely scared to death. I was just terrified to meet him because I felt like my brain was a toilet seat compared to his. And it was.

But I remember him unrolling this drawing and he spread it across a table. He looked at it, and he was very complimentary even though it wasn't that good of a drawing. I'd even written on a rock in the drawing – there's a big chunk of the dam in the river, and I had scrawled across it – Ken Sleight was here for the ride. Ken Sleight was one of his [Abbey's] dear friends, so he spotted that. "You know Ken? Have you met Ken Sleight?" [Sleight, who still lives in southern Utah, was the inspiration for the character Seldom Seen Smith in *The Monkey Wrench Gang*.] I had just met Ken a couple weeks before so I was in hog heaven. I had met in the space of ten to twelve days Ken Sleight and then Edward Abbey.

The other thing is, I don't begin to want to portray myself as having the kind of friendship that [Doug] Peacock did. Peacock and Ed were like brothers, and their relationship was ongoing and never-ending. My relationship was sporadic, and sometimes I wouldn't see Ed for months, or even a year. He'd come to Moab and I'd see him, and it wasn't, I'd say, 'til the last two or three years that I finally started finding confidence in myself to feel like I could engage myself in real conversation with him and disagree with him.

I don't know how many times Ed invited me down to Tucson to join him on a camping trip with John DePuy [another close friend of Abbey's], and I would never go. I just felt scared, I felt intimidated. I felt like I was imposing on John and Ed, especially on those camping trips.

Finally, Ed, in 1988, said, "Stiles, I have invited you and invited you, and you never show up. I want you to come down and visit me." Being the way I am, I arrived in Tucson, and I went and I got a motel room, and then I went over to his house. He said, "Get your bags, you're sleeping in the office," and I said, Ed, I didn't want to impose, I got a motel room. And he's like, "What the hell's wrong with you? This is ridiculous, of course you're...oh, well, you paid for it tonight, but you're sleeping here the rest of the time."

I think in a way he actually kind of liked doing that – because I didn't assume I could stay with him – because if you ever read his journals, there are a few references to people who moved in on him who wouldn't leave. Anyway, that was the only time I ever asked Ed if I could take his picture. It was on the late afternoon of March 14, 1988, exactly one year to the day before he died. It's a beautiful picture. He was out chopping wood, and he's got leather gloves on and he's barefooted, and it's a profile shot of him looking into the sunset.

It was such a great time. He had just bought this Cadillac. He was so proud of this red Cadillac, not because he owned it, but because he knew how badly it was going to annoy people.

Ed and I, we decided to go to a baseball game. This was March and spring training is in Tucson, you know? The Giants used to play at Hi Corbett Field. So I remember this ride to the ballpark with Ed in his '62 Cadillac with the top down and the white leather interior, blasting our way down Speedway Boulevard. The vehicle had completely no shocks. I just remember bouncing every time we went under a viaduct or something.

But, anyway, we got into this debate about humanity

and for some reason I was, like, defending humans, and Ed was—I remember distinctly, his line was—"Stiles, what the hell's wrong with you? You know 90 percent of all people should be put up against the wall and shot. They're all swine." And I said something like, Ed, you know damn well that you personally could not line 90 percent of the world's population up against the wall and shoot them. And he looked at me and he said, "What the hell's wrong with you? Do we have some goddamned liberal or something?"

Anyway, so we got near the ballpark and it was a fairly big crowd. So, he said, You buy the tickets and I'll go park the car. So I went and I bought the tickets, and then I waited for Ed to show up. I waited and I waited and I waited and 45 minutes went by. And finally here he comes. He used to wear this big white cowboy hat with a real wide brim and it had a hatband made out of pull-tabs from beer cans. So, Ed, even from a distance, he towered above the masses, and you see this guy coming toward me and he had this terrible scowl on his face.

He finally walks up and he says, "Did you get the

goddamn tickets?" I say, Yeah, I got them like 45 minutes ago. It's already in the second inning. Where the hell have you been? He says, "I couldn't find a damn place to park the damn car." And I said, Well, if you didn't have a car that was 36 feet long you probably would've found something a little bit easier, and he looked at me and he just broke into this big grin, and, "Yes, Stiles, but then what would I have to complain about?"

I remember sitting there during the game, and he actually ordered a beer. It was the first beer he had in, like, three years. A ballpark beer. Because Ed had to quit drinking altogether. So we sat there and drank a beer and I don't think we watched any of the game, we just talked throughout the whole thing. I'd give anything to remember what our conversations were about but.... Anyway, I ended up spending the rest of the time sleeping down in his office, where he died a year later.

That's not the last time I saw him though. He came to Moab in December of '88, and he was promoting *The Fool's Progress* – then at the time, Ken Sleight had a bookstore, so he was selling copies of his book. Ed used to hate those book signings. He only did it to sell books and to meet girls. This middle-aged woman came up to him and she said, You know, Mr. Abbey, I'm an author too, and I'd like to ask you a question. How long should a novel be? He looked at her and he said—I can't remember exactly—"Um, 313 pages." And she said, Thank God, I'm almost done. And he looked over at me, because I was just kind of sitting in the corner. That was the last time I saw him.

Then I told him about the *Zephyr* and the plan, and he thought it was great and he said, I want to put a story in there. So, then in January, I heard he was really sick and I called Clarke, and at the time there was a total coverup with Clarke: No, Ed's fine, everything's fine, no worries. So I went, Alright, but I still continued to hear these rumors.

Well, then I knew he was sick to some degree and in February here comes this story. He sends this original story with a letter, and I don't have the manuscript of the story, but I still have the letter and it's a letter of apology. He says, "Stiles, here is the story I promised you, however, I must tell you it has never been published in the United States or in the English language, but it is not what I had intended. I wanted to write something just for you, but I am trying to beat the deadline for *Hayduke Lives*, and as soon as I get that done I will send you something just for the *Zephyr*." I mean, here he is dying, trying to get this book done, and he still remembers to send me this story, you know? That was Ed Abbey.

JZ: I imagine that your decision to start the *Zephyr* very much followed your interest in Abbey. Today, would you say you're trying to carry on the spirit of what he was doing and saying?

JS: It really is. I mean the big difference is I know I could never fill Ed Abbey's shoes. Nobody could ever do that. Ed Abbey was unique and no one will ever be like him again. All I tried to do is continue the passion that he had for the land, and his honesty and his integrity. Nobody could ever match his talent or his intellect, or his ability to move people, but I would have never started the *Zephyr*...my father wanted me to be an insurance salesman for Allstate Insurance.

It's very rare, I think, where you can look back on your life and you can say there was this moment where your entire life was changed completely by one event. And it was my father's friend, Bill Parker, handing me a copy of *Desert Solitaire*. Then just the icing on the cake was meeting him [Abbey]. Whether I ever met Ed Abbey or not, I think I would probably still be doing the things that I do. But then to meet him, and to meet the man and to know who he was and what was really a part of his soul...

JZ: Today, you're trying to address these issues that he did. What do you think about the idea that we need another Ed Abbey?

JS: I'm really glad you said that: Where are the Ed Abbeys? I think there are Ed Abbeys out there, but they can't be heard. Ed Abbey came at the right time where he established himself as a real icon of the American West and American literature, to where they couldn't refuse to publish him. He was a voice that people wanted to hear, and whether the editors of the magazine agreed with him or not, they knew that he was going to sell magazines for them.

But try to say something now that goes against the grain, and you can't get your voice heard at all. I think there are lots of writers—and like I said, he's unique —but I think there are Ed Abbeys out there who are trying to do that and they just can't. All I can do now is put out this little paper [online since 2008] that doesn't reach that many people.

JZ: I agree with you, on one hand, that there are writers and other crusaders of sorts trying to raise some of the issues as Abbey did. But what has turned into your passion—fighting industrial recreation, commodification of resources, and the corporate influence on environmental groups—is that getting lost in a larger debate, or have we passed on those issues?

JS: The longest thing I've ever written in my life was in the August/September '08 Zephyr, "Greening the

Wilderness, Part 2," it was like 12,000 words. I went back into the old Grand Canyon Trust magazines all the way back to the mid '90s, and we found a quote where they said that all things recreational and the urbanization of the rural West are going to destroy it more than anything else that we're fighting. They admitted the problem more concisely than I have. But then they just walked away from it. They backed away from it because, as more and more of this money poured into the Grand Canyon Trust, the people who sit on their board have no interest in seeing those kinds of restrictions and those kinds of messages being put out. So, go to the Grand Canyon Trust website and just look at who's on their board of directors. It will blow your mind. The words private equity keep jumping up...private equity, private equity, banking, banking investment.

But, you know, sometimes I think the biggest problem is that we're just not reading anymore. I think it's just the dumbing down of the culture. I keep doing these 2,500- and 3,000-word stories in the *Zephyr*, and all I do is get complaints, like, I don't want to read that much. They want 15-word sound bites.

In this next issue of the *Zephyr* [the October/ November 2009 issue], I started a page called the Twit Page. What I'm doing is I'm taking famous speeches or works of literature and I'm printing the first 140 characters. Then I'm printing how Sarah Palin would turn it into a tweet. So, first is the first 140 characters of the Gettysburg Address, and then the second is how Sarah Palin would tweet the Gettysburg Address. I was able to do it in 135 characters.

A Noble Warrior:
A Conversation with Doug Peacock

Interviewed by Joshua Zaffos

When Edward Abbey published his classic novel, The Monkey Wrench Gang, *in 1975, his character, George Washington Hayduke, a feral and damaged Vietnam vet, roused a generation of young environmentalists to protect the remaining expanses of unroaded public lands from mounting industrial pressures. Hayduke was modeled on Abbey's close friend, Doug Peacock, a Green Beret combat medic who served in Vietnam and found sanctuary in the wilderness when he returned from the war. The monkeywrenching antics chronicled in Abbey's book are mostly fiction, according to Peacock, but Hayduke and his band of anti-industrial, wilderness crusaders inspired the creation of Earth First! and a new tide of activism in defense of wild places.*

Throughout the 1970s and '80s, Peacock would spend months alone in the backcountry of Yellowstone and Glacier national parks, living among and observing grizzly bears. His memoir, The Grizzly Years, *published in 1990, details his experiences, and established Peacock as a keen and passionate advocate for bear conservation and wilderness preservation.*

His 2005 book, Walking It Off, *chronicles flashbacks from Vietnam, Peacock's travels around the world, and his relationship with Abbey, including Abbey's final days and his desert burial in March 1989, carried out by Peacock.*

Peacock still writes on the importance of protecting bears and large carnivores and of preserving wild places. He is also a board member of Round River Conservation Studies, a nonprofit organization that supports international conservation research and education. He agreed to speak to me during the annual meeting of the Western Literature Association in October 2009. We met on a cold afternoon inside the Holiday Inn in Spearfish, South Dakota, and were immediately confronted with some news that made both of us ornery: The hotel bar wouldn't be open for an hour.

Joshua Zaffos: In your mind, what makes Abbey and his work still matter twenty years down the road? How has that changed at all?

Doug Peacock: I don't think it has changed. He was a lot more unique than we imagined and that's hard to believe, knowing him as I did from 1968, right after *Desert Solitaire*, all the way to his grave.

But he told the truth. He didn't bullshit. He told the truth and he kept his promises. He was trustworthy almost always…like, you'd trust your life to him, but not your woman.

You know, that is so rare. He was able to come at the issues of his day – our day, they're all the same. He was unique because right off he saw what was important: that the wilderness is the only thing worth saving, and to identify that nut really clarifies your vision.

And then he would take on, I wouldn't say enemies, but he took on all these adversaries with a fair amount of grace and humor. He could laugh at himself, and he could collectively make us laugh at ourselves, and that is so needed today. I'm ashamed of myself sometimes when I lose my sense of humor.

JZ: I've been reading your book, *Walking It Off*, and you use the phrase, "humorous fanaticism," which seems to capture Abbey's injection of humor into situations. But there was also his level of cynicism, and a certain machismo. It seemed like he introduced a kind of personality to wilderness preservation and, while he might never have considered himself an environmentalist, he put this really human face on the grand environmental movement.

DP: Well, he certainly gave a style, and that style was wacky and attractive, and also effective. That why's *The Monkey Wrench Gang* sold I don't even know how many copies, just by word of mouth. It never got reviewed by anybody in the East.

And that's why Earth First! just picked it up: They already had a persona around which to form their group. They were young men at the time. They were almost delusional; they thought they were Hayduke. But nonetheless they were effective and it expanded the dialogue about what's important and how to fight for conservation causes—you know, no compromise. The Sierra Club looked really right in the middle of things once Earth First! showed up, and I thought that was good, a real service. They [Earth First!] modeled themselves almost directly out of that spirit of *The Monkey Wrench Gang*.

I'm distinguishing really...it wasn't his persona so much; it was his work. He wasn't a unique character, he wasn't even comfortable in the limelight, to tell you the truth. When he did give a performance he was sort of ashamed of himself for not being more serious.

JZ: Abbey's work gives voice to anger or frustration with where things were going in the world. Reading your work, it seems like, for obvious reasons, he really resonated with where you were mentally, and I imagine where a lot of people were, at the time.

DP: Well, you know I just happened to be at that place in my life where I felt like it wasn't even worth the devil anymore. When I met Abbey I was just one crazy sonuvabitch.

[Before going to Vietnam,] I was an antiwar activist at the University of Michigan. I invited Norman Thomas [the 1960s-era Socialist presidential candidate] to come in and talk. Tom Hayden [the cofounder of the Students for a Democratic Society, and civil rights activist] was my mentor. I invited Martin Luther King to come talk, nobody else did that, I did that on my own.

I went from there to a war and I came back out again, and I may be antiwar but I'm certainly not nonviolent. I think I have written that I was probably looking for a noble war worth fighting, aimed in the direction of life. Abbey had already identified his battleground and we just, without discussion almost, shared this point of view on the importance of wild places.

JZ: For people like me, who found Abbey in the '90s or even more recently, *Desert Solitaire* is still a very powerful book in terms of environmental writing. At the time when it first was published, was there a pretty instantaneous response?

DP: I was dodging bullets when *Desert Solitaire* came out, I was still in Vietnam. But I came back to visit my friends and they had read this book, and it did, it changed their lives all of a sudden. First of all, some of them weren't even outdoor-wilderness kind of people, conservation kind of people. And maybe they were only talking about pulling up stakes, but they were doing that and it was a giant leap.

There was one simple reason for that, and that was Edward Abbey.

JZ: It seems like he helped move along American environmentalism from having been this appreciation of the sublime to a movement where you can really work through your issues and in doing that you're working on these larger issues as well.

DP: You also saw these same places that you found of value—wild places—being destroyed, going away, just as you're discovering how important they are, and you're discovering them on a personal level and maybe on a species level.

I don't think the human species have much of a chance these days, but what little chance we have still depends, just like Abbey said thirty years ago, on the defense of big, wild places and, by inference, the corridors and linkages that make for a world, which is really going down the tubes.

The global picture is so critical. I think you'll live to see your life dramatically changed. Wait for just another big iceberg to fall off Antarctica. You got sea rise up to over twenty feet, that's enough to displace billions of starving people in the world to then go someplace else, and we're not going to be able to grow things. I'm talking about the climate. There's going to be war, water's going to go away, and this social and political and economic fabric that we've all counted on since I was born, I believe, is gone. Not just going away, but gone.

You know, the simple equation is that which evolves doesn't continue to exist without the conditions of its creation, or its genesis. We didn't evolve out of an agrarian-industrial landscape. We evolved out of Africa and other places. Human intelligence was born of hunting and living in places whose remnants today we call wilderness.

JZ: On the other side, what are the successes you see since you and Abbey first met? We have a lot more protected wilderness in the US and elsewhere in the world.

DP: We see this and that, but on the whole we've lost ground. How much wilderness do we need? Abbey asked that question a long goddamn time ago, and he said, at least as much as we've got left. And we've lost a lot since then.

Someone asked me about SUWA [the Southern Utah Wilderness Alliance] today. They've got this nice little plan for connecting this wilderness area with that, and sometimes they are adjacent [referring to America's Red Rock Wilderness Act, a bill before Congress that would protect 9.4 million acres of "wilderness-quality land" in Utah]. Without that, the loss is for the mammals and reptiles and birds and plants that need to move, and that's pretty much what we've done. We started saving pretty places like national parks and we've just compromised the hell out of big wilderness. We just don't have any left in the continental United States.

JZ: In the '70s, you began to spend time living among grizzly bears in Yellowstone and Glacier national parks. How directly did your relationship with Abbey and other folks from that time lead to your decision to go up to Yellowstone and Glacier?

DP: No. That wasn't it. I was headed off on my own, and there was no mistake.

Abbey and I were already solid. He was the most difficult close friend in my life. Don't get me wrong, he was a fucking nasty, cantankerous sonuvabitch and I was awful, I was awful. But nonetheless, it lasted all that time. When the final days came, I was right there again.

But, no, just those first few years after I came back from Vietnam, I just couldn't be around people, and I just camped out in the Rocky Mountains, basically all the way up and down. I'd run into grizzly bears, so that just propelled me. But in the winter I'd get back here [to the Southwest]. Abbey visited me up in Glacier. It'd be perfect, but every trip we took to the Grizzly Hilton [a site in the park where Peacock observed grizzlies], he never saw a bear. Only one in the world who went to his grave talking about the alleged griz, you know? He never saw one. I mean he went down fucking rivers in Alaska and didn't see one.

JZ: There's certainly part of Abbey's humor directed at a level of womanizing and machismo. How does that connect with the wilderness ethic that came out of his work?

DP: Abbey would poke fun at this [referring to the submission guidelines for this issue of *Matter*, which include, "We're not interested in gratuitous violence or sex, or misogyny, bigotry, etc. Just because Abbey was a womanizer and misogynist at times in his writings doesn't mean we gotta be, too."]. I could say he'd hate it but…

I resent that. He was not a misogynist. He loved women and he treated women as equals. Now I knew him through a lot of women, all ages, our daughters, our mothers, our wives, girlfriends, everything, and he was never condescending, and he was not a misogynist.

I never saved any correspondence—Ed and I just wrote to each other, I always just tossed them—but he'd get these terrible letters from these feminists, and he'd show them to me. He'd write back, just making an appropriate retort. He had a great sense of humor and he rattled their cages, and he loved rattling their cages.

He was anything but a misogynist. I take exception, I resent that.

The worst of machismo: Go down to a narco town in Chihuahua or anywhere in the Sierra Madres and you'll see it at its rawest, ugliest fucking self. It doesn't care about life because it was born of nothing. It wants to subjugate everything—plant, animal, woman—and that's the heart of it. It doesn't respect life. Abbey was the opposite of that.

JZ: In reading his books, including *The Monkey Wrench Gang*, Abbey always refers to stashing guns and peanut butter. Did you guys used to eat a lot of peanut butter back in the day?

DP: We did stash some things. I still have a .44 Mag buried in Mexico that I use when I'm down there, that I'll carry again, and that started from the old days.

But a lot of the stuff out of *The Monkey Wrench Gang* is just talk. It was cheap. And that's not all we did. What we did was fairly lightweight in the grander scheme of things. It was as much recreational as subversive. It usually involved some pranking. It was something, well, we'll be sitting around here, why don't we go out and do something?

JZ: Do you see the benefits even if monkeywrenching wasn't going to stop the gears of industry?

DP: It made a few people open their eyeballs and say, well, not everybody approves of this. And that's worth doing. That's worth doing.

JZ: Do we need to be doing more of that today?

DP: Yeah, at least. This is a totalitarian government with the leftover terrorism laws, and they have every way to fucking look in on you. Ed Abbey would have gone crazy with the amount of governmental surveillance of private citizenry. They're crazy.

What'd they do when Ashcroft—asshole—got his antiterrorist laws approved? He went after those pathetic poor people who burned down the condos in Colorado. What a fucking chickenshit, you know? Instead of going after real armed, dangerous people. It's sad sometimes. But you can never get too enamored with your own image, and once you start reading your own press, you're dead.

JZ: In *Walking It Off*, you share the scene where Abbey dies and you say the real Hayduke died then.

DP: Hayduke was a great fictional character. He [Abbey] borrowed elegantly and he nailed things like posttraumatic stress—before there was such a word in the English language—accurately, just by observing myself, in this case. And he really did it well in *The Monkey Wrench Gang*.

But Hayduke is a great creation of Ed Abbey, superficially based on a lot of me, but I am not Hayduke, and Hayduke isn't quite Abbey either.

He had a life unto his own and that's fine with me. I just didn't want anybody running off and claiming that ground. I don't know why anybody wants to do that, but they did.

JZ: The character is this kind of great hero/antihero and...

DP: A dolt. A great, big, strong dolt.

JZ: As you said, here's this character who's walking around with—what everyone in our post-Iraq world would call—PTSD, and is there a resonance today as we're going to have this generation of men and women who are leaving military service and probably dealing with a lot of these same issues?

DP: I wish they'd take it on the road and pull a Hayduke for us, you know? Every single one of them. I mean that's also pretty good therapy. You're always doing something. It's better than being quietly desperate.

JZ: You literally had Ed Abbey standing next to you, but there were obviously plenty of people in the '70s who never knew Abbey personally. Do you think he had the same effect on them?

DP: Yeah, that was his real hope between monkey wrenching and political hope. It was to inspire thousands of independent cells and activists all over. They'd just spread out like brush fires.

The FBI conveniently waited for Ed to be dead before they busted those suckers in Prescott [activists in Arizona accused of cutting power lines]. The morning they busted those guys, they also busted Dave Foreman [an early leader of Earth First!], and they were at my front door in Tucson, but I wasn't home.

JZ: Do you think we need, I hate to say it, another Ed Abbey? How major of a role do you think writers or anyone else plays these days?

DP: They're not doing much of a job. They aren't. We really do need Ed Abbey. We don't have him. That's not working.

We live in a really timid world. We're timid, we're scared, we're endangered species biologically and, at some level, we know it. We're having all kinds of physical, *Time-Magazine*-type political problems, wars, economic pressures, and then we've got this totalitarian government that really almost is a police state and wants to be.

I don't think Obama's going to be able to walk us out of that one, or if he'll have enough time. We'll see, we'll see. Maybe there's some hope on a political level. I never trust that level to affect change very much, but you can't lose all hope and I haven't lost hope.

My prognosis is pretty fucking grim. But I'll fight to the end. And so would've Abbey.

No Government Should Ever be Trusted:
A Conversation with Charles Bowden

Interviewed by Todd Simmons

Following the truth wherever it leads has guided Charles Bowden for the last thirty-five years as an essayist and journalist into drug-crazed border towns and corrupt economic disasters. Known for searing prose and top-notch investigative stories in such books as Blood Orchid: An Unnatural History of America *and* Murder City: Ciudad Juarez and the Global Economy's New Killing Fields, *Bowden's insight into matters dark and deadly is always brutally honest. Bowden met Edward Abbey accidentally in the early 1980s, but a friendship soon formed and lasted for the latter part of Abbey's life.*

Honesty flowed from the phone during our conversation in late 2009, and I was impressed with the care Bowden took to make sure I understood the differences between the myth of Edward Abbey in comparison to the man he spent time with. Abbey's memory hung thick though transparent in Bowden's fond remembrances. Issues that infuriated Edward Abbey most during his life have only escalated in the time since he died—fragmented or destroyed natural ecosystems, unchecked industrialization and the exploitation of people for profit. Bowden's literary efforts to date seek out the same gritty truth.

TS: Thanks for talking with me about Edward Abbey. Start with when you first read him or when you got to know him personally.

CB: Well, I can tell you when I first got to know him. I was a reporter for a newspaper in the early 1980s and I was sent to interview Dave Foreman, one of the founders of Earth First!. He was staying at Ed Abbey's house, and that's how I met Ed, and we became friends. It was an accident.

TS: So you knew who he was?

CB: Yes, but I had never met him. And frankly when I got the job, I just went there, I didn't know it was his place. We just hit it off, it's hard to explain things like that. I just liked him, and he seemed to not dislike me too much. We became friends, and we used to have lunch a lot. After that, I ran a magazine there in Tucson, and he used to write for me. What I liked about him was that he was thoughtful. I didn't talk about the environment with Ed, because we both knew we agreed, so there was really nothing to say. We spent more time talking about politics, books—we were both big closet readers, so we'd argue about writers, talk about writers, and eat lunch.

TS: Did you disagree about anything in particular?

CB: No, not really, partly because of my own nature—if I feel like people are honest with me, I don't much care what they say. It doesn't bother me if I disagree with them. I know Ed was a little excessive with some of his comments, like rounding up everyone with AIDS, and isolating them in the desert in some sort of concentration camp, because he was afraid that they would ruin one of his joys in life—sex—with this disease. He liked to write things like that. He became famous, or infamous, for saying every illegal Mexican should be stopped at the US border, given a Winchester rifle, and a case of ammunition, and be sent home to fix his country. Obviously it was not a policy he thought would occur, but it was seen by some as racist. But I always thought people like that didn't understand polemics. He liked being kind of rasty with what he wrote. What I'm trying to tell you was the person I knew wasn't like that at all. He was rather soft-spoken, and liked to listen to classical music, particularly Charles Ives. The reason people still read Ed is because he is fun to read—he's kind of rollicking. He told people that you can belong to the West if you're willing to defend it, and it's one part of the world left worth defending.

TS: How do you think we're doing on that?
CB: I think we are failing. The greatest defense of the West I've seen in my lifetime is the current collapse of the American economy. It's the only thing I've seen stop this endless expansion of housing in an area with no resource base to possibly sustain these populations. I think Ed would agree with me, but it's hard to speak for him. Actually there's no need to speak for Ed, he left enough in his writing that you can know pretty much what he thought about anything.

TS: It would seem like most of his arguments are still relevant today.
CB: That's because they were rooted. What he was as a writer was a classical anarchist, meaning, if you read Bakunin and the classical anarchists of the 19th century, he didn't think anybody had a right to have power over anyone else, he didn't think any government should ever be trusted, and to the degree anybody thinks government is necessary, the least amount is the best

amount. There's no question how he'd feel about the Iraq wars, he wouldn't think one nation had the right to invade another nation, just like I don't have any question about how he'd feel about gun control. He was a grounded person, take-it-or-leave-it type of thing.

Ed was the editor for one issue of the literary magazine at the University of New Mexico in Albuquerque, and then he was fired. He put on the cover a famous quote by Voltaire, and I'm quoting from memory: "I want to live long enough to see the last king strangled with the entrails of the last priest." Ed put it on the cover of his first issue, but he attributed it to Louisa May Alcott…[intense laughter]…that was the end of his editorship. Apparently they were humorless back in the early '50s up there at the lit mag at Albuquerque. Actually, Ken Sanders, who runs Ken Sanders Rare Books in Salt Lake City, has a copy of that issue, he showed it to me once. I always thought it was folklore, but it isn't, he actually did it.

TS: A lot of people don't know what to believe about him—there's a huge myth surrounding Edward Abbey.
CB: There always is—he's always giving these phony addresses where he was living because he was, he told me, one step ahead of some sheriff demanding alimony payments from his ex-wife. He would give these fictitious towns that he was living in…well one of them, Wolf Hole, up there in the Arizona Strip, has been uninhabited for at least 50 years. He did that, and of course he wrote this kind of Paul Bunyan-esque stuff sometimes.

TS: He understood the power of myth, and he moved it along sometimes.
CB: He became a captive of it. He wanted to be taken

seriously as a novelist, and instead, he became a legend. He was of a generation where the Great American Novel was the thing to achieve, you know, the late '40s, early '50s, when he really got into it, and that's what he wanted to be judged as. Instead he became Cactus Ed, famous for his non-fiction and his polemics, with the exception of *The Monkey Wrench Gang*, the novel he wrote thinking it would become a movie and then he could never worry about money again. That's one thing I think your readers should know—he never made much money. I'm sure he's been a better breadwinner dead than alive.

TS: Yes, he's still holding steady in his popularity.
CB: A lot of writers survive because they are assigned in universities. Ed's not one of those. People actually just read him, like Mark Twain or Kurt Vonnegut. He actually has a readership, particularly in the West. His ideal was magazines all the time in the East, with an occasional novel. And they really don't know who he is. When I mention Edward Abbey, they'll either think I'm talking about Abbie Hoffmann or Edward Albee.

I know when he died, because he told me, almost all his book sales were west of the Mississippi. He was read in the West. I think since then he has become more national, but I don't know, because I'm not his publisher, and I don't know what his sales are, but I know that I see his books sold at a lot of places, because they're easy to read. They're written clearly, they've got humor, and they've got bite. What's not to like?

TS: The rumor is that once again they are trying to make the big screen version of *The Monkey Wrench Gang*.
CB: I heard that too. Ken Sanders actually keeps abreast

of that stuff. I don't. *The Monkey Wrench Gang* has been optioned every year since it was written. There have been times that it got close to being produced. It's a movie that can only be made in a certain quirky moment, because what it endorses is destroying public and private property. Not many movies do that.

TS: How much did he help your own writing career, or did he help it along?

CB: Not at all. He tried to. I wrote a book called *Blue Desert*, and he told me where to send it in New York to this agent, which was his agent, and the guy rejected it out of hand. Which is what you'll find, and I'm sure you have making these phone calls—Ed helped everyone, or tried to. He'd write a note for almost anyone to whatever connections he had in publishing. He was a generous person. It just so happens that his efforts on my behalf were to no avail. He was always sending postcards to people, encouraging them. You could fill a decent sized auditorium with people he tried to help get published.

TS: I read Doug Peacock's book on grizzly bears because of his connection to Ed, and it was a great book. Any others writers connected to Ed that we should read?

CB: Ed was also a champion of Terry Tempest Williams, a quite different kind of person. He taught this non-fiction writing class for a couple of years down at the University of Arizona. I know he would try to help students get published. He had an interesting criteria for his class—you couldn't get an A in the class unless a piece you wrote for the class was published in a magazine that paid you money. It was actually a pretty rational standard. Students are taking the class to learn how to write non-fiction for magazines…well that's how you got an A, actually sell some of this shit... (laughter)... I don't have any bad memories of Ed, except he died on me.

TS: Do you think that Ed had too much fun with what he was doing for people to take him seriously?
CB: I don't think that at all. I think he was too serious and too radical for people to want to take him seriously. He really thought the planet was overpopulated. He really thought that Industrial Civilization was a mistake. He really thought that half of Arizona should be declared a wilderness. Period. That I know because he wrote an op-ed piece when I was working for a newspaper, and they wouldn't publish it. It was an interesting piece. Classic Edward Abbey—he wanted 50% of the state of Arizona made into a wilderness. And he wanted to be generous, so he gave humans half, and every other organism the other half. It was kind of charming to read. And he wrote another op-ed piece about a huge new sewage plant in Tucson. He wanted to name it after the biggest developer in town because he'd done more than any other human to fill it.

TS: What's your favorite work of Ed's?
CB: "A Writer's Credo," an essay in one of his later collections. It's about what he thought writing should be about, and frankly he thought writing should be about truth. It's based on a speech he gave at Harvard. But hell, I enjoy the fun stuff too, like *The Monkey Wrench Gang*. The book I had the most trouble with was probably *Desert Solitaire*, mainly because I agreed with it all, so I thought, why did he write this? I was flabbergasted that it became this big book. I just realized how insulated I was. The book changed the way people talked about things like National Parks, etc. The thrust of the book,

toward the end, was that they (National Parks) are not for people. It was a full blast attack on Industrial Tourism, as he called it.

TS: Yeah, I worked for the Park Service for a few years after college, fighting bureaucracy the whole way, and had to get out of that system.

CB: I've talked to others like you who had to get out. The same thing is happening in the National Forests. Used to be you started in the Service and you found your forest, and then you died in it. You became a steward and knew every square inch. Now you get off career track if you do that. I think it's led to a deterioration of care and understanding of the forests. It's too bad. When I was a kid, having a job at a National Park was one of the greatest jobs in the world. They pay you to be outside. I think things change. We'll have to restore the Park Service I guess. Now they are very worried because visitation for a number of years has been declining. Apparently people would rather watch the Discovery Channel than visit the real thing. I'm not sure that is bad. I think the Parks were getting beaten to death. I know the Park Service is concerned. They've been starved to death for decades in real dollars. They are tattered. They keep adding, for political reasons, cannonball parks, which take money. They don't add real money to maintain the parks. So you ruin them. It's a fact. Seems to me that Homeland Security means nothing if it doesn't take care of the land itself.

TS: As far as writers who make the land the central character of their books, Ed probably hated the term nature writer.

CB: He looked at it as a ghetto. He wanted to be known as a writer, and not as a Western writer. Neither do I.

At the end of September, I give the keynote address at the Western Literature Association, and I don't really have any interest in regional writing, *per se*. They are like ghettos. Writing should just stand. I don't think Dostoyevsky is a good little writer from St. Petersburg, Russia. Tolstoy, Interesting Count from Central Russia. I don't think he wanted to be a nature writer, a Western writer—he wanted to be an American Novelist. He wrote about what he knew. Most of his books take place in the West because that's where he spent most of his life, deliberately, since he saw it out the door of a boxcar in '44, before he had to go off to the war. I think he got it done, personally. When he died he'd said what he wanted to say. He'd established both a criterion and credo with what to do about the land. He was interested in the wild land; he isn't like Wendell Berry. Wendell Berry has been interested in sustainable agriculture, out there working his teams in Kentucky. I'm a fan of Wendell Berry, *The Unsettling of America* is a great book. He has basically been saying the same thing as Ed was, in a difference circumstance.

TS: Does anything surprise you with what is said about Edward Abbey these days?
DP: It's kind of odd to have someone who was a friend, and then have him become a demi-god or legend. I'm glad it happened, but it's a misunderstanding. If Ed Abbey ever ran into a guru, and Ed had a gun in his hand, he'd shoot him dead. If you actually read his stuff, he'd tell you to think for yourself, not become an acolyte. Defend personal freedom and the ground you stand on. He's certainly a clear writer, you can't misunderstand what he means. I used to tell people that I wanted to live long enough so that no one would read Edward Abbey, because they would all agree with him and protect the

land, that reading him would be unnecessary. I think it's going to be a while. He'll be necessary for a long time. We're still going through a fire storm of hypermoney, overpopulation—a human population that exceeds the carrying capacity of the land in North America—we can't sustain this many over the long haul. So yeah, it'll be awhile. I was just reading Saint Augustine, and he's been dead for 1600 years. Some things don't wear out if they address the right questions.

TS: How hard did he have to work on his writing?
CB: Very hard. I've seen his drafts. He'd bring this shit in to the magazine or newspaper to publish, and it was all scratched out, and lines drawn everywhere, looked like a bunch of snakes. Anybody who writes so it seems effortless has spent a lot of effort to get it to that point. One of the obvious points of writing is to get your reader to forget that they are reading, just experiencing it and hearing it. He worked most of his life with very little recognition. He worked as a ranger until the 1970s, up in fire towers and everywhere else, because he couldn't make enough money writing to eat, and his eating standards were pretty low. A can of beans and the bullets he needed to poach a deer from a beat-up truck. He didn't need to live high off the hog. He was dedicated to what he did or he never would have done it. He left a considerable body of work that was original. If you read Joseph Wood Krutch and some others before him, these people are from another planet. These people are appreciating the mountains and desert. Ed's devouring them. It's like having a guide to a savage fucking feast. He's a creature of appetite for what he writes about, instead of a person trying to convey an aesthetic.

TS: Ed seems to take a lot from Thoreau.

CB: I've never been a real Thoreauvian. Ed was; he worshipped Thoreau. Walden Pond has never been quite the size I needed. And frankly, I think Henry would've written a little better if he'd fucked a few more broads, but that's just my opinion. Sitting out there a mile from Concord watching ants isn't enough of a life for me. I think he was in many ways a tortured person. The thing that redeems Thoreau was that he was right—he was right not to pay his poll tax to endorse a government that endorsed slavery; he was right about the Mexican War, it was a terrible mistake. He was right about the importance of wilderness. I wouldn't say Ed was envious of Thoreau, but Ed loved writing aphorisms, and I think he got that disease from reading Thoreau. His journal was full of his efforts to craft aphorisms, which would then show up in his books. Some of them are pretty good—"I'm a humanist, I'd sooner kill a man than a snake." Some of them have a real ring to them. He was always good company to me. I've missed him every day since he died, because there's one less person to really talk to.

TS: Any parting words on Edward Abbey?

CB: I'll give you one sentence. If you can't understand him, you haven't listened. What I really like about him, as far as reading him—it's been twenty years since he died—is that he's always good company. Just like you can walk into a bookstore, killing time, and pull some Vonnegut off the shelf, crack it open and read a page or two—he's always good company too. They're both from the same strain of American writing. They're oral, meaning their writing comes from hearing people tell stories. It's always got a rhythm, a rollicking nature to it. He's the guy on the barstool next to you who you turn to because you actually want to hear what he's saying.

Wilderness Calendars and *Ms.* Magazine:
A Conversation with Ken Sanders

Interviewed by Sara Eden

Ken Sanders owns and runs Ken Sanders Rare Books in Salt Lake City, Utah. He also runs Dream Garden Press, which published the illustrated edition of The Monkey Wrench Gang *(illustrations by R. Crumb). A man of many talents and interests, Ken worked with Edward Abbey on a number of publishing projects, Earth First! events, as well as became his good friend.*

Ken Sanders Rare Books is described as a "destination" instead of just a bookstore. Ken's passion for books guides the store and his life. His curious mind never seems to rest, and he's always coming up with new and varied projects.

Sara Eden: You give lectures about Edward Abbey. How did that start?

Ken Sanders: Well, I knew Ed back in the day. We did a lot of things together and I published some of his books. I became friends with him. When he died, for those of us who knew him—even if by knowing him it meant you just read his books or maybe met him once at an autograph party or something like that—it left a huge, huge hole. People were gathering in the Ed Abbey sections of bookstores hanging out 'cause they just didn't know what to do with themselves. I couldn't— for years I didn't want to—talk about Ed. It was too raw and painful in the beginning. The thing is, Ed was a forceful personality and a very large man physically. When he died, people came out of the woodwork kind of putting their arm around the ghost of Edward Abbey, saying, "Oh and Edward Abbey was my best friend," and all this nonsense. They could get away with doing that because the spine was off the cactus; the rattle was off the snake, so to speak. They'd never in a million years do anything like that when Ed was alive because he would've tore 'em a new asshole! (laughter) Literally! But dead he couldn't fight back and I found it disgusting.

But a few years ago various friends of mine who teach at universities around here said, "Hey I got this class, we're doing Environmental Literature, will you come and talk about Ed Abbey?" I thought, well, what the hell. The classes were an hour long, twenty or thirty students. No big deal. I actually found myself liking it. And the students seemed to really like it. I'd get feedback from them sometimes. They'd e-mail, "Ah, we thought we were going to have this boring lecture about an old dead guy we never heard of, and instead we got you and wow, that was really interesting."

SE: Do you feel that Ed's been exploited since his death by movements like Earth First! or other environmental movements?

KS: Well, in its first days, in the '80s, Earth First!—the original Earth First! was very much inspired by Ed, and *The Monkey Wrench Gang* in particular. So I would say, no that's not true. He actively supported and encouraged them. He gave them money. He showed up to Earth First! activities. I was heavily involved with Earth First! from '81 to '85, beginning with the cracking of the dam in '81. But by the mid-'80s, things had gotten ugly and strange and that's when I left. I could see the handwriting on the wall. I don't mean to denigrate these other movements, but Earth First! was about saving ecosystems and biotic communities and wilderness, and all of a sudden—partly because of Foreman[1*] and company recruiting on college campuses—we got an infusion of young people into the group. We weren't all that old ourselves then. I was in my late twenties to early thirties. At first it was a breath of fresh air and I think Earth First! accomplished a lot through guerrilla theatre, in particular. These guys were so crazy that they made the Wilderness Society and the Sierra Club look like old fogies.

I think Earth First! served a purpose. But over the years it degenerated into all these movements within movements. ELF and ALF and vegan rights people and people interested in this, that or the other. That didn't necessarily have anything to do with wilderness. It became very splintered, very contentious and infiltrated by agents, provocateurs and undercover FBI. I told Foreman and the rest of the founders, "Look, we should have a hippie-style party and bury this thing because it's out of control." I didn't like the limelight. Foreman had this whole rootsy-Texas-Baptist-preacher thing, and he really embraced the limelight. I kind of ran from it horrified. I'd organized a lot of events for him over the years from nuclear waste issues to Glen Canyon dam. I didn't want to become responsible for all these young people's actions and lives, as mistakes became increasingly serious. The people on the other side were using bullets and playing for keeps. We didn't have any intention of hurting anyone or blowing anything up, but they did. And they would blame it on us.

Anyhow, things did go horribly awry in the late

---

1   * Dave Foreman, one of the five EF! founders.

'80s. "They," whoever "they" are, blew up Judy Bari[2*], the redwoods activist, in her own car! They planted a bomb in it! She lived but they blew her pelvis up for God's sake! Things got really ugly.

SE: Is that when you started your bookstore Cosmic Aeroplane?

KS: In the '70s. It was an old hippie shop from the '60s and we turned it into a legitimate bookstore. That was when I met Ed, around the time *Monkey Wrench* was published. He was sleeping in Moab, Utah, at the time. He moved down to Tucson because after *The Monkey Wrench Gang* was published in '75, Moab got to be too small a town for him. The locals didn't care for that book. *The San Juan County Record*, the newspaper down there, said, "The author of this book should be castrated and neutered." In print. They published that.

SE: That's a strong reaction.

KS: Ed actually liked it because the book evoked that kind of response from both the radical right and left. Neither one liked Ed.

SE: That's part of his power. For me anyway—just recently getting introduced to Ed Abbey—he evokes very strong reactions. It's visceral.

KS: When I was doing little talks that culminated two years ago at Westminster College, I thought I was doing another classroom talk, you know, twenty or thirty students. How bad could it be? Didn't seem like there'd be any consequence if I made a fool out of myself. Then Bill tells me, "Well, it's in the auditorium."

---

2   * Judy Bari, EF! organizer who survived a 1990 car bomb attack but died of breast cancer seven years later.

SE: Oh, no.

KS: Auditorium? How big? "Oh, it's about 300 seats." I said, "You've got to be kidding me. What the hell am I going to do in an auditorium with 300 kids when only thirty people show up? It's going to be a disaster!" "No, no, no—people are going to come." I don't have any shyness anymore about public speaking because I've done it for so long. It doesn't faze me anymore. But this did! Long story short, not only did the auditorium fill up, but it overflowed.

SE: Oh, my god.

KS: I thought, well, I don't need to worry about people coming anymore, but now they're going to expect something. I said to myself, "Sanders, you better pull something out of your ass." (laughter) I don't work from scripts. I have to do things sort of intuitively. To make matters worse, an old friend Doug Peacock came through town the day before. He's the basis for the Hayduke character in the novel. He and his wife said, "Hey, we heard you're doing this Ed Abbey thing tomorrow night and we're going to come to it." I thought, oh great, now I'm going to have Hayduke in the audience. (laughter) I'm going to be talking about Ed Abbey in front of a man who knew Ed better and longer than I did!

SE: (laughter) No pressure.

KS: Yeah, but being nobody's fool, I asked Doug if he would come up and address the audience. I saved him for the very last, though. There's no way in hell I'd introduce Hayduke in the beginning. (chuckle) I'm not letting Hayduke upstage me! And Doug and I are both kind of old now, so no one in the audience even recognized him sitting up there front and center. So it made a really great surprise at the end when I said,

"Well, maybe some of the more attentive of you have noticed that we have a certain George Washington Hayduke, a.ka. Douglas Arapahoe Peacock, in the audience with us tonight. Doug, would you come up here and say a few words?" We did a Q and A together afterward. It had a powerful impact on the evening. And at the beginning what I observed was that a lot of the audience was incoming freshman. Young people, just turning eighteen years old. At the time, Ed had died eighteen not twenty years ago. It occurred to me that none of these kids were even on the planet when Ed had died. And that's more true today at twenty years, the twentieth anniversary.

SE: When Todd[3][*] first told me about Ed Abbey and the theme of the issue, I thought, "I don't know who this guy is." It's strange how great an impact he had and yet I don't hear about him. That frustrates me, because we have to put his work out there so everyone knows. So upcoming generations know.

KS: What I've tried to give through presentations is a reanimation. We use a lot of video and audiotape because I want people to see that visage and hear that voice. People don't have the opportunity to meet him now, but he is still alive. Through his twenty-one books he does still live to a new generation of people. He's not some dusty, boring Victorian writer that no one ever wants to read again. In his introductions, he really lets his hair down and talks to you directly. The introduction to *Desert Solitaire* is priceless and the same for Journey Home. In the introduction to Journey Home he claims, "I am not and never have been a naturalist." He goes on to claim that the only birds he can recognize in nature

---

3   [*] Simmons, Pub. MJ.

are the roast turkey and the rosy-bottomed skinny dipper. I tell people, if you don't think Ed Abbey's a serious writer, take a random paragraph out of any one of his twenty-one published books and attempt to edit it. See how well you do. See if you can cut a word or phrase out. You can't. He thought about things deeply. He read stuff that would bore me to tears. He was a philosophy major and he'd read some really weird shit. Every time you saw him he'd give you books to read. He turned me onto Cormac McCarthy, gave me a copy of *Blood Meridian* to read in 1985.

SE: Have you found that your bookstore is a good place to interweave Ed Abbey's works?
KS: Oh yeah, it's a bully pulpit, if you will, a 4000 square-foot shop in downtown Salt Lake. At the head of it there are three or four aisles and he's the opening author alphabetically. Fortunately, there are very few authors that come before Abbey alphabetically. It's hard to beat A-B-B. So he has the first entire case in the literature aisle. It's devoted to nothing but Edward Abbey books. And in the front are all the rare editions, signed books. In the '70s and '80s Dutton was his publisher then and they never printed more than 5000 copies of his book. Ed called me up one day grousing because Dutton was remaindering the hard-bounds to *Journey Home* and Ed was mad about it. I told him, "Ed, with your author's contract we could buy them real cheap. So you buy them up and let's have them shipped here and I'll sell them. We'll pay you some money on the side as we sell them." So I bought 4500 copies of *Journey Home*, hardbound, and paid a dollar each. The retail was $9.95, so in order to compete with the paperback, every time Ed would come through town I would make him sign cases until

he would get so sick of signing books he'd throw the pen across the room and refuse to sign anymore.

SE: I can just imagine him throwing the pen. (laughter)
KS: He was a good sport, up to a point.

SE: How did your publishing relationship develop?
KS: He used to come through periodically. We ended up over the years sponsoring things—a fundraiser for the Wilderness Association. He and the then, unknown Barry Lopez came to town and did a dog and pony show. Barry had just published *Desperate Hopes* and nobody had ever heard of the guy. That's changed. Then Ed and Utah Philips, this Wobbly[4*] folk singer-labor-rights-Joe Hill kind of guy, who's also a friend of mine, did a concert together that was another fundraiser. Whenever Ed came through Salt Lake I would always talk to him. Then I started pestering him about publishing projects, and that led to the calendar. He'd call me up. (You wanted him to call you. Ed hated telephones, so I learned early on not to call Ed because it was like having a Zen phone conversation. He would just sit there with dead air so you'd better have something to say because he wasn't going to contribute to the conversation.) So Ed would call me, "Ken, I'm down at the Lone Rock campground. If you want to talk about that silly calendar come on down." He was kind enough to let me do an Edward Abbey western wilderness calendar for ten years. It morphed into a whole line of wilderness and national park calendars that I used to do back in the '80s, and that's what Ed ridiculed me for. (chuckle) I'll never forget doing the river trips with Ed, sitting down on the banks of the Colorado at Spanish Bottom and

4   * The Wobblies were union members of the IWW, International Workers of the World.

Ed would say to me, "Ken, you're not going to make those silly calendars for the rest of your life are you?" (Laughter).

Then Ed and I started to do book publishing projects together. I hit him up to do a new hardbound, tenth anniversary edition of *The Monkey Wrench Gang* that was only available in paperback at the time. I wanted the underground '60s cartoonist R. Crumb to illustrate it. Well, Ed didn't necessarily think much of that idea but I could just see how Crumb would be perfect for that novel. He couldn't illustrate *Desert Solitaire*. That would just be horribly wrong. But *The Monkey Wrench Gang*, the exaggerated, over-the-top prose was just perfect for Crumb. I tried to get him to illustrate the book and he turned me down cold (chuckle). I went through two years of hell and trying out all these other artists and nothing worked, nothing worked. And I could just see the R. Crumb characters walking off the page of that book. So, genius that I am, I wrote him again. This time I offered him more money and I sent him a copy of the paperback. R. Crumb had never heard of Edward Abbey. That's why he had turned me down. Once he read the book, I wouldn't have had to pay him a dime, he would have done it for nothing. He called me up on the phone all formal-like, "Well, are there people in real life who go out and do some of the activities that the characters do in Mr. Abbey's novel *The Monkey Wrench Gang*?" He was absolutely fascinated. And the two of them could not have been more different. Talk about a Mutt and Jeff situation. This funny little urban guy who's always in his little hat and shiny shoes and button-down black vest. Very formal. And big ol' sprawlin' rangy Ed Abbey. But they hit it off quite well.

We published the book in the spring of '85 and had a giant autograph party down at the group campsite at Devil's Garden at Arches Park. We created probably the first and only traffic jam and gridlock that spring. Arches Park consists of a twenty-three mile long road that goes from the bottom up to the top through all the rock formations. And 300 people showed up for the dinner! We completely gridlocked the park! It was crazy.

SE: Do you have a favorite Ed Abbey quote or excerpt, or something he said to you that you keep coming back to?

KS: There's one piece that people really need to

read. I always read this whenever I do an Ed Abbey presentation. It's from his last published collection of essays, *One Life at a Time Please,* and the essay is called "A Writer's Credo." He writes about the moral duty of a writer. I usually read the first page and a half. But the entire essay is brilliant and he just rips other writers a new asshole. He tells you exactly what you're supposed to do and why. It's one of the best essays he ever wrote, but people don't seem familiar with it at all. It's really a good one.

As far as quotations, well, "Growth for the sake of growth is the ideology of the cancer cell." "The wilderness needs no defense, only more defenders." My favorite from The Monkey Wrench Gang is, "Looking like a weed doesn't make you organic." (laughter)

SE: That's another thing I love about Ed Abbey. He's funny!

KS: His writings are all very first person, personal. He uses himself as a character in his writing, and humor is a huge part of that because he uses himself as a foil. Very few writers can tell you their own personal experiences and make them entertaining and philosophical and educational at the same time. Usually the weight of the person speaking overwhelms everything else.

Another thing people should read is the introduction to *Journey Home.* It is hilarious. His sense of humor can be pretty juvenile at times, too. He was so proud of himself that one time in the late '70s, maybe early '80, he wrote Gloria Steinem and *Ms.* magazine a letter.

SE: Oh, no.

KS: He started it out, "Dear, Sir." She took it in stride. He printed both his letter to her and her reply. And it's pretty damn funny. He goes on about tatting doilies. He's trying to imagine what these women do, see. It's just a complete send-up letter. Left-wing people would get very angry at Abbey over issues. Women: Was he a misogynist? Race: Was he racist? Particularly toward Mexicans? But he had a more complicated personality than that.

SE: Not just black and white. Right or left.

KS: Exactly. And for a younger generation he's very accessible. We sell a huge amount of new Ed Abbey books, but we also buy a ton of used books and can't keep them in stock. They disappear off the shelves. He speaks to a whole new generation.

SE: He's accessible to the upcoming generation because what he says is relevant.

KS: It is relevant. In December of 2008, the BLM here in Utah, in the waning days of the Bush administration, tried to ram through hundreds of oil and gas leases for bargain prices in sensitive wilderness areas and parks. A group of local protestors, college kids from the University of Utah, went to the BLM and protested in the snow that day. One of them, Tim DeChristopher, decided protesting wasn't enough. He went into the auction and inside a security guard said, "Are you here as a bidder?" and he just thought, "Yes, I am!" He registered as a bidder for the auction and held his paddle up in fourteen different oil and gas leases in and around Arches and Canyonlands National Park. He out bid the oil and gas industry people and monkeywrenched the entire auction. He threw it into chaos. They arrested him and he's currently facing fifteen years in a federal penitentiary for his actions. His trial probably starts here soon. But he did it. He literally evoked Ed Abbey.

At this library thing I did recently, Tim DeChristopher was my guest. I pretended to talk to Ed Abbey, looking up at his face on the screen and said, "You know, Ed, I don't think burning down billboards is going to cut it anymore. The stakes are even higher than they were back in the day."

The Grand Dame of Western Environmentalism:
A Conversation with Katie Lee

Interviewed by Sue Ring deRosset

In June 1953, Katie Lee was the 175th person to float the Grand Canyon after John Wesley Powell and was among the last to float the Glen before a giant hydroelectric dam was constructed in 1962. She ran the Colorado River sixteen times in that bittersweet decade. Rowing boats with oars (this was before the era of rubber rafts), she and her friends spent weeks at a time on the river, singing around campfires, "night-flying" downstream under the stars, and hiking thousands of miles and swimming in the emerald pools of a myriad unnamed side-canyons that were later submerged beneath the rising waters of Lake Powell. She knew the Glen and its tributary canyons like no one else. Most of the rest of us have no idea what was lost.

Nine years before Silent Spring, *at a time when other thirty-something women were settling into suburbs of lush green lawns and electric washing machines—the very conveniences for which Glen Canyon Dam was built—folksinger and actress Katie Lee was singing songs to save the Colorado River. Once, when she asked her good friend Burl Ives for professional advice, he told her to "Get the hell out of Hollywood and take your songs on the road!*

Which she did. This adventurous river-rat, folk guitarist, and singer/songwriter took her songs on the highway all the way to Chicago and New York City. She took her songs along the jeep trails of the desert Southwest. She took her songs down the river-canyons of redrock country, for the enjoyment of her friends and boating clients. On the same July 1954 river trip when she met Ken Sleight (of "Seldom Seen" fame), Katie Lee learned of Floyd Dominy and the Bureau of Reclamation's plan to build a dam and flood Glen Canyon. So she wrote articles about the grandeur of these imperiled canyons, and stood up and spoke out—passionately, fiercely—for their protection.

In 1971, after she sent an early novel to the author of Desert Solitaire, *Edward Abbey recommended that she rewrite the novel as "a straight-forward autobiography." Katie Lee's manuscript thus became* All My Rivers Are Gone *(1998), which was republished as* Glen Canyon Betrayed *(2006) with a foreword by Terry Tempest Williams. Katie Lee has also published* Sandstone Seduction *and* Ten Thousand Goddam Cattle, *recorded ten music CDs, and appeared in documentaries. She currently serves on the board of directors of the Glen Canyon Institute.*

The interview below was braided from three phone conversations. For Ms. Lee's generosity with her time and her stories, and for her work to save the wild Colorado River, I am most grateful—we all are, Katie. Thank you.

I: RIVERS & DAMS

Note to the Reader: On 11 April 1956, the Upper Colorado River Project Act was passed and, on 21 January 1963, the diversion tunnels around the giant, new dam were closed, causing the river to back up into Glen Canyon and the side-canyons, across the Arizona border some 170 miles into Utah. Although this body of water is called "Lake Powell," it is in fact a reservoir.

Sue Ring deRosset: In *Inside/Outside SW*, you call the dams that form a chain of reservoirs along the Salt River, east-northeast of Phoenix, "aneurysms," and "the most hated blobs on the planet." The old joke: Okay, so how do you really feel?

Katie Lee: [Laughing]. The rivers are the lifeblood of our planet. When I do presentations for school kids,

I ask them, What's the most important element in the body? They say, "Water." They know we're composed of this high percentage of water. But what else? I ask them. What else is inside us, something without which you could not exist? "Blood," they say. If you stop the blood, you die, right? That's our planet. Those veins of water are like the lifeblood veins in our body. They get that. And I say, You can't keep damming it up.

SR: From your book, *Glen Canyon Betrayed*, I learned that we had a law that made it illegal to build a dam or reservoir in a National Park or National Monument. So how is it, with Rainbow Bridge National Monument just upriver, that construction of the Glen Canyon Dam was able to go forward?

KL: That's why we didn't even get upset. We said, "Well, we have the law to protect us. There's not going to be a dam in here!" And that fucking Senator Moss, from Utah, he just went in and he changed the wording. That's all he did. He changed the wording! Then they voted on it, and said, Okay, we knocked that out, now we can build dams anywhere.

SR: What do you, personally, want to see happen to the Glen Canyon Dam?

KL: I'd like to see someone just blow the fucker up! [Laughing]. Get the Grand Canyon all cleaned out, get a river down there where it belongs. I'd like to see Mother Nature shake up the Earth there.

SR: What was your response when the Colorado River herself injured the dam—nearly irreparably—and almost reclaimed the canyon in 1983?

KL: I was on my knees praying, "Go! Do it! Do it! Go, girl! More, more, more! Drown everything, hurry up, don't waste any time!" [Laughing]. I can't believe that a couple of plywood boards saved them. That's all right. The river's gonna eat around the edge, they don't need gates or anything else, the sandstone is gonna give away one day. They pump caulking and iron tubes back into that right wall constantly. To hold the dam in place. They were told never to build it there in the first place, because of the sandstone being so porous. . . .

SR: I read in your book that it was considered a very bad site.
KL: But [Floyd] Dominy was already on his way, saying, "We'll build it here." If they'd built it in Dinosaur [National Monument] not half would've been lost that was lost in Glen Canyon. Dinosaur doesn't have all those side-canyons.

SR: What was your reaction on learning that the Sierra Club's then-executive director, David Brower, had gotten behind this controversial trade, wherein the Glen Canyon was sacrificed in order to spare the upper Green? He said it was the biggest mistake of his life.
KL: Dam-building was in rapid-flow at the time and nothing was going to stop it. David went to the grave saying if he'd just made that phone call, he could've stopped it. I said, "David, that's not true. Would you get that off your back, please. Because you could not have done anything about it. I'm sorry you didn't see the Glen first. But you can't do everything. Please, look at all the good you've done. Don't take that one in your soul. That's not your fault."

SR: After Glen Canyon was dammed, you refused to go on any river trips, from 1963-1974. What changed in 1974? Why did you start running rivers again?

KL: The head of the Sierra Club back then, John MacComb, came by one day with [his then-wife] Joanna and said, "We're gonna run the San Juan." I said, "Good luck!" And he said, "Good luck, hell! You're coming with us. It's been too long. You haven't been in the water, and you need to find out a few things." So they yanked me by the hair and took me back to the Glen. Brandy, my husband, had just died, and I figured, Well, shit, I can get away more, now, and I need to do something different. So I said, "I'll go on this *one* trip with you, but—" … that started it again.

SR: When you visited Glen Canyon post-dam, after the formation of Lake Powell, how was that for you?
KL: The upper half of the San Juan river was still there. We ran to Clay Hills Crossing. . . and I just recalled everything that had happened before, all the side-country. But I tried to turn it off as soon as we hit the still water. Because in those ten years, I must've hiked 2000 miles, in different canyons. The White Canyon drainage, Cheesebox, Hideout, "Fart Knocker" Canyon—not *Fort* Knocker, it's Fart Knocker! [Laughter]. That's what the cowboys called it, the Mormon cowboys. All those canyons with drainage into Glen. Good Lord, we hiked Death Hollow before anybody had ever gone all the way down it. We had to swim half of it. You could hardly raise your arms without hitting the wall! Amazing trenches, they were just beautiful. Incredible, *incredible* canyon. Death Hollow's one of my favorites, for hiking. Down on the river, I never had any favorites there, on the Glen. They were all so perfectly beautiful.

But you asked me how I dealt with the fact that it was gone? How did I manage? [Reading from page 36 of *Glen Canyon Betrayed*]: "Now, as I write, every mile of that canyon, and what was hidden in the side ones, is incised on my memory, complete with remembered conversations there, with smells, with springs, with redbud trees and heron nests; with owl perches, pink lizards; with good camps, and bad camps... What fascinated me? *Enslaved* me? How did it, and why?"

Well, I did it just by repeated trips. You cannot *get* a place with one trip down The Grand Canyon. Or grand *anything*. You have to learn it. You have to go back. You have to study it. *It* has to study *you*. That's why I quit going with the groups. Tad [Nichols] and Frank [Wright] and I just went off by ourselves. I said, I don't want to see all these people... I just want to feel this place, I need this, I need this. ... Well, don't you think that's enough about me? Let's talk about Ed Abbey.

II: EDWARD ABBEY, BOOKS, & MUSIC

Katie Lee: I'm not a great or prolific writer, by any means. I write for a reason. I write for a belief. I write the way I talk, from my emotions, and I do what Ed told me to always do: "Write what you know about." That's why, when he read my novel—you see, he ran the Glen once, and only once, and he didn't run the whole thing. He had to get out at Cane [Creek] because there was a big sign where they made everybody get out. You couldn't go down because they were working on this dam. The coffer dam was already up so you couldn't have gone clear to the dam site anyway. But he uses the river to do what he usually does. To philosophize. Of course, he sees [the river], and it's a beautiful place, and he thinks it's incredibly stupid for this [damming] to happen, and he's railing against the government, like he always does. Ed writes like he talks, too, but from his intellect. And I can hear his voice in the way he writes... gravelly, deep-throated, almost like a gargle. To many people it sounds kind of gruff. But he's very soft-spoken. Except when he's mad, or when he's drunk, then that's a different matter. Or if he's singing.

SR: Did you and Ed get together quite a bit to sing around campfires?

KL: I never sat around but one campfire with Ed. He was a ranger down at Organ Pipe National Park down by the border, and his wife Judy [Pepper] had just come back from university and [his daughter] Susie was in her crib. His family was there, too, so I got to meet his mom and dad. His mom and dad were inspirational; they were wonderful people. I sat at the campfire with them and Brandy, my husband at the time, and I'd brought my guitar, like Ed had asked me to. We sat around and sang, and sang. Later that evening, I asked Ed where to camp, and he said, "Go up there where the sign says, NO CAMPING, you pull off the road, go up the creek bed—you've got a dune-bug—go around the bend, nobody will bother you."

SR: [Laughing]. And you were about to say something about your novel…?

KL: I gave Ed my novel to read. It was deeply felt, but it was [fiction]. I wrote it that way because I could not write in first person without crying. I would break down into miserable tears. I just couldn't do it. I told him that, and he said, "Well, your first book is in first person" [referring to *Ten Thousand Goddam Cattle*]. Yes, it was. But I wasn't as close to the subject, even though it was the subject of my life, which was music. It didn't involve a heart-wrenching loss. I was just trying to put people straight about who wrote these [folk songs everybody was singing]. They didn't fall out of the sky; they were written by somebody, and they ought to be credited.

Anyway, after reading my novel, Ed—who I know had a certain amount of respect for me—he said he wanted my book to be remembered, not as a story, but as a real-life happening. It wasn't going to come out that way if I didn't write it off my journals, like I should have. I just couldn't do it. He said, "Yeah, you can do it! It needs to be done. Nobody's done that canyon as many times as you have, who has the writing ability." And he said, "By the way, don't go to any writing school. Just write it your way, hunh?" I never did understand why he told me not to go to a writing school. I only [took a writing class] once, in defiance, and that was because of Gary Paul Nabhan—I love him and it was a great experience and I had a wonderful time. And I did learn some things.

Ed wrote because he was a writer; I write because I'm not. I think he saves his passion for the women that he's always been so fond of. I put my passion down in writing. I mean, I put it right there, because it's tearing me to pieces. I want someone to understand, as best they can, that this [losing the river] is no different than having a lover die. This is no different at all. In fact, sometimes it can be even more potent. If they take from you something that you have taken into yourself as your very own skin, and your life, and it has done as much for you as that river did for me, then that's a passion. That's a love that cannot ever be destroyed.

SR: There's a gorgeous line in your book about not abandoning your lover as he lies dying in his bed—you go back and you hold his hand.

KL: That's right. That's what it felt like I was doing. But I couldn't watch it go all the way. I couldn't watch it totally die. I had to say goodbye after a couple of years. I couldn't watch the water rise any higher, because I'd been in all those places, and I wasn't going to torture myself. Enough is enough.

SR: How did you and Ed meet?

KL: Brandy and I were on our honeymoon up in Castle Valley, out of Moab, and I was reading *Desert Solitaire* for the first time. I said, "Hey, let's take a ride, up on the road—they were building the road around the La Sal Mountains—you know, the Loop Road? Where you went in at the south end at Pack Creek Ranch and came out in Castle Valley. They were going to pave the La Sal Loop Road. Well, I thought that's the dumbest thing I ever heard. So I pulled fifty day-glo stakes and threw them off into the canyon, and I took one of the stakes and glued it to my album and sent it to Ed at Organ Pipe. He wrote me a card that said, "Come visit! Bring your guitar!"

Over the years, I visited him many times. In the parks, up at the North Rim of the Grand Canyon and Four Peaks—the fire lookouts—and Organ Pipe, and another place, Aravaipa? I get the names mixed up. See, there's another canyon down by the border, Arivaca, where we used to hunt boar, javelina. Now it's a big drug center, a really horrible place. Anyway, the place between Tucson and Globe, where Ed was the game-keeper, that was Aravaipa. He was guarding the game from the hunters, the poachers. Oh, that was the other campfire I spent with Ed. In the morning, Ed, Renee, Bruce, and I hiked Aravaipa Creek, up the canyon, and we saw mountain lion tracks. And then we saw a mountain lion! Absolutely beautiful! But while he was there, Ed had a confrontation with these asshole hunters who pointed guns at him; they wouldn't get off the game reserve. After that he gave up his position.

SR: Many of us—who didn't know him—might think of Ed Abbey as not only a great storyteller and powerful voice for wilderness, but also as a witty misanthrope, a cynical curmudgeon, or a rabble-rousing, macho Westerner. Some women think of him as misogynistic, but none of his male friends seem to think so.

KL: He was *not at all* misogynistic.

SR: So what's coming through in his writing? Why do you think people call him misogynistic, or chauvinistic?

KL: Well, I don't know. To me, he was a very gentle sort of person. But his anger and mine were equal, about the country, and the land. We would get into tirades agreeing with each other. I always said, Well, Ed, you always say it better than I can say it. He puts [his argument] in strong, concise words, backed with quotes from an ancient historian or philosopher, or some other great writer. He was philosophical. But he was those other things you said, too. Was he a misanthrope? He might've been. He was a cynical curmudgeon, that's for sure! So am I! And a rabble-rouser, a macho Westerner? Well, he was when he felt like being that way.

SR: You'd mentioned earlier that he saved his passion for women. What was his particular charm? What do you think attracted them to him?

KL: I don't know how he attracted his women!

SR: Did you ever fall for him?

KL: I was way too old for him. That's probably one of the reasons there was never any question that there was any sexual attraction, to me with Ed or Ed with me—that I know of, anyway. He liked twenty-five year old girls! Or younger! I always thought that that was kind of stupid. Because they couldn't come up to him, in any way, regardless of their age or how brilliant they were. They couldn't come up to his intellect. I think he got most of his intellectual stimulation through his men friends. I know he did. But no, no way. I did not fall for him.

SR: What did Ed teach you about activism?
KL: To protest the destruction any way that I could. He'd say, "You do it by singing." I would get so *mad* at these meetings that I would blow it. I'd get up and call them what they were, right smack out in front of the audience. Ed told me, "Katie, you should just shut up and sing!" And you know, he was right. Because singing gets through to somebody a lot quicker and stays with 'em longer than a bunch of words. I knew that. I just couldn't hold it back. I said, I can't sing at those meetings. He said, "Yes, you can."

SR: So did you?
KL: I did a couple. When it suited the purpose. [Singing "The Wreck-the-Nation Bureau Song"]: Three jeers for the Wreck-the-Nation Bureau/ Freeloaders with souls so pure-o/ Wiped out the good Lord's work in six short years! *[Rest of verse: They never saw the old Glen Canyon/ Just dammed it up while they were standin'/ At their drawing boards with cotton in their ears./ Oh, they've gone and dammed the Frying Pan/ You're next, old Roaring Fork./ And when they built Glen Canyon dam/ The San Juan got a cork./ No river's safe until these apes/ Find something else to do./ So have your fun in Cataract,/ 'Cause after that, you're through!]* Singing called attention to these guys. During one meeting, two of them walked out in the middle of the song and I said, "Wooooo! There they go!"—boy that really pissed them off!

SR: I'll bet! During those years, were there other women doing what you were doing—attending meetings, singing and traveling around the country, running rivers?

KL: This business with, what do you call it?

SR: Feminism?

KL: That always made me laugh. Shit, if you have to bitch because some man opens the door for you, you're sick in your head!

SR: Is that how some people define feminism then?

KL: Well, I guess! [Laughing, lowering her voice]: "I can open my own door!" Well, great! You see, I never felt these restrictions that seemed to have been around. Maybe they were there, and I just did not notice if I were being singled out, left out. I am an entertainer. Entertainers go and do their thing: They audition. They're either what the person wants, or they're not. I'd certainly put it down to that, and not the fact that, "I'm a woman." I was born and raised in the theater. Everyone works together there. No man is more important than a woman in a show. That's the way I was brought up and the theater instilled that in me even stronger. Until I got to Hollywood and found out that there was a Star System. They say you gotta push everyone else down in order to get to the top of the heap. That's one of the things about Hollywood that was driving me nuts. I know you have to manipulate to get somewhere, but I *don't like* manipulation. I hate women for their *manipulating*. And they are good at it. I'm not a *woman* person, I'm a *man* person.

SR: Most of us—men and women—don't even know what's being destroyed, or what's already been lost. Which is part of the power and beauty of your book,

Glen Canyon Betrayed. I cried while I read it—and I'm not one to cry—but I was crying because I never knew what had been lost. I never *knew.*

KL: That's what I hear every time I do a lecture. People come up to me after saying, "We're mad! We're angry! We got cheated!" I say, Well, then. Go out and do something about it. If you've got a place, that you love, you had better watch it. Don't tell anybody about it—except your very closest... I know you want to share. Because sharing is part of human nature; it makes you love it even more. But. Be careful. Because it will be gone when ten people arrive there. You'll never see it the same again. So just be prepared. Prepared to lose it. If you love it, be prepared to lose it. Because this country is on its way to destruction. And nothing's going to stop it. Nothing.

SR: That's the saddest thing I have heard.
KL: Yep. I know... But I'll go out feeling great. Because I did whatever I could. I watched myself; I didn't overdo things; I didn't grab too much. And I got lucky. Oh boy, did I get lucky. I came at the right time, at the right spot—and that was a happening I had no control over. It was given to me and I could've taken it or left it. I had to take it.

SR: Who were your mentors?
KL: Burl Ives, Josh White, and Carl Sandburg...

SR: I loved where you mentioned, in *Glen Canyon Betrayed*, that Burl Ives called you "Sergeant."
KL: He also called me Bitch! That's because he knew I did things my way. I wasn't going to take any shit from anybody. I have another friend who calls me Cowtoots, which I love. And another nickname is Eco-Bitch.

SR: [Laughing] Is that all one word, ecobitch?

KL: I don't know! Maybe it's on one of these badges. I have these badges, all strung up on a string. Like this one: "Reclaim the Bureau: 600 Dams, 100 Years, Too Much." And "I Can't Wait to Run Dominy Falls." That's what we always called it. You know, over the Glen Canyon Dam!

III: EARTH FIRST!, POPULATION GROWTH, & THE FUTURE

SR: I'd like to talk about Abbey's most controversial novel. Some of the characters in *The Monkey Wrench Gang* were based on people: Doug Peacock as the inspiration for Hayduke, Utah river guide Ken Sleight as Seldom Seen. I'm thinking Doc Sarvis—the shambling bear of a man, the brains behind the operation—was somewhat autobiographical, but who the heck was Bonnie Abbzug?

KL: Well, you are about to learn who Bonnie Abbzug was! My friend M.L. Lincoln just interviewed her, back in New York. M.L. is doing a movie on the beginnings of Earth First!. She's interviewed everybody—*everybody but Ed!*—Dave Foreman, Doug Peacock, me, and Peg Millett, who went to jail. She's finally got a hold of this person who everybody thinks was Bonnie Abbzug. She's some sort of mystery woman. M.L. is like a dog on a bone, boy! She goes where she finds them, and she interviewed this woman. I have no idea who she is—I haven't seen the footage yet.

SR: I can't wait to find out! What did you think of Earth First! when it got started?

KL: Dave Foreman, Mike Roselle, Howie Wolke, Bart Koehler: It started with the four of them. Earth First! was a great starter for action. It was a great group of people. There never were members; there was no membership. That group was a milestone. It put ideas in people's heads that they could actually get off their asses and do something—*and* have fun at it. There's your secret, you know, like "Shut up and sing!" [Laughing].

SR: [Laughing]. You've written: "Saving a wilderness takes enough people to ultimately ruin it." What a bind! We need to go out and get to know a wild place so we fall in love with it and protect it. But we're loving the wilderness to death…

KL: It's a catch-22 that you can't do a whole lot about. I'd like to just see it left alone. But that's not possible. And the reason it's not possible is because there are just TOO MANY FUCKIN' PEOPLE FUCKING! If we don't stop this pretty soon—and have only one or two children—we are gonna FUCK ourselves off of this planet! You wanna know how I feel about that?! That's how I feel!

SR: How do you really feel, Katie? [Laughing]. So what do we do?

KL: You've got to stick your nose out! Like the Center for Biodiversity did. They have done something really funny. They have these things they're gonna send up to me: *Endangered Species Condoms.**

SR: [Laughing] With a picture of an animal or plant on the condom?

KL: On the package it says, "Endangered Species Condoms," and I'm going to hand these out… But everybody's afraid to even talk about [human overpopulation]… I would like to see every single one of these "pro-life" idiots—*fanatics*—all packed up, put into a great big bundle, and sent to the moon—no, sent to Mars. It's hotter up there. They go out and kill abortion doctors! It's the most insane bunch of people I have ever heard about. They're sickening. For some man to stand up in front of me and tell me I can or cannot or should not have an abortion—I'd like to just walk out of an abortion clinic with a baby in my arms because they've refused… And hand it to him and say, "You take care of it, asshole. See how you like it."

SR: [Laughing] Many of them seem fascinated by space travel anyway. So about the future—you said earlier there was nothing to be done about the destruction of the Earth…

KL: We can slow things down. But I just don't know if we'll be able to, because there's too many of us. This is the root of all evil, and nobody's paying attention to the ROOT. All you have to do is look at past civilizations. Read Craig Child's *House of No Rain*. He talks about all the civilizations buried under Rome, under Mexico City. They all get wiped out eventually because they overindulge in whatever it is that finally runs out. The Earth has only got so much.

As far as the [Glen Canyon] dam, Mother Nature will take care of all kinds of wonderful things, but I'm quite sure that dam is here for the next millennium. And I hope it will be. Because I want it to be a monument to our stupidity—to *Floyd Dominy's* stupidity, to *Wreck-the-Nation's* stupidity. Not *mine*; I thought they shouldn't put it there in the first place. It'll go its own way. The river will make its way around it, and the dam is just going to be insignificant. My eternal hope is with Mother Nature. Glen Canyon will flourish again—in possibly a slightly different way. But I am certainly *against* having it in the National Park. It's too delicate a place.

In the Afterword of *Glen Canyon Betrayed* I talk

about this [page 260]: "National Parks are for anyone at any time. Glen Canyon is not. Invite a herd of buffalo into your rose garden and you'll know why... Glen deserves *heavy* protection from *us*. Its ecosystem was, and is, intricate, fecund, seminal, and, above all, fragile. Between the protective walls of Glen was the cradle, the nursery, an almost two-hundred mile, quiet river-breeding-ground for a diverse ecosystem that once fed Grand Canyon—a river canyon now starving without those healthful nutrients and life-giving silt... We've got to speak out for the river-canyon's survival."

SR: Still stirring up any trouble, Katie?

KL: Yep! Still a shit-disturber—and not always out of anger. Sometimes for the betterment of everyone. Last couple of years, I've been giving seed money to our town to try to get it off the grid by generating electricity from our springs. Our water comes from up the mountain quite a ways. And the pressure is so strong we need pressure gauges on our pipes to keep them from blowing. So why don't we tap into this by using hydraulic generators for electricity to the town? After much ado, we've gotten a grant to study the situation— hire a hydrologist, an engineering firm, someone to do the research and get us off the grid by tapping into what's already here.

This is very important to me, to use what we've got. So I've become involved to make this happen. I think Ed would be proud of me, don't you? Like, I don't sing much anymore, Ed, but I just can't shut up!

Editor's Note: If you want to stick your nose out, go to: www. EndangeredSpeciesCondoms.com. To find out more about Katie Lee, and her books and music: www.katydoodit.com.

Bob Dylan & *The Monkey Wrench Gang:*
A conversation with Gary Burden & Ed Pressman

Interviewed by Todd Simmons

The Monkey Wrench Gang *as a novel stirred up a revolution and became a classic. The film version of the novel is developing a similar, almost-mythological history. Robert Redford, Sean Penn, and Matthew McConaughey are part of the on-going history. Optioned since it was first published in 1975, the book has almost been made into a film ever since. I spoke with the two men who are currently working to get the film made: Gary Burden, the famed counter-cultural artist who's worked on album cover art for artists such as Neil Young and My Morning Jacket, and Ed Pressman, who's worked on films such as* Wall Street, Reversal of Fortune, *and* Thank You For Smoking. *Overly generous and forthcoming, the two men showed remarkable dedication to a controversial and difficult novel-to-film adaptation. With these two men on-board, my summation is this: Hayduke will live! (on the big screen).*

Todd Simmons: Thanks for taking the time to talk with me about *The Monkey Wrench Gang.* Considering how long this film has been in the works, are you waiting until the public can't stand it anymore, and then that's when you'll release the film?

Gary Burden: That's it, we're holding back. We could've put this film out ten years ago…

Ed Pressman: Walter Salles is going to do the movie, but we're still trying to find a screenwriter to match his vision. We're getting very close.

TS: All the information that can be found online has Catherine Hardwicke directing, and William Goldman writing the screenplay?

EP: That's all in the past. Catherine would still like to do it, but she's gone on to do *Twilight* and other things, becoming a very hot director. Walter Salles really wants to go back to the original source, to the book. Having read the script and read the book, he still feels the book hasn't been captured the way he sees it. I think he's right.

TS: Did he feel a certain element was missing, or just an overall feel?

GB: Walter really has turned up something that most people have missed—he's going for the humor first, and the message second. Most people are so overwhelmed by how Ed Abbey targeted the problems in the environment, and how people were dealing with it, but I'm quite sure that Ed intended this to be a comedy. Most people want to preach about the environment. I think Walter's idea is right up Ed's alley, and I think it is the best way to present this material. I think if you get people laughing, then they're much more receptive to any ideas you may want to lay on them. I think it's brilliant that he saw that. He wants to do it more in the style of a Coen Brothers, or Terry Southern—just make it a wacked-out, absurd comedy. Certainly that is there in the book, but no one has mined that approach. I think it's absolutely what we've been waiting for.

EP: Terry Southern, who's not around anymore, or Buck Henry, who wrote some of the great, sophisticated, politically engaged comedies—*Shampoo, The Graduate*... anyway, I think that's the spirit of the book.

TS: Who do feel will be the hardest character to cast?

EP: In the beginning the prototype for Hayduke was Jack Nicholson, and as the years went by, it evolved as such that some of the actors who we thought would be Hayduke are now ready to play Doc. I remembered when Dennis Hopper wanted to direct it; his first thought for Hayduke was Jim Carrey. When Catherine came on board to direct, Jim really wanted to do the role, but Catherine thought at that time—it was a few years ago—he was too old to play Hayduke. He was trying to convince her that he could act ten years younger than his age. The prototype for me is still the young Jack Nicholson that we knew from *Easy Rider*.

GB: I agree with that, or maybe from the next generation, Sean Penn.

EP: Yeah, he was also interested in the role, but he's probably more suited to play Doc, in terms of his age. We've been talking more about writers with Walter at this point…

TS: Hayduke is the central pivot to the book, so he seems like an important character.

GB: The only actor that Walter mentioned was Sam Worthington, who is in *Avatar*. I'm not familiar with him, but that's the only name that's been thrown out so far.

TS: As far as the new script, are you setting any sort of timeline, or are you just letting the film evolve as it needs to evolve?

EP: Walter will be in LA this December [2009], and we're hoping to narrow down a writer by the end of the year, and hopefully have a script at the early part of next year. It's always been a film that we have to shoot in the spring or the fall, in terms of the seasons for shooting in that area of the country. I would think that the target would be a year from now, in the fall, or if it's delayed, the following spring. We're talking about a Fall 2010 or spring 2011.

TS: Speaking of filming, do you feel like you'll have a good working relationship with the National Park Service, or do you feel like you'll need it?

GB: What we've come to realize, for a lot of reasons, is that we'll try to shoot the whole film in New Mexico, and have a small, second unit that would go to Lee's Ferry and Monument Valley and places like that. We've done three survey trips and have found every location in the book in New Mexico. The reason is partially financial because the state of New Mexico offers big tax breaks that will make it more possible to make the film.

EP: One of the things to bring up is the importance of the musical artists who've committed to working with us, and have been for some time now.

GB: There's a long list of people. Well, I'm in the music business, and have been for the last forty years. I've worked with everybody from the Doors to Crosby, Stills, and Nash. I still do all of Neil Young's artwork. Now I'm working with younger artists like Conor Oberst from Bright Eyes and Jim James from My Morning Jacket, so all of those guys are into the project.

TS: Was that the Monsters of Folk album?

GB: Yeah, I did that artwork as well. Actually Jim and Conor were on the rafting trip with Ed Pressman and me that we did with Ken Sanders last spring down the Rio Chama. They're all part of a new generation of musicians and songwriters that get this book.

EP: Even Bob Dylan wants to be a part of it.

TS: I remember reading about Abbey denouncing Dylan back in the day, but I don't know if that's true or not.

GB: I think it is true. I've heard it enough times. Ed Abbey was a pretty cantankerous guy and I think his musical tastes went more toward classical music and country and western. I think he thought Bob Dylan was some sort of poser... he didn't get him. He actually made fun of him, the way he talked. Nonetheless, Bob did actually read the book for me—it took him six months to do it, but he did read it—and he was so pleased with it that not only did he offer to do some music but he also offered to do a cameo, which is pretty cool. With all due respect to Ed Abbey, I think Bob Dylan would bring something to the film. He certainly would bring an audience to it, much like he did in *Pat Garrett and Billy the Kid*.

TS: Describe your aspirations for the film—commercial, artistic, revolutionary?

GB: To change the world, no big thing.

EP: My son is a junior in college, and his generation looks at the spirit we were growing up in, and in some ways the glamour and engagement that they missed, and I think the timing of this film is more important than it's ever been, because the film could strike a chord with our generation and their generation in a way that films don't often do. When Gary says change the world, I was in the movie business in '69 and the early '70s and the feeling was that films and music could change the world, and films were very engaged with political issues that studios nowadays shy away from. If it's done with a sense of humor that Gary is talking about, I think it's easy to be corny, and say it could be an *Easy Rider* for the 21st century, but in the back of our minds, that is what we hope for.

GB: I think that is totally possible. Having been a part of the music business in the 1960s and 1970s I have no problem saying that what we all were doing contributed to changing the world—from stopping a war, to opening up opportunities politically and socially. From working with these young singer-songwriters, and knowing their friends and compatriots and how they all think, most of them are in their twenties, and I think there is a group of people now who are, if not exactly of that same mind, they are at least respectful of it. Todd, how old are you?

TS: I'm 34 years old, so I've been waiting for this film my entire life.
GB: That's great, thirty-five years ago it came out.

TS: Are you going to try to set the film in the mid-to-late 70s? Ed wrote in the front of the book that everything in this book happened one year from today.
GB: It all happened one year from today. I think it's important that it is set in the period, and not be made as 2010 or 2011, but to be in the 70s, for many reasons. First of all, the powers that be have always tried to stop this film from happening because they consider it to be a dangerous story that could incite riots or incite people to blow shit up, that kind of thing; that puts an additional difficulty on our being able to make the movie. Whereas if it's in the period, it's almost like mythic in a way, like once upon a time this happened. If you tried to make it contemporary, it would somehow weaken it, that's my opinion. Ed Pressman and I have always tried to keep it in the setting that Ed Abbey intended. Also, if you think about it, the thing that dates stuff that happens in that part of the West, are the pick-up trucks; I mean, Monument Valley and the

river, they haven't really changed since that time—of course there are more buildings and things, but really it's sort of a timeless area.

TS: Since people readily confuse acts of sabotage with acts of terrorism, and since terrorism is more prevalent in people's minds today, how will you address that issue, or will you even try?

GB: Ed Abbey was very careful about saying things or expressing through his characters that they were not violent people—except for maybe Hayduke. In fact, they were not terrorists, but amateur saboteurs who attacked the tools of terrorism—the bulldozers, and those things that have changed the world not for the better. It's almost impossible to get away from it, and I think that contributes to a great extent to why this film has not yet been made, it is perceived by the powers that be as being very dangerous. In fact, it probably is. I know from Earth First! to ELF—they are inspired to a great extent by Ed Abbey and by this book. I think there is a way to make the point that they are saboteurs and not terrorists, although there will be a certain faction of the population that will never accept that, they will always think that it promotes terrorism.

TS: This book started a movement, and there aren't a lot of novels out there that have started movements or revolutions. *On the Road* is another novel that started a movement, or captured a movement. Do you find it interesting that a couple of novels are making it to the big screen around the same time?

GB: Ironically, Walter Salles is the director of record for *On the Road*, and he's going to direct that film with Francis Ford Coppola producing.

EP: What Walter did, because the film *[On the Road]*

hadn't happened yet, he decided to do a documentary basically tracking Kerouac's journey that he took on the road, and filmed a personal documentary following the route. He's actually done that, being frustrated trying to do the movie itself, he made his own version of it.

TS: As a director, is he particularly drawn to revolutionary narratives, does that fit his worldview?
GB: If you see other films of his, like *Central Station* or *Foreign Lands* or *The Motorcycle Diaries,* there is a political side to them, but not politics that get in your face. They are part of the story, in a good way. I think he's a socially conscious guy, and a good person, and he sees things in the world, and he certainly brings them in. He's a really political guy, in a quiet way.

TS: *The Monkey Wrench Gang* will certainly bring a lot of scrutiny to how we protect, conserve, and take care of our land…how controversial do you feel this film will be?
GB: I would say appropriately controversial. I think it will encourage people who are sympathetic to the Earth and want to protect Her, and I think it will encourage them in their efforts. And I think that people who believe the environmental movement is all bullshit, this film will give them material to argue their points. I guess that's a good thing. If this movie did nothing but caused people to discuss the issue, then it will have succeeded in a big way.

TS: Ed, any thoughts?
EP: It's actually asking the question, too, whether you are prepared or should risk injuring other humans in protection of the land, and I think there's an internal debate between Hayduke and Doc about that question. The book to some extent addresses it, but raises the

issue about how far you are prepared to push it. It's ambiguous in a sense, because Hayduke is the hero, but Doc gets the girl.

TS: Ed, how long have you been involved with the film?

EP: Gary, how long?

GB: Ed's been involved for fourteen or fifteen years, and I started twenty years ago, more or less. I remember when I first got involved. I've always loved this book and I watched what was happening with it. I was not a filmmaker and I didn't know much about that, but I always felt that someday it should get made as a movie, and in my own quiet way I started pursuing the rights. When they became available, I thought, well I'm going to try and get involved. I spoke with Jack Loeffler, an old friend of Ed Abbey's, and people who were around Abbey, without really knowing his widow, Clarke. Prior to that I had wanted to make a film out of *The Milagro Beanfield War*, and I actually got the rights from John Nichols, the writer. Out of the woodwork came Robert Redford who as a front person had this person named Montezuma Esparza, and I relinquished the rights because there was a Chicano activist who wanted to make the film, so I acquiesced. I thought it was a good idea, so I backed out. Turns out it wasn't Montezuma Esparza, it was Robert Redford. In the last throes of getting the rights to *The Monkey Wrench Gang*, after having big name Hollywood producers come after it, Robert Redford flew Ed's widow up to Sundance and tried to romance her into giving him the rights, and in the end she gave them to me instead. Ever since then I've felt a huge responsibility to Ed Abbey who is, in a cosmic way, around me all the time. I had a mountain lion on the patio of my house one day…[laughter]…

this is funny…during a period of time…[laughter]… when we were thinking about Matthew McConaughey to play Hayduke. It would have been expedient perhaps, because we could have gotten the movie made, and I had sort of gone along with that idea, and then this mountain lion showed up on my patio, and scared the shit out of me, and I thought that perhaps that was Ed telling me what a bad idea it was.

TS: Everyone thinks Matthew McConaughey would have been a bad idea.

GB: Sometimes you go, well shit, if it will help us get it made. Fortunately, Ed Abbey stepped into the picture and put the kibosh on that.

TS: Any last words on the film?

GB: It would be fair to say that both Ed Pressman and I have put our asses on the line for a long time for this film, and we are committed beyond a sane commitment to getting this made.

EP: I think some of the greatest films from fiction have taken the longest time; the prime example is *One Flew Over the Cuckoo's Nest*. It took eighteen years from the time Kirk Douglas wanted to do it, to the time that Michael Douglas actually did produce it. I think *The Monkey Wrench Gang* is still my most personal commitment to seeing a film get made. We're not like a studio, we can't afford to commit so much time and effort and money to something unless we finally see it through.

The Last
Four Boats on
Lake Foul

A novella by Dylan Quint
Illustrations by Lauren Howell

The Characters

Artemis

Weasel

Georges

Maggot

10 September 2010
9:45 p.m.
Denver, Colorado

Strange how, on that last night at the hospital, the woman in the photograph seemed to glow. She'd never glowed before. Many people, in fact, had never even noticed her.

Relative to the grand gallery of the slot canyon, she was tiny and stood looking up from the canyon floor toward sandstone cliffs towering so close and so high above that only a pinch of sepia light reached her face. The lid of the canyon was itself like a camera's aperture, or the glottis to a windpipe. A fishing hole in lake ice. One could almost imagine, near the surface where the sunlight poured in, the swifts like fishes flitting the narrow gap between streaked walls. But as the light trickled down the shaft, it scattered irreversibly, and became stratified and sickly. Leagues below, in the shaded depths of the scene, one could almost hear the restless clicks and bubbles rising from chilly soft things astir in the sand.

The little goddess submerged by granular shadows possessed nevertheless a gigantic psychic presence. It was like she generated her own light, much like one of those oceanic bottom-dwellers who navigate the darkness with bioluminescent deeley-bops held aloft on slender stalks like lanterns. She posed in the benthic reaches of the canyon waiting for something to happen—or capture.

With one arm akimbo on a cocked left hip, the right foot steps upon a skull-sized stone as she palms her pale thigh. Her other foot lifts from the agitated surface of a puddle. Lustrous hair cascades like a dark streak of lichen down her back as she tilts her round chin and lifts her right breast to the lightfall. A classic "hero pose," except that the expeditioner, Emily Sevo's mother, is naked. And it's her nudity that imbues such a confident pose with a certain vulnerability, so that one doesn't think so much of a conquering as a belonging. Even if it is to a world that no longer exists.

For the past fifteen years that Dr. Emily Sevo had worked in the hospital, this matted and framed 8x10 photograph hung over her desk and conscience. The other anesthesiologists on occasion had commented on this Canyonlands image but none had remarked on the tiny woman in the lower left corner. One doctor, whose hobby was watercolor, loved the composition and intriguing perspective (from where had this picture been taken?) as well as the textured chiaroscuro of the cliff walls. Another, a weekend rockhound, pointed out the Moenkopi chocolate-cake layers of Triassic shales and, near the top of the photo, the shine of desert varnish on the Wingate sandstone, the faint wall-marks that may have been petroglyphs. He'd also said something about dinosaurs, and, ever since, Emily had imagined their giant white bones floating in the sightless depths of sediment among the stains and stamps of palm fronds and beetles with flared wings, an entire ecosystem pressed between the pages of Earth's book and flattened like so many silverfish. Oddly, in all those years, not one of the other doctors had asked, "Now, which canyon is this?" or even mentioned the minuscule, nude human. To be sure, Emily's mother was very small in the photograph, and her curves and skin tones nearly blended with the walls of water-scrubbed rock, but how could such observant scientists not have noticed this radiant nymph?

Emily set a stack of files in the last box and wiped her nose with the sleeve of her synchilla jacket. She regarded her mother's photo. Emily herself had never felt graceful, radiant, or soft; she'd never belonged anywhere; she'd never loved anyone as much as her parents had so obviously loved one another. At once both open and cold, she'd had many lovers but had never been in love. She didn't really like anyone at all. Least of all her patients, down whose ten thousand windpipes she'd threaded ten thousand trache tubes.

It was a blessed thing that she rarely had to speak to these people while they were conscious; she couldn't imagine the workaday drudgery of the physician who spent hour after hour listening to patients whine about bunions and heartburn and depression and insist on the latest "ask your doctor" pharmaceuticals. How lovely it was that her patients lay inert as hibernating toads beneath the bright lamps and blue drapes. How exhilarating it was that, while the patient's consciousness sank like an anchor through the strata of anesthetic stages, and the surgeons scrubbed and joked and gowned, and the nurses cranked up the tunes ("Jump! Jump in!"), Emily Sevo could flip a switch, ignore almost everybody, and be completely ON. With the concentration of an undersea diver, she drew her focus to the breath—her patients's—and all the hurly-burly of the world fell away. While the megalomaniacal surgeons disemboweled and hacked away with their little blades into the patient's innards—nicking arteries, dropping eyelashes onto the mesentery, troweling out tumors as hard and purple as onions—Emily Sevo, the real hero, kept the heart beating, the lungs ventilating, the blood pressure just high enough to perfuse such must-haves as the brain, liver, and kidneys. The lungs. The kidneys. How terribly under-appreciated, these blood-cleansing organs of filtration, excretion, and acid-base metabolism! So important, in fact, are the respiratory and renal systems that the God of Carbon-based Life Forms, whoever She might be, saw fit to install not just one kidney and lung but two of each. We only get one heart, one liver, one brain. But two kidneys! And two lungs! Anatomic profligacy? Accidental redundancy? She thinks not. It's evolutionary C.Y.A. Practically proof of the indispensability of the body's trees and rivers.

In sum, Dr. Emily Sevo didn't love or even care that much about the patient; she just didn't want to make a mistake and compromise the function of a lung or kidney. She even believed that if she'd cared more about the slumbering sick person as a whole Emily wouldn't be as good as she was. And she was good. In fifteen years, not a single anesthetic death until last week. Agreed, medicine seemed an unnatural career choice for this avid misanthrope, but, from the first day of medical school, Emily had had her reasons. Namely one: Anesthesiologists make enough bank to buy some seriously nifty toys. And what better job was there for an angry adrenaline junkie with an aptitude for medicine, an addiction to the life-and-death drama of the surgical theatre, a deep-seated greed for unspeakable wealth, and a score to settle with the Bureau of Reclamation?

Now she'd made as much money as she was ever going to make. It was time to finish packing, leave for good, go home. Really go home—home to the Canyonlands. But she lingered. It's never easy to say goodbye, even when clearly it's time to go.

Most nights, after Emily returned to her lonely bungalow near City Park, she whipped up a collard-greens-superalgae-kale-and-parsley smoothie and descended the stairs to spend an hour with the speedbag while blasting the Dixie Chicks on her thousand-dollar stereo system. After her workout and a few glasses of her verdant elixir, she'd often slump in the dark and weep from exhaustion. Even after a good day. Coming down off the headiness of the high-stakes hospital work to once again have to face herself at night, alone, her body would feel like a punching bag, or—she would perhaps realize, if she were ever to stoop to such self-conscious banalities as pity or extended metaphor—she was herself a kind of surgical patient: anesthetized by the media and psychotropic prescription meds, colonized by the cancer of progress, palliated by paychecks.

Anyway, it was Friday, the last day of work not just for the week but for her professional career. Time to go home to no one to begin her real work on the planet. There was nothing else to do here, nothing else to pack. She lifted the framed portrait of her mother from its nail above her vacated desk. She brought it close and peered over the tops of her spectacles, running her left thumb over the picture glass. The picture jiggled; her breath limped into and out of her lungs; she had to sit. So she sat for the last time in her chair, drained the last sip from the first can of Coca-Cola she'd drunk in some twenty years, and studied the familiar and mythic and haunting topography of maternal rock and flesh.

The photograph had been taken by Emily's father on May 2, 1962. It was the day that Frank Sevo and Mildred Hodgkiss, on a boating expedition down the muddy Colorado through Glen Canyon, had eagerly scrambled up this unnamed tributary of the lower Escalante and, quite unexpectedly, conceived Emily. In 1963, Frank and Millie married, and the canyon in the photo, and everything in the canyon—petroglyphs, granaries, cottonwoods, monkeyflowers, lizard eggs and swallows's nests—was drowned and preserved in deadly stillness beneath Lake Powell's shellac, where nothing much stirs today but water-skiers and brain-eating amoebas. A few days after Mildred had died of breast cancer in 1985, Frank gave his daughter the photograph and a blown-glass dacryovial of muddy Escalante riverwater suspended from a thin gold chain. He told the story behind the artifacts while he sobbed. It was the first time Emily had ever seen her father cry and it had unhinged her—left her feeling for years like a house without doors, both open and cold. But when she'd turned the frame over and discovered that Millie in her perfect, looping penmanship had self-deprecatingly entitled the photo, *Defrocked*, they'd both laughed so hard, in their desperate need for release from grief, that for a moment they'd nearly forgotten the funeral.

She flipped the picture over. Beneath her mother's indigo orthography, Emily was now surprised to see that she had transcribed, in some forgotten past, a favorite Edward Abbey quote in her own boxy capital letters: SENTIMENT W/O ACTION IS THE RUIN OF THE SOUL. Emily touched her mother's ink; she trailed a fingertip and smeared her own graphite. Then coughing she placed the picture face-up in the last box, on top of her framed diploma, on top of textbooks and two peacock-feather earrings and a medical file with Anna Lee Kravitz's anesthesiology report and letters from the lawyers and her bound copy of the malpractice lawsuit. Her fingers reached instinctively for her sternum. At some point in her twenties, she'd lost track of the necklace and vial of riverwater (unconscionable loss!). She frowned as if at a ghost's intrusion—a fragmented memory or forgotten promise—but it was mist; it evaporated. She stood and scanned the grey office, with an unsentimental glance out the slot-window that gave onto a parallel wing of the hospital.

Beneath Denver's orange night sky and helicopters, the regimented squares of lit windows marched in yellow columns and rows across the artificial canyon of concrete and steel. Some canyons were fortresses. Some were prisons, ruinous to the soul. But others were sacred love-grottoes, or secret passageways to magical realms from whence luminescent otherworldly creatures came: fish with lanterns, iridescent damselflies, the glowing Mothers of God who'd asked their warrior-daughters to keep their own most sacred and terrifying promises. And some canyons were corridors to the warm beating heart of the earth.

Emily hefted this last and heaviest box to her cocked hip, her mother's photo riding on top, then, with a grunt, lifted the box to her flat chest. She strode from the room, wheezing and leaving the empty Coke can on her desk and the door wide open; reconsidering, she returned to the threshhold and slammed the door shut. In the hallway, the only sounds were her shuffling footfall and the ubiquitous, maniacal hum of the building's ventilation system, which Emily would not miss.

The lost promise circled again, hummed a little ditty, retreated. Like surf it ebbed, gathered itself, then came at Emily again, rushing in and materializing from the mist of her mid-twenties into lyrics. Don't dam the river, leave the river alone.

A few months after her mother's death, Emily went looking for the canyon in which she'd been conceived but had never found it; the chasm like a capsized vessel may have lain some two hundred feet below her canoe in the lifeless crypts of the reservoir. But on that trip, she'd had a fling with a very hairy river guide and, while in college, gave birth to a daughter, whom she'd put up for adoption. Her mid-twenties were crazy alcoholic years of radical ecofeminism and running rivers in the American Southwest, but she still managed to graduate with a Biochemistry degree and a respectable GPA. Upon graduation, however, she'd felt torn in two: Her wild self needed to wander in the Utah wilderness, while her security-seeking self wanted a career, a home, a black Toyota Landcruiser. She'd compromised—ah, the treachery of compromise!—having taken not the road less traveled but the highway into the U.S. Army and medical school. By thirty-three, she'd finished her anesthesiology residency. All those years reassuring herself that, one day, after she'd made and saved enough to finance a certain "river restoration project," she'd return for good to the Colorado Plateau. Maybe someday she'd even find her daughter. The goal-year she'd set for herself was 2012, when she—and Lake Powell—would turn fifty: her mother's age when she'd died.

Emily Sevo was now a forty-eight year old millionaire. She had a modest bungalow near Denver's City Park, a shiny black Landcruiser, a speedboat on a trailer in her driveway, and terminal breast cancer, which had metastasized to her lymph nodes and lungs. Leaving her office and her lucrative career in medicine, she was the picture of success, perfectly miserable, and still, unbelievably, right on track. Or, more precisely, back on track: thanks to Anna Lee Kravitz.

Last week, Anna Lee Kravitz, a woman her age—with short blue hair, peacock-feather earrings, and two young children—had died on the operating table. It was Emily's first anesthetic death. Her first irreversible mistake. How she feared and loathed Irreversibility! Her heart had been cowering all week in the crawlspaces of her chest. All week she'd been unable to run, or eat, or sleep. All week she'd avoided her downstairs weight-room and Dixie Chicks. All week she'd sustained her blood glucose levels with shots of tequila at night, and shots of espresso come morning, and now, sliding the slippery slope to certain ruin, she was drinking carbonated sugar-water beverages chock full of chemicals. She'd always suspected that one who wasn't living in accordance with one's deeper values would do terrible damage. She'd just assumed the damage would be done only to herself. Anna had proved her wrong. Or naïve.

Now her mother burned, for the first time in twenty-five years, like an incandescent bulb from the old sepia-toned photograph. The unfrocked joy of Mildred Sevo was the lantern Emily would borrow to find her way out of this devastating Aesculapian maze, and escape beyond the sprawl of this unquiet city of concrete canyons and helicopters. But Emily had to swim close to her mother's light. And closer still, to see what shadowy thing held up the lantern. Emily had to get so close she could look behind the light; and for that she needed to trust that the memory which lurked behind the bulb's attractive glare was benevolent, and not a red-eyed, lumpy-jawed monster with serrated teeth and fins of poison. In short, Emily had to trust her instincts, after her instincts had failed her.

Walking the corridor, Emily recalled her oath, and pieces of an old Peg Millett song that she, everyone, used to sing around the campfire came back to her: *Born in the Rockies, of high mountain streams/ running down the valleys, the ocean in its dreams.* Now her timid, remorseful heart picked up its cadence, and it shot like a wild mustang across the windblown terrain of her chest as if it had finally shaken itself free of bit and bridle, reins and rider. Something was breaking loose. It was as if she were waking up after sleeping through someone else's life for twenty years. The River Restoration Project!

Emily had done nothing wrong.

Any anesthetic procedure carried risk. Every single time.

And everybody died.

If not today, then tomorrow; if not this year, then next.

Coughing as she descended into the cold, dimly-lit stairwell, waddling gracelessly down the stairs a step at a time with the heavy box clutched to her chest, Emily said to the portrait, "Millie, it's time to make history."

2 May 2012
7:30 a.m.
East of Moab, Utah

A month or so after the twenty-third anniversary of Edward Abbey's "death," four middle-aged Earth First!ers are en route to rendezvous near Moab. Three of the four believe they are meeting to roast s'mores over a campfire, get shitfaced and maybe laid, and discuss the environmental progress made in the American West since March 14, 1989. And a fine day it is for a rendezvous: It's early morning and springtime on the plateau, and the redrock canyons shimmer with foliage and bright yellow songbirds. The upper Colorado River, swollen with snowmelt from as far up as the Nokhu Crags of the northern Colorado Rocky Mountains, slithers like an infinite serpent down the canyon alongside the river road, gulping creeks, dragging snags, and churning with a mighty borborygmus as it grinds the two-billion-year-old sediment down another monumental inch. The air smells of non-native tamarisk and clay.

Georges Nondairy, a moustachioed draft-dodger of sixty-three years, arrives from Moab by iron donkey (actually, a "cro-moly donkey") at the trailhead to

Negro Bill Canyon. He pedals in ratty black Converse "Chuck Taylor" hightops. He is skinny the way only old vegan men can be skinny, in a not-unattractive but somewhat spent and yogic sort of way, his cyclist's body exhausted from over sixty years of consuming all the lipids in his muscles, blood, and liver. An autopsy of Georges, he might be proud to know, would reveal zero intra-abdominal fat and the ticker of a man half his age (as well as pus-pockets in his liver and a joint mouse developing in his elbow, which he would not be happy to know). He reaps all his calories and nutrients solely from spiceless gobs of beans and rice, and from whatever edible treasures he can dumpster from the parking lot beside the Moonflower Food Co-op in Moab. He takes his EFAs and a vitamin a day to keep the blues and B-12 deficiency away. But his omnivorous associates who often crash at his camp have lately become concerned that Georges's supplementation is inadequate and that he suffers from a paranoia induced by VNS. Vegan Neurologic Syndrome! Obviously factory-farming propaganda! He is not worried about VNS. He is worried, however, about dangerous things that actually do exist. Like cars, and what might lunge and snap at him from beneath.

On this cool morning, Georges Nondairy (for his nonpatronymic he prefers the French pronunciation: *nohn-dayrrrEE*) has dressed practically. He wears a hemp necklace ghost-beaded with juniper berries, a thin pink ribbon tying back strands of wispy grey hair, striped socks, and layers of black cotton clothing beneath an oversized pink T-shirt with a fist encircled by the female symbol and a slogan that reads: ANOTHER CAR-FREE VEGAN ECO-DYKE FOR PEACE, *AND I VOTE!*

He has arrived before the others but figured this

would be the case. He pedals across the dusty parking lot, which is disturbingly full; he dismounts and tilts his bicycle with its two weathered canvas panniers and homemade fenders against a wooden post. First thing he does is squat to check beneath the chassis of the nearest vehicle, a black Ford Escape with New Jersey plates. One can never be too careful in these parts. There are giant landsharks with hides like steel-belted radial tires that lumber up from the river to bask in the heat of engines, drive shafts, and mufflers until the sun climbs high enough. They can eat a man alive, flense a guy in seconds, but generally only eat flesh-eaters, rarely vegans—actually only those vegans who crave cheese and secretly enjoy the smell of sizzling bacon. But, like any intelligent creature, landsharks have been known to make honest mistakes.

Georges has mostly seen landsharks near slaughterhouses and feedlots in Louisiana, where they lurk in polluted lagoons waiting for discarded offal or giblets or for the unsuspecting meat-packer on a cigarette break. But one night in Silver City, New Mexico, he came across a real live landshark thrashing in a ditchful of frogs near where he was camped and, even though he knew he was probably safe, considering his pristine diet and cravings, he decided to move to another campsite. Which turned out to be a smart move. Because in the papers the next day a hobo was reported missing only a block away from behind a steakhouse, where a waitress had seen the man dumpster-diving. But Georges knows exactly what happened to him. There are perhaps millions of landsharks infesting the Southern states by now, Georges reckons, but the Freddies suppress this information to avert pandemonium. And who can blame them, really.

At the trailhead to Negro Bill Canyon, at seven-thirty on this flaming pink Beltane, Georges gets the willies. No humans anywhere—familiar or otherwise—but he is surrounded by parked Suburbans and Dodge Ram 2500 pick-ups and Vanagons with bike racks. The bigger the vehicle, the bigger the landshark it can conceal. There must be two or three dozen of these giant cars shoehorned into the parking area between signage for the trail (Morning Glory Bridge/ 6th Largest Natural Bridge in the World/ 2 miles) and a dumpster stuffed with greasy McDonald's sacks, diapers taped up in neat white packages, and ripped, bulging garbage bags in which metallic-green bottleflies blithely mate and lay their eggs. Landsharks like basking under dumpsters, too. For the heat of decomposition.

Georges screws up his courage. He peers under each and every automobile and the dumpster, too. Safe, this time, for now. Yawning with relief, he returns to Melanie (his gallant white 1970s Peugeot with Reynolds 531 tubing), hooks his skinny tanned thumbs in his belt loops, sucks on the overgrown fringe of his salt-n-pepper moustache, leans proprietarily against the Ford Escape with the New Jersey plates, and waits. "Eh, bien," he thinks to himself, in his francophilian French. Hungry as always, he briefly considers eating the Luna Bar ("pour les femmes") that he scavenged earlier, but instead decides to save it as a treat to share with his old friends. He does not check his watch because he wears no watch. The others, he knows, will be arriving soon enough. A certain level of disorganization is to be expected if one prizes freedom above all.

Time passes. Georges sits crosslegged on a sandstone boulder beside his bike and closes his eyes. He tries to clear his mind of doubt. Imagines his fears as puffs of cumulus cloud that scud harmlessly across the blue expanse of his mind. They're coming. They haven't forgotten. Clouds form, poof, gone. But form again, build into a thundercloud: They wouldn't change plans on him, would they? Did they decide behind his back that he was too shifty, too unimportant, too much of a. . . liability?

He gives up on trying to meditate. To tranquilize his turbulent mind and twitching body, he pulls a used paperback copy of *The Monkey Wrench Gang* from his handlebar bag. On the dedication page, a former book-owner has scrawled a quote and Georges rereads:

> "I look forward to the day when somebody with a terminal disease is gonna strap a load of TNT around his waist and go down in the bowels of Glen Canyon Dam and blow that ugly thing to smithereens. That would be a good way to go."
> —Edward Abbey, 1983

Bien sur!, thinks Georges. He then resumes reading where he'd left off the night before, with the characters on a river trip nervously making plans and pacts at night by the campfire. But after only about a page, he imagines a gorgeous blonde in tight jeans and a daffodil-yellow bikini top approaching his bicycle. She asks him what he thinks about Edward Abbey, about environmental issues, about life and art and truth and our moral duty to defend nature. Would he have a few minutes to share with this naïve apprentice the pearls of his wisdom? He'd be nuts to say no: It's the only way these days that Georges gets to rant uninterrupted.

Uncle Ed published hundreds of essays, articles, columns, and letters and a whopping nineteen books in his known lifetime, and even a couple of books posthumously, which feat, to someone like Georges Nondairy, is incontrovertible evidence that Edward Paul Abbey did not, actually, die—from pancreatic disease, or esophageal hemorrhage, or anything else. Georges has heard the term "ghost-writer" but thinks it's a bunch of bull-huckie; and even if ghosts did somehow exist, they wouldn't be able to push the stiff old keys on Ed's Deluxe manual typewriter.

"You really think he's still alive, Georges?" his numinous blonde asks, stroking his bicycle's naugahyde seat. She smiles at him. Then moves around his bicycle, coming closer, batting her lashes and calling attention to her breasts by adjusting her yellow bikini top.

"You know *Hayduke Lives!*, the sequel to *The Monkey Wrench Gang?* It was supposedly completed after his death, right? But one day I was thinking real hard and realized the title doesn't refer just to a novel character, or Douglas Peacock, or the spirit of monkeywrenching. It refers to Abbey himself." Georges, like many intergalactic eco-pilgrims, and especially those that hail from the Vega solar system, has received regular messages about Uncle Ed's whereabouts. Last week, Georges scouted a campsite for tonight's rendezvous up Onion Creek, east of Castle Valley, based on from where Ed's pheromonious "messages" were coming in the strongest.

"Oh," says the blonde babe, moving close enough for him to smell her mockorange-blossom breath. "And what is that book you're reading there? *Hayduke Lives?*"

Georges picks it up, shows her the cover. "No, it's *The Monkey Wrench Gang*. It's my favorite." He was long ago set afire by Abbey's story of Hayduke, Seldom Seen Smith, Doc, and Bonnie. Something about that story stirred up Georges's own rewilding desire and his fantasy of doing something that mattered. Not just talking, but doing. Stirred up something fierce, like a fightin'-dragon dislodged from slumber by the prick of the philosopher's pen. By gawd, if the Sierra Club and other namby-pamby spineless-gumby advocacy-litigation groups couldn't stop America's machines from ransacking the earth for raw material and profit—killing us all!—then something else had to be done!

"Have you ever done anything, Georges?"

He squints at his projection suspiciously. "I'll tell you, mon petit chou, when I know for sure that the statutes of limitation have passed."

"Do you believe that the 'master's tools can be used to dismantle the master's house'?"

Georges frowns. "I'm not sure what you mean."

"Just tell me what you believe."

He scratches his head. "I believe we have a moral duty to stop the machines, and put to rest the ideologies that kill the earth and all the creatures who live here," Georges explains. "Before the machines and ideologies kill everything we all depend on for life. I believe biodiversity is a good thing. Monoculture's a bad thing. All living things have a right to live wild and free."

"Which includes humans," the buxom apparition purrs.

"That's correct," Georges says, pleased that his protegé is such an astute pupil. "We are a part of the quote-unquote Circle of Life. Which is actually a Spiral. But it pisses me off when mainstream environmentalists say idiotic things like, 'We need to protect this river or that desert for the next generation, for our children's children, blah blah blah.'"

"That's always pissed me off, too."

"As if humans are the only creatures worth saving!"

"So anthropocentric!"

"See, they're just trying to appeal to the CEOs of giant multi-national corporations. Corporations like Maxxam and Peabody Coal and Dow Chemical and Ford and, and Monsanto and, and, and Shell Oil and that, that evil Texas-slimeball company that is nuking the forests of Borneo. These D.C. enviros are thinking, Well, let's see if we can get these family-minded CEOs to change their ways by pulling at the heartstrings. Only it doesn't work, see! If these CEOs had any heartstrings, they would've already been pulled! The companies would not be doing what they're doing! But they don't care! Not about their children or grandchildren or even their own health and heartstrings! A corporation—from corpus, meaning body—is an oxymoron! Corporations don't have no bodies! Corporations don't have no mind or heart either! They are clinically psychopathic entities that don't give a poop about anybody! So how on earth are we supposed to raise sympathy for the plight of some poor desert toad or bat or tortoise?"

"People should just say, We need to protect these wildlands into perpetuity for the javenila piglet and the spadefoot tadpole."

"Mais oui! And to protect wilderness for its own sake!" He holds a fist in the air and gleefully shouts, "No Compromise in the Defense of Mother Earth!"

"Oh," his novitiate says, clearly moved by Georges's passion. "What does that mean, No Compromise? Is that a slogan for the group you belong to?"

"It's about loyalty, it's about love. No Compromise means we love something so much we'll stand up and speak out and put our bodies on the line to defend it. It's what powered Uncle Ed's writing. Love—not hatred, not cynicism, not nihilism, not misanthropy, and certainly not misogyny—"

"But he objectifies women in his novels," the scantily-clad blonde bombshell interrupts. "Like in describing characters. Even when he's trying to write a feminist character. This man's a doctor, that man's a river guide, and that man's a Viet Nam War veteran, an ex-Green Beret, a loose cannon. Men do things. Then there's the girl. She's the doctor's assistant and she's beautiful, of course. The girl just is. She doesn't do, she's done to, passively moved around by plot and the desires of men. Also Uncle Ed uses last names to refer to the male characters and first names for the females. Sarvis, Smith, Hayduke, and Bonnie. Blech!"

"Don't all authors do that? Even the dude who wrote about the Divine Feminine in *The Da Vinci Code?*"

"And some of them don't even give their lesser female characters names!" She pouts and crosses her arms across her voluptuous bosom. Georges feels her pulling away from him, emotionally. He's afraid she doesn't respect him anymore as her mentor, her guide, her rinpoche.

"Okay, maybe a little misogyny, but only because of maybe a little misanthropy, see?"

"He cheated on his wives!"

"But you must understand! Deep down it was a love of life, any life, especially the love of any living thing—vultures and scorpions, kissing-bugs and cacti and—" he looks at his girlfriend, "—blondes in yellow bikinis—the love of any living thing that stands between the developers, ranchers, uranium and coal companies, Army Corps of Engineers, Bureau of Wrecklamation, *et asshole*, and their profits. This is why Uncle Ed and I are so close," Georges summarizes as he brings his hands together, interlacing his fingers to symbolize the degree of closeness. He clears his throat. "It's because we're both devotees of the life project."

Georges Nondairy, for instance, has never personally denied another human, dog, or housefly a meal if he or she were hungry, and has always lent a hand if someone were in trouble, needed a bandaid or had a flat tire. "Even if that flat tire belonged to a Sahara Clubber's gas-guzzling, cryptobiotic soil-crushing, tortoise-squashing, planet-poisoning, global-warming ATV?" his fantasy probes, rhetorically.

"I know it's hypocritical," Georges concedes, sitting like a guru on his boulder, "but c'est la vie." Georges holds up an index finger and says, importantly, "Only love can power a movement effectively for over thirty years."

"Love, you say?" The woman leans forward and doodles her fingers up his thigh.

"And as an expression of that love," he continues, "why not use every tool in the toolbox?"

"I certainly agree," she says. "*The Monkey Wrench Gang* is an inspiration and a blueprint for saving the whole world. It should totally be a movie."

Georges considers: *C'est vrai?* Is this statement true, the part about the blueprint? If his fantasy believes something, that means he believes it, right? Are we using every tool in our toolbox to solve the world's environmental problems? And if not, should we be? He's been specially-selected to be part of this meeting to discuss exactly this question, so he should probably figure out what to say before the others arrive. He truly believes they are meeting to put a finger on the pulse of the direct-action movement, take stock of victories and missed cairns, dig out the old 1981 ecodefense map and compass, and chart where to go next.

The woman strokes his thighs as she nestles her breasts between his knees. She lifts her dewy, admiring eyes; he hardens. The sexual attraction is undeniable—but what if Artemis, the Amazon-Surfer of the California Coast, who'll be arriving any minute, wants to sleep with him again? Would he be cheating on his numina if he gave in to Artemis? Mostly though—if he could just stay focused for one second here—he is excited by this imminent tete-a-tete of the movement's Great Minds; to have been invited to this auspicious gathering of the Council of Elders is arguably the best thing that's happened to Georges in twenty years. There is so much to talk about! He has so much to say about the future of the direct-action movement!

"We're all looking to you now, Georges," she says.

"Yes," he says, and lowers his lashes humbly.

A red SUV pulls into the parking area and his apparition evaporates. Georges misses her immediately. As he goes limp, he feels the sucker punch of loneliness again, the loneliness he felt as a boy when his mother sent him South to live with his Aunt Martha and his blunted cousin Darryl, and overnight he lost all his friends. The shock of the loss always takes his breath; it happens every time his lady friends sublimate to cirrus and cumulus.

You'd think by now he'd be used to the feeling. But Georges is not a macho man. Georges is in touch with his feelings, and he feels his feelings, leans into the fear and pain and discomfort, the anger and the grief. Like a true warrior, he must be strong enough to feel and still have the energy and courage to survive and to fight for what he loves. Who today will raise the fierce yawp of dissent, if not him? Is *The Monkey Wrench Gang* still a blueprint for ecodefense? Georges Nondairy, who would never shoot a Slow Elk or toss a beer can out a truck's window or utter four-letter words or do anything violent to anyone or anything, isn't sure. But he wants to hear what the others have to say. Especially the Medical Maggot. And especially especially Artemis Jade Bison-Wallow.

The red Chevy FreedomFighter with AWD, moonroof, and independent triple-axis 4th-dimension suspension squeals to a halt in the parking area. The woofers pound out a driving bass rhythm that rattles the tinted glass of the sport utility vehicle. Georges Nondairy's blue eyes rise beneath his sun-bleached lashes to beam the driver a message of love and peace and at the same time he mumbles, "Thanks for sharing what you call music with the whole world, you unenviable person of limited awareness."

The door behind the driver swings open. A voluptuous fifty-something woman, with a babushka tied over a kelpy thicket of hair, slides barefoot to the sand and pebbles of the lot. Something about her seems familiar. She adjusts her long brown T-shirt and long brown skirt and, thanking the driver, she smiles. Someone hands her a backpack to which several glass gallon-jugs of water have been clipped to carabiners and nylon webbing. Again she smiles as she takes her pack. Then she clicks shut the door, shoulders the pack, and sweeps her eyes across the packed parking lot before fixing her wall-eyed gaze on old Georges. She waves! As the red Chevy squeals out of the lot and onto the river road, Georges frowns and straightens his spine, thinking, Does this mademoiselle know me?

"Well, goddamnit all to hell, if it ain't George 'Hayduke' LaRue!" While Georges spiders down off his boulder, the voluptuous Goddess barrels across the lot, head down and pack waggling like a bison hump atop her broad back, water jugs swinging like bovine mammaries. A couple of meters away she holds out her arms and he braces for the smothering hug and clasp of massive armflesh and unrestrained breasts. After an airless minute, he is released. Smell of patchouli incense. "It's me! Artemis! You haven't forgotten me, have you, Hayduke LaRue?"

"No, uh, I go by Georges *NondairEEE* now, so please don't call me Hayduke anymore. That was a phase." Artemis wears a red, gold, and green cotton cloth tied over her dreads and a treasure trove of necklaces: goddess spirals, Zuni fetishes, rastafarian beads, a little glass vial of brownish water, a black Sharpie pen. "Uh, so I see that, uh." He is more nervous than he thought, seeing her again.

"You didn't believe I'd actually make it, did you. Ah, George, *Georges*, of course I'd come! I wouldn't miss this rondy for the world—jesus, what a surprise to get The Weasel's call! What a hoot! We have so much catching up to do!" She scans the dusty lot. "But where the hell are the others? Where's The Weasel? And where the fuck is Maggot?"

Georges unable to meet and hold her gaze. His eyes flicker over hers. Her wall-eyed hazel irises, one globe slinking off to the side while the other locks in on a point where his brows merge. Of course, Artemis. How could he ever forget? At the 1991 Round River Rendezvous—or was it '92?—they went at it like wildcats in heat all over the pinewoods of Southern Colorado.

"I knew you'd come for sure," he says, chewing a thumbnail. He stares at his striped black and pink socks, ratty black chucks, and the scuffed brown-white rubber over the toe with the drawn-on smiley-faces, and feels stupid. Then he stares at Artemis's wide feet with their arcs of dirt beneath long yellowed toenails and the tufts of hair on the toe knuckles. Her feet are very dirty, deeply soiled and encrusted, especially in the ducklike interdigital webbing. One of her big toes is swollen and misshapen, maybe broken. Her ankles are thick and muscular and stocky as a draft horse's. Also like a horse or a Selkie her legs are furred with thick dark hairs that lie in flat streams against her dusty shins. He loves the way she smells. He wants to look at the crowsfeet across her temples and assess the state of her teeth but can't bear to bring his eyes to her brown moon-round face. Instead he turns and raises his embarrassed eyes to the rim of the cliff where a pale trumpeting of daffodil announces the imminent arrival of the sun.

"But personally I think Maggot's been. . . absorbed," he says, adding, "Indoctrinated. I seriously doubt she'll come, but you never know about people."

"Indoctrinated," Artemis echoes. "But The Weasel told me over the phone that she was the one to call this meeting, so she better fucking show!"

"Oh." News to him! He thought all this was The Weasel's idea. What else is the ole gang keeping from him? Their eyes snag accidentally; he smiles and blushes.

"And speak of The Weasel, where is His Mighty Highness, Mr. Punctuality with a grandfather clock shoved up his ass? Oh, shitfuckinggoddamnit-alltohell, you wouldn't happen to have any TP on ya, wouldja George?" She drops her pack to the dust, sending up a cloud. The glass bottles clink against metal zippers, biners, and D-rings.

Shrugging, but happy to have something useful to do, Georges Nondairy turns on his holey soles and strides to his pannier, from which he extracts a sandwich baggie containing a neat stack of restaurant napkins and a book of matches.

He hands them to her, saying, "Just be careful, you know, check under the cars, and also they might have videocameras everywhere now so, you know."

Artemis smiles wanly as she takes the baggie. "Check under cars?"

"Yes, under cars. You know. It's traditionally a Southern thang, but now. . . they could be. . . ." He nods once and returns to his pannier, embarrassed and nauseated by the attention, wondering if she thinks he's crazy. The unanticipated resurrection of long-buried feelings. The suspicion and jealousy aroused by the thought of Artemis and The Weasel having a long telephone conversation. He wants to feel angry toward The Weasel for withholding that it was Maggot of all people who organized this rondy—but when he peeks over his shoulder and sees Artemis's hips parting a thicket of poison ivy, he prays to the pantheistic godlike entities she isn't eating the flesh of animals these days. Not just because of the health impact of RAFinGS— Rotting Animal Flesh in the Gut Syndrome—but also, of course, because of the landsharks. He hopes, too, that she remembered to bring some Mendocino marijuana. And he furthermore hopes he gets his own joint sucked on this trip because he can't even remember the last time he laid himself naked beside or inside a real, actual woman and it sure would be nice, *yessirrEEE.*

Artemis Jade Bison-Wallow pushes aside branches of poison ivy, *Rhus toxicodendron,* with her ample arms and wide hips. She lifts her skirt and yanks down her panties and squats in the sandy soil of the side-canyon, exuberant to finally have arrived after hitching for six days from the California coast. Wasn't anything like it used to be, hitch-hiking. These days everybody has cars and hardly nobody will stop, and those that do are weird fucking bastards, first they lay down the dog blanket across the back seat and squirt a little Lysol around, then say it's okay, she can get in now. It's not like the lice or fleas in her dreads are all that contagious, for fuck's sake! The parasites know they've got it good sticking with her boat; no way they're gonna jump ship for something unknown. How insulting anyhow.

In the parking lot, Artemis thought she had to poop but now decides she only has to pee. She pisses a hearty stream of urine into a puddle between her big feet and it soaks into the earth. Relieved and happy as a javelina in mud to be back in redrock country, Artemis giggles as she wipes herself. Reconvene indeed! A BRILLIANT fucking idear, grrrlfriend, wherever the hell you are. We shoulda done this years ago. Exactly what the movement needs: Four EF!-elders converging in Mobe—Center of the Universe!—to examine patterns and trends, look at the big picture. Something Artemis does extraordinarily well, if she says so herself. Which she does. Get a little stoned, do a little skinny-dipping and river-surfing, sing a couple of the ole Dana Lyons, Janet Planet, and Peg Millett riversongs for old time's sake, bed her old lovers—maybe, this time, all three at once?—then look at what the fuck happened over the past twenty years.

Artemis pulls up her panties and adjusts the cotton moonpad, snugs it into her crotch. The perimenopausal spotting hasn't been bad. She can't wait to see Maggot. Heard all kinds of rumors, like Maggot's shaving her legs and pits now and drives a Landcruiser and reads Madonna biographies and listens to insipid pop music. Ha-ha, wouldn't that be something to see! Maggot, sittin' one shiny knee hooked over the other in a fancy restaurant listening to Josh Groban or Norah Jones and sipping champagne. Is it all an act? Where's her heart and soul really these days? And, most important, is she still a hot bulldyke with a buzzcut, a nice butt, and rippling biceps? And what about The Weasel, with the sexy bod of Baryshnikov, the mischievous spunk of Napi, the temper of Zeus? Jesus H. Fucking Christ, ten years in prison, a wilderness-lover's bound to be supremely fucked up after that. Especially an alcoholic egomaniacal EF!er who was angry and fucked up before he was even incarcerated.

The sun like a newborn crowns the rim. A long-fingered shaft of light illuminates Artemis's bronzed forehead and colorful scarf. In the thinning grey hair at her temple, just under the fabric, a scurrying flea is caught unawares by the searing sunlight. It pulls a U-ey and paddles beneath the scarf again. Artemis closes her eyes and inhales. Touched by the Sun God in the land of timeless beauty, far-fucking-out! It is going to be a great day for a witch. She is ready to cast some spells and shake up the universe. Cleaving the poison ivy patch again, she thanks the plant for keeping idiots and assholes out of this primordial ravine of cottonwoods and laughingbirds and seeps full of spermlike tadpoles. If I was a plant, she thinks, I'd be fucken poison ivy.

She parts the drapes of guardian foliage and stares at weird little Georges clad in his offensive pink shirt. His wispy hair floats around his head as he paces beside his bicycle. Gross, she thinks. She won't be proposing no orgy on this trip! She can't believe she once slept with this repulsive little squirt. She hates when men pretend they're feminists and wear the slogans and paraphernalia of the eco-babe. Vegan eco-dyke for peace? Shit, he may as well be wearing a pink NARAL ballcap embroidered with, "I fuck to come, not to conceive." Hunh!

A rattling car has pulled up, gasping and squealing,

into the lot. Artemis watches Georges look up from beneath his pinched monobrow, half his moustache in his mouth. It's a small mid-'80s Honda with a big guy driving. No doubt The Weasel hath arriveth, pissy little bastard's gonna get all the attention now just because he's been on the inside, but what the hell, he deserves some tribal support especially since word is he got locked up not just cuz he got caught inoculating 300-year-old Doug firs with ceramic spikes, but cuz he refused to snitch on others who may or may not have been with him at the time. Which is commendable indeed. Especially considering the pressure the FBI puts on an activist these days under the new eco-terrorist laws. It's not like the old fuckin' glory days! Used to be all the old macho authors could brag about the shit they did, write it up, even get paid for putting it in print. These days, the only folks who talk about doing shit are the ones who'd never do shit. Fucking people.

Sometimes Artemis worries that maybe she's too much of a selfish, man-hating bitch to hang a shingle and call herself a green witch. Othertimes she's pretty damn sure that she's such a grounded herbalista that she can heal whatever ails anyone, whether a chest-thumping hairy redneck or a savvy Mexican dyke or anybody in between—and lots of EF!ers, she's noticed lately at the RRRs, are some nongendered in-between. Speaking of Yin muddied by Yang: There's Georges watching the rattling car try to find a spot to park; Georges stands with his hip cocked and an elbow bent, the wrist dangling limply against his ribcage. Georges is not well, she diagnoses. She wonders if his liver needs cooling: she'll introduce him to the root allies *Rumex crispus, Arctium lappa,* and *Mahonia.* With their blessings and permission, of course.

Having accessed the Divine Healer Within, she immediately feels better.

The sun mounts the cliff. The sun is full on naked hot and gold. The sun dances on the bartop of the canyon's rim, which is the ancient floor of an ancient inland ocean, and here's Artemis standing at the bottom of the bottom of beyond, five hundred feet below the ancient seabed of yore. Mind trip! She's instantly transported to some 350 million years ago when the continent, steepled by the Ancestral Rockies, was hovering around the equator and the plants were ten-foot tall mosses and *Equisetum* and giant ferns and palm trees. Then to 150 million years ago when ten-ton dinosaurs with elegant necks tiptoed through the foliage, dislodging monstrous dragonflies that droned overhead like today's helicopters. At night, from the place where the sun now stands on the canyon rim, you wouldn't have been able to see the North Star, cuz this continent back then was equatorial. Weird, hunh? And Artemis realizes—in a dazzling flash of insight—that the dinosaurs of what's now called "North America" must've used completely different constellations to navigate by.

Mike Weiselmann, bald and pale as a cave fish and sporting prison tats of serpents up both arms, unfolds from his parked, rust-bucket Honda and scowls into the searing sunlight. He lifts the temple-pieces of his old near-sighted prescription glasses so the lenses slant down, and he tilts back his head to see who that is moving around over there at the other side of the lot. Visoring his eyes with his hand he sees Hayduke LaRue beside his bicycle and they wave as Hayduke minces toward him, and Mike Weiselmann's thinking, Oh christ, here comes that self-righteous vegan. So quickly he unbuckles his spiked leather dog collar from his neck and the bracklets from his wrists and his holstered pistol and belt, too, and tries to stuff everything under the front seat. But that's where he's stored all the Northern Arizona/Southern Utah road maps and nautical maps of Lake Powell that Maggot asked for, so he has to stash his leather in back. He covers the contraband with his satiny blue and red "SuperWeasel!" cape. Not because he's trying to appear to be someone he's not, but because if Hayduke LaRue's tick-sized brain latches onto the topic of cowhide and guns, even thrift-store cowhide and inherited guns, said embedded brain will get stuck in the rut of a tiresome rant and suck all the lifeblood from their rondy. And there's so much more to fight about this week than just leather and weapons!

Watching LaRue's twiggy, effeminate approach, he can't believe the Medical Maggot wanted him to contact this feeble-minded nutcase. Cannot imagine why. But he was thrilled to have been rung up and put in charge, so to speak, of organizing this rendezvous. He needs to hang with his people, needs to laugh and relax, needs this shot in the arm before returning next week to his deadening nonprofit office job, where nothing ever really gets done, and his one-bedroom apartment in the sprawling metropolis of Salt Lake City. He didn't even realize he was burnt-out, and nearly as depressed as he was in prison, until now. Thank god for Fermin!

Scanning the parking lot for the others, he sees Artemis's huge bronzed forehead poke up from a rustling bustle of poison ivy. She carries a plastic baggie—ah, she's been toileting in the wild. Three of four present and accounted for. He checks his Triathlon watch: oh-eight hundred thirty. It bothers him that he's late, but at least he's not last in, and anyway it could not have been helped. His Honda has developed an abscess in the crank case, bastard strangles from the unholy marriage of antifreeze and engine oil, and he had to limp Rusty the entire thirty miles from Crescent Junction past Arches into Moab along the shoulder of 191, going fifteen miles per while eighteen-wheelers torpedoed by at eighty. Considering everything, it's a wonder he's not later. In fact, he would have been, had he not started out from Salt Lake City with a two-hour lead time on top of the four hours he'd allocated, just in case.

If the past twelve years of Grand Juries, prison, and wageslaving have taught The Weasel nothing else, they've at least impressed upon him that it is essentially, crucially, important to not only have a Plan A—and a bomb-proof one at that—but to have in place a Plan B, a contingency plan, as well. And an exit strategy! Because environmental work is serious business. And because humans are notoriously stupid when predicting outcomes and consequences. Humans don't know shit and the smallest oversight can fuck everything up.

The three aging Earth First!ers, arthritic of joint and wrinkled of skin, loiter by The Weasel's suppurating Honda and smoke some of Artemis's Mendocino medicine in a fatty. If any one of them is worried about possession or use of a Schedule I controlled drug, no one shows it. Georges is a little twitchy, and smokes it with his head lowered beneath hunched shoulders, but that's just Georges. The Weasel has decided that he deserves a toke on his vacation and has let his figurative hair down a little. There are many cars but no other humans in the parking lot. No one to see them. The sun climbs higher and beats mercilessly on the silvering hair of their heads—and The Weasel's bald head—and glances off car hoods and glass into their unprotected eyeballs.

"I doubt she shows," says Georges Nondairy.

"She'll fucking show," Artemis fires back. "Ye of little faith."

"This is her baby. She's coming," The Weasel reasons, and he shakes his triathlete's watch down over a serpent's inky tail. Nine twenty-three and forty-two seconds.

"She's on dirtbag time. That's a good sign, I think," Artemis offers. She stares at a spot above his glasses, at The Weasel's shaved brow where his eyebrows used to be. She takes in his clean-shaven face. Sharp-angled bones beneath the pale skin. Smooth upper lip. Which she wouldn't mind licking. She's never seen his mouth and lip and chin before.

"What's wrong with you?" The Weasel asks Artemis.

"Maybe something horrible happened to her," Georges says, too brightly. "Maybe she was hit by a semi last night coming over Vail Pass, and she's lying somewhere in like a bloody ravine beneath a ski chalet and RPHs."

The Weasel and Artemis stare at Georges.

"RPHs? Rich People's Houses?"

"Jesus, Georges, but that's a terrible thing to put out into the universe," Artemis chastens him, and Georges wilts, thinking, No way is she going to sleep with me. He withdraws to marinate in a bitter sauce of nostalgia for the freewheeling early '80s when he was a desirable, edgy, draft-dodging punker who'd just discovered the mail-order company that made vegan Doc Martens from recycled materials.

Finally he whispers, snottily, "I'm not wishing she did, I'm just saying she might have."

"We can't afford to lose nobody," Artemis says, between clenched teeth. "So don't even go there, okay, George Hayduke LaRue?"

"Georges *NondairEEE*."

"Whatever."

"If she's bleeding in a ditch somewhere she knows what to do. She's a doctor." The Weasel hands the joint to Artemis, who sucks on it and hands it back to the Weasel, who sucks on it then gives it right back to Artemis, and each time their fingers touch they share what Georges would call a certain look. His ears flame with envy and he withdraws further.

At ten o'clock they split Georges's lemony Luna Bar three ways—his attempt at reconciliation—and as The Weasel licks his fingers he proposes they hike up Negro Bill without the turncoat, which incites an ugly argument between the three old comrades. Artemis holding forth on the virtues of open-mindedness and giving people the benefit of the doubt; The Weasel contending that life is too fucking short to waste on tardy narcs and traitorish straights; Georges, in his desire to sting Artemis, defending the other male's perspective that if you blow off your tribe you don't belong with the tribe anyway.

Georges says to The Weasel, "I agree! Maggot's sending a clearly hurtful message that she has better things to do than get together with a bunch of lowbagging losers to rehash the good old days of direct action. She probably never intended to come! For all we know, she's probably a snitch who's gonna sic the FBI on us! I say to heck with her, and let's migrate."

The Weasel seconds the motion proposed by Georges, but adds, "If she gets here in the next few hours, she'll find us anyway. She'll know to come on up to Morning Glory."

"You two assholes go on then."

"You're not coming?"

"Me and my herb will await the sister as planned."

"Damnit," The Weasel says. Women activists, he believes, have a passive-aggressive bass-ackwards way of leading just by deciding not to follow, and it's always driven him catshit-crazy.

The three of them lounge in the scanty shade of a juniper until the sun moves higher and makes them sweat and pant. So they walk the length of the lot and cross the river road to take a dip in the Colorado. Talking idly about this and that. Catching up on folks they used to know—who's a lawyer now, who's a cop, who's in jail or a housewife or exactly the same. Who's organizing this year's big Round River Rendezvous. Sharing activist news from around the country.

On the mosquitoey riverbank, Artemis strips down to her ample folds of luscious skin and dives in. The men on the bank wait for her to surface. Finally, far out where the river speeds by like a train, she rises, shrieking with delight. She is carried downriver a ways. The men lose sight of her; she is the same color as the river. A hundred meters away, she begins her slow, powerful surfer's crawl back to the bank, swims a series of eddies upriver to her friends, and, not even winded, plunges in again, holding her breath for a minute or two as she dolphin-kicks underwater, far out and into the current, eyes wide open to the brown murk. When Artemis was twenty she won an underwater breath-holding contest: four minutes and twenty seconds. Even now, her lungs remember their training and capacity. Her webbed hands and feet splayed like the finned appendages of a seal, she is a naturally strong swimmer and former surfer from the California coast who pulls against the wild current in ecstasy. She surfaces, turns, and waves at the boys as she rides the river down-canyon.

The Weasel leaves his glasses with Georges. He cannonballs into the river wearing his unbelted jeans and Tevas but stays closer to shore. His bust is an artful shiver of alabaster in the mudbrown medium. Artemis has drifted downriver again and returned, grinning. But Georges, he will not go in, no way José, he sits on the eroding red-clay riverbank in the vegetation while his compadres giggle and clutch at sprigs of tamarisk so they don't drift downriver in the roiling current. He imagines their shins entwining in the opaque run-off. He feels sick to his stomach imagining how their flashing legs would appear to a landshark coming up from the silty depths of the river. He sits hugging his knees inside the longjohns, occasionally flapping his arms or nonviolently blowing mosquitoes from his wrists. He looks pallid and terrorized.

"Can't you swim, Georges?" It's Artemis. Mocking poor little Georges.

He shakes his head. It's not that, he wants to tell her, but fears ridicule. It's the twenty-foot long landsharks with carcass-ripping jaws and skin like tire treads. For a moment Georges watches his friends dog-paddling in the chocolate river, The Weasel floating behind Artemis, then yelps, "Eh, you two don't eat meat these days, do you?"

"What?" Artemis hollers back. "Just get in, Georges!"

"What did the little man say?" The Weasel asks Artemis, then drifts out.

"Uh, I bathed last week," Georges explains. "Also I get cold very, very easily, and I've never really been a strong swimmer, per se. When I was a boy in Louisiana,

I fell into our kiddie pool, see? Or maybe I was pushed? And my cousin Darryl, he—"

"GET IN!" Artemis yells.

"Uh," says Georges, and he points downriver.

She turns: The Weasel has gotten carried away, far downstream. He has become a bald, bobbing white buoy in the current. He raises a hand. Artemis groans and plunges into the swell.

Back in the parking lot, dripping water into the dust and sand, Artemis stands next to The Weasel, who is still coughing and shivering and badly shaken. She checks his pulses and puts her ear to his naked chest to listen to his lungs. "Let me see your nailbeds," she says, and he shows her the pale bluish ovals. "You seem fine now," she says. "You'll warm up soon. *Hooo-WEEE!* That was exciting, wasn't it?"

"I almost drowned," The Weasel says, as angry as either of them have ever seen him.

"Why are you pissed at me?" Artemis asks. "I saved your fucking life, asshole."

"That's why he's angry at you," explains Georges, the only local expert on male behavior. "His male ego has been wounded."

The Weasel pushes his glasses up his nose. "Go to hell, Hayduke LaRue."

"Georges *NondairEEE*. And why are you pissed at me now?"

The Weasel swallows hard. He considers the question and thinks back to his Anger Management Class in prison, to the avuncular bearded man, Steve, who would prompt them to explore the emotion beneath the rage. Why is he so angry? "I just got scared, I guess." He inspects an abraded patch of skin across his hairless pectorals and under his shaved armpit.

"That's where I held you, to tow you in," Artemis says. "Sorry I was a little rough."

"It's weird I don't remember it."

"You blacked out."

He touches his lips and frowns his browless ridge.

"I had to give you mouth-to-mouth," Artemis says. "You weren't breathing. Tonight your abs will probably hurt, too, where I squeezed your belly and pounded on you to get all the water out."

"I almost died."

Artemis remembers a swim with The Weasel in the Piedras River back in 1990, when he wore hair down to his hips and a full hippie-beard. Or was that 1991? The cold mountain waters were rushing and roaring through a piney gulch of granite boulders but they'd both navigated the river without incident. She says, "I thought you could swim."

"I can. Or I used to. Before I started lifting," The Weasel says, but adds with humility, "And maybe the river was just too much for me this time."

Artemis squints at The Weasel, thinking, *This isn't The Weasel I used to know.*

"So, wow," Georges says. "You blacked out. You almost drowned."

"Yeah." The Weasel rubs his shining pate. "And there was nothing going through my head. Nothing at all. It was like I was totally, completely, eternally at peace." Then The Weasel thinks, *Shit! What would've happened to Fermin?*

Another hour passes and The Weasel, having changed into dry clothes, checks his cell phone for messages from Maggot. Georges, disgusted that one of his peeps has bought into the trappings of the telecommunications industry, sulks beside his trusted steed Melanie with Her vegan saddle and squeezes Her comforting orange and blue hemp-wrapped handlebars.

"No messages," The Weasel announces, dejectedly.

They decide to hike Negro Bill and even Artemis agrees to go along this time, mostly, she rationalizes, to keep an eye on her nearly-drowned friend. With the Sharpie around her neck she defaces the trailhead sign: "Phaenicia—Hike the effin' trail!" *Phaenicia* is the codeword they'd agreed to use if plans changed in Moab; the word had some significance for the Medical Maggot.

Artemis stashes her backpack in The Weasel's car. They are able to convince Georges to stow his panniers and handlebar bag inside Rusty as well, but his bicycle won't fit inside. Not that he wanted Her to; Melanie would want to be locked inside a car about as much as Georges himself would. The Weasel locks his car. Against Georges's wishes, The Weasel conceals Georges's bicycle in an alcove behind boulders, the juniper shrub, and some rabbitbrush.

"No one is going to steal it," Georges complains. "This is a stupid, fear-based action."

"Fine, it's fear-based," The Weasel says, arranging shrubbery over the handlebars.

"Better safe than sorry," Artemis chimes in. Georges winces at her voice, which has begun to grate on his nerves ever since she put her whoring lips on The Weasel's.

On the way up the trail, a white-haired couple, wearing matching visors and sunglasses and apparel more fit for a tennis court, is coming down-trail, and they say, "You're almost *they-yah*!"

Not that Georges, Artemis, or The Weasel either asked or cared.

Artemis retorts, "We're already there! In fact, we're already *here!*"

The man and the woman stop in their tracks, mouths agape.

Then they *har-har* in New Jersey accents, "Oh ahn't you kids hilarrious! *Har-har-har!* Of course, you're already *they-yah!*"

"That's right!" Artemis happily shouts back. "We're already here! Just like that!" She snaps her fingers, a hip hop artist performing a magic trick.

"You do know," the New Jerseyette says, leaning in as if conspiratorially, and Artemis notices the ruddy skin that tonight will be a sunburn and in three days will peel away in stretchy sheets. "You do know that they-yah's a natural ach at the tap!"

"It's not actually an arch, per se, but a bridge," Georges says, helpfully.

"What?" Artemis teases the couple, ignoring Georges. "Only one arch? The guidebook promised two golden arches—and a swimming pool! I was looking forward to poolside Big Macs and french fries and ice-cold Cokes! I want my money back!"

The New Jerseyans stare until they get it. "Oh, har-har-har! You kids! You're locals!"

"Har-har!" Artemis laughs. "Ha-ha!"

"You kids have a great hike!" they shout, laughing and stepping down the ledgy trail.

"Toodle-loo!" Artemis bids them adieu.

"Must you be so annoying?" Georges tells her, after the couple is out of earshot.

"I'm just having a little fun."

"Everyone needs a hobby," The Weasel quotes, but Georges stomps on ahead like a petulant child and soon he's already ten paces up the trail.

It's two rocky uphill miles to the natural bridge, everybody's destination and a blessed respite from the sun. The sandstone bridge runs parallel between the flanks of the narrow box-canyon. Vibrant trees and plenty of shade, poison ivy and a sandy-damp puddle rippling with mosquito larvae provide just the setting for a picnic. Obnoxious teenagers, too old for such infantile games, play chase, widening their game to include our dour EF!ers who came for quiet and privacy and got spoiled anvil-footed American child-teens and their obnoxious parents.

Our three sit in the sand and stretch their legs. Artemis wiggles her bare hairy toes. She has always adored her feet and ankles: They are wide and muscular and webbed between the toes, with tortuous veins running all over the place; her big toes are asymmetrical, one bigger and lumpier than the other, an old break; and her little toes with their hard calluses curl like shiny brown pond-snails. She loves her feet because they are the notebooks the earth writes on as Artemis gypsies around the West. She loves her feet because they allow her to swim oceans and rivers like a sea lion, otter, or eider. She flares her webbed digits, fans them out in all their glory. Tendons pop in fan traceries along the instep.

Someone throws down a rappel line from the far strip of blue sky and our three misanthropes raise their faces, in unison and disbelief, to the gap between bridge and canyon rim.

"You have GOT to be fucking kidding me," Artemis says. Her toes tuck reflexively.

A large boy backs over the rim between the cliff and the bridge—a paunchy black silhouette against the royal blue—and a picnicking parent yells, "You've GOT it, Danny! Woo-hooooooo! Lookit you go!" Danny, the kid a hundred feet up with his hand on the rope, lowers himself in spasmotic jerks down the rock face. His hand yanks up and down above the rappel device, a masturbatory gesture that embitters Artemis and excites Georges, who watches Artemis watch the yanking high above.

Artemis says, "How the *fucking hell* did people get up there?"

"There's a road up there," Georges explains. "There're these companies that take tourists rappelling, drive these rich people in Jeeps way back into these places, set up the rappels and rope 'em in, so all the client has to do is lean back."

"That's sick," says Artemis. "I think I might throw up."

"You've GOT it, Danny!" the parent shrieks. "Lookit you go, woo-hooooo! Hey, looky down here a minute, I'm gonna take your picture." She sets her crinkly bag of Cheetos in the sand and picks up her digital camera. "LOOKY HERE DANNY!"

"Unbefuckinglievable," The Weasel mutters. His upper lip twitches.

The teenagers playing chase go wide, hurdle Artemis's hairy legs, and crash into the island of poison ivy, which is lit by a magnificent beam of sunlight in the gloomy canyon. Artemis smiles. She presses her shoulder into The Weasel's and whispers, "You know, poison ivy seeds could be collected and planted in strategically important places, to keep people out."

Georges overhears and runs with her idea. "Like National Park campgrounds, jeep trails, and hunting camps?"

"Subdivisions," The Weasel riffs with glee. "Shopping malls, car dealers."

"Motocross courses," Artemis puts in. "Real estate office-parks!"

"County fairs!"

"Baseball diamonds!"

"Football fields, event centers, and zoos!"

"Not zoos," Georges says, taken aback. "Zebras are very sensitive to poison-ivy oil."

"No, it's giraffes who are sensitive," Artemis says, but wonders if she's right, or if she's just feeling contentious and making shit up. For good measure, she adds, "And okapis."

"Aren't okapis extinct in the wild?" The Weasel asks.

"No," Georges says. "It's the horse family who are sensitive to rashes, such as hyraxes."

"What? Don't be stupid. Hyraxes are in the elephant family."

"No, tarsiers and tapirs are in the elephant family. Hyraxes are in the horse family."

"And capybaras?" The Weasel interjects, just for fun.

"Capybaras are in the rodent family."

"What? No, they're in the platypus family," Georges tells Artemis. "With echidnas."

"Nobody's in the platypus family," The Weasel says. "Except the platypus. Sorry little man, but you are wrong."

"I have all two hundred zoo cards in my tent at home," George says. "I'll prove it to you."

"Georges, you are so full of shit," Artemis proclaims, with stinging finality.

"Well, so are you," Georges meekly answers. Nobody ever believes poor Georges!

Our three learned zoologists and guerrilla-botanists watch the tourists eat Cheetos and take photos of another fat kid rappelling the canyon. "That's it, Bobby, you got it!" the parent yells. Artemis curls a lip. She's feeling testy. Just when their game seems to have ended, The Weasel stage-whispers, "Ivy League campuses, corporate business parks, golf courses."

"Elementary schools and playgrounds!" Georges says.

"Not playgrounds." Artemis apprehends Georges with a fierce mother-griz look that nearly claws out his eyes. "Children are innocent."

"GMO tree farms," The Weasel says. "Scenic overlooks."

"Wal-Marts, military training camps, prisons," Georges adds.

"Not prisons. Christ, it's hard enough. Plus, probably half the inmates are political prisoners or were falsely convicted, set up. Innocent."

"The tops of overrun canyon rims and natural bridges," Artemis murmurs.

The others grunt their approval and watch—Bobby now, is it?—get dropped like a G.I. Joe action figure to the sand. There is much cheering from the tourists. The moment is ruined.

"I wonder how Melanie's doing," Georges says, petting his moustache.

"Who the hell's Melanie?" The Weasel asks, and coughs a little. He hacks up a giant loogie and spits: It's clay-brown with Colorado River water.

"I grow weary of this scene," Artemis says and stands with a sigh. "And the medicine isn't working. Let's go, Rangers."

On the way back down the trail, Artemis wants to stop at a shaded pool with a foot-high waterfall splashing white bubbly water into it. A soak is just the thing to improve her spirits. Georges "Buzzkill" NondairEEE whines about his bicycle: He doesn't want to delay their return to the trailhead because of his fear-based concerns. Artemis, already sick of Georges, rolls her eyes and downclimbs to the pool. The Weasel follows behind her. Georges eventually does, too.

The water is clear and the three sink their feet into it and watch for the stealthy advance of bluish crawfish among the pebbles and twigs at the bottom. Presently tiny fish come round and kiss their toes. They share another joint and another and let the fish nibble, suckle, tickle, and kiss kiss kiss their feet. Artemis, whose feet are quite tough and callused, nevertheless giggles. Her former lovers find her ridiculous and they laugh at her until the three of them are chuckling like a clutch of cartoon chipmunks, stoned on *Cannabis sativa* and pawing each other and sailing high as a kitefest of ravens in the joyful blue sky. The descending laughter of a canyon wren joins in, a flute-call falling like a leaf and ending with a funny grunt. Like best friends who've been separated neither by decades nor mountains, they recap the chat with the har-haring New Jerseyans and cruelly mock the picnicking parent. "Work that rope, Danny. Woo-hooo! Lookit you tug that thing!" Still the little fish pucker and buss their toes. Artemis is in heaven: She's in a religious daze, baptizing herself with her friends in the church of the canyonlands, giddy with the sensuousness of the trickling stream and the men's fingers on her skin and the kissing fish, feeling spiritually connected with the Divine just knowing this little seep meets a larger stream to join the sacred Colorado River and bigger fish, trout and squawfish and possibly those primitive plated sturgeon. Eventually, whales. It's hard to imagine a world without dams or reservoirs or water pipelines and ditches. Where wild rivers ran singing all the way to the sea. For instance, the Colorado River used to flow all the way to the Gulf of Baja California, and, maybe, someday, will again. "That which rules, lies beneath and below," she quotes Lao Tzu to her affectionate comrades. "The ocean is the king of rivers."

The Weasel laughs and strokes the furze on her cheek. "The king of rivers?"

"I was just thinking how, before I die, I want to swim with the whales."

"What about after you die?"

Artemis takes it as a serious question. "I'll still want to swim with the whales." But The Weasel grins mischievously, so she punches his shoulder. Meanwhile, Georges has become convinced that a particular crawfish is out to get him.

"Which one?" The Weasel asks, peering into the shallow pool.

Georges points. "That little duder there. One with his pincers up. He's out to get me for sure, doesn't like the looks of me at all. Thinks I'm some sort of. . . extractive industry politician, some oilman or vivisector. I'm beaming the villain vibe." Georges frowns with the advent of a migraine and withdraws his waterlogged feet to the rock on which he's planted his bony ass. He stares at his wrinkled toes. He clears his throat. He rubs his temples and the back of his head. "The aliens are sending again. Dang it! I hope we don't have to change our campsite plans. Hold on a minute while I prepare to receive their message."

Artemis and The Weasel exchange looks. The Weasel snorts. He pulls his long, pale feet and shaved ankles from the pool and stands, reaching for his Tevas. Artemis glares at Georges and says, "Why do you have to be such a fucking buzzkill."

Georges receives his new directive. After they meet up with Ed Abbey in Onion Creek, Georges's expertise is needed in the Yukon Territories to help found a separatist group of vegans who will grow giant bok choi in greenhouses near the Arctic circle in order to save the world. He is to ride his bicycle the entire three thousand miles. If he leaves next week, as soon as their rendezvous concludes, he should arrive before the first big blizzard hits.

Instructions duly noted (and shared enthusiastically with the others), he thinks of Melanie (his heart leaps at the thought of her shining white diamond-frame soaring across Canada, the warm clasp of her hemp-wrapped handlebars as the first flurries fly), while working his striped socks and tattered chucks onto his wet feet. Nodding importantly at his comrades—who are so impressed they're speechless—he sucks the salt from his moustache and waits for them to climb up the rock to the trail. Feeling important and wanting to impress his comrades further, he follows them, saying, "Well, not that anybody asked, but before I die I want to steal something, something small and meaningless and yellow, and get away with it."

"Well that's fucken noble, Georges."

"I've never done anything dishonest in my life," he tells them, scampering after Artemis's swinging dreads and swishing skirt. Illegal, yes. But not dishonest. Not for no reason.

The high, early-afternoon sun is blindingly white in the sunburnt pinkish-red canyon. The shrubs of Mormon tea and blackbrush have withered in the heat. The marijuana has begun to wear off and Artemis feels dehydrated and more than just a little pissy; she'd like to knock somebody's head off and impale it on a walking staff in the middle of the trail.

Oh, and here come some tourons now.

The woman leading the gaggle wears an astro-pink visor, astro-pink heart-shaped sunglasses, white T-shirt, and astro-pink short-shorts pleating at her crotch. She smiles and asks The Weasel, How much longer?, and Artemis retorts, Til what, bitch?, and Georges anxiously asks if the pink lady saw a bike hidden at the trailhead, and the lady appears to read Georges's own pink shirt

(VEGAN ECO-DYKE FOR PEACE!) and says, If it's hidden how the hell could we have seen it?, and The Weasel thanks them, ushering Georges and Artemis along, but Artemis turns to warn the tourists about a plague of aggressive black widow spiders under the natural bridge at the top.

Is this what the sum total of her activism has devolved into—smart-assing the tourists? Stationing herself along a savagely beaten path in a popular canyon, where assholes can pay some canyoneering company several hundred bucks to get driven to the top anyway? She is hardly defending the wilderness on this well-trammeled trail.

The problem is that Artemis Jade Bison-Wallow no longer knows what her calling is. What is she supposed to be doing to save the world? It used to be so clear and easy, so black and white. There were good guys and bad guys. Now everything is painted in shades of grey. Is the American West a better place now than when she started protesting the coal mines in Arizona thirty years ago? So why bother anymore? Either she's burnt out, or has gotten used to compromising, or she's growing up, as they say, becoming a barely-left-of-center middle-aged liberal. Sometimes she fantasizes about taking a Real Job—but doing what, for fuck's sake?—so that she can have health insurance, take a trip to Hawaii or Baja or someplace to swim with the whales, get that periodontal work done on the exposed roots of her molars, and have some orthotic shoes made for her enormous, flat feet. Teeth, feet, whales, and tourists. One, two, three, four. Walking down the hot-hot canyon trail. One foot, two foot, whale foot, blue foot. Just teeth, feet, whales, and tourists—okay, and a little mary jane to entwine the divine. Sometimes she wishes she had a tail. Like a mermaid's, elegant and sparkly. Or the fluke of a Blue whale: a powerful boat-smashing tail! This is her life, after thirty years of daring front-lines activism? After thirty years of the Sea Shepherd, and tree-sits, and lockdowns and barricades, and protests and demos and marches on the Capitol? This is her life—looking for tourists to hassle and wishing she had a tail? At least she had a pome published once in the *Earth First! Journal,* so her life isn't totally meaningless.

Our three continue to pick their way down the trail, with The Weasel leading, Georges taking up the caboose, and Artemis sandwiched between and feeling superficial, peevish, and bloated. The Weasel's pallid neck and bald head are getting sunburned; to take her mind off her self-loathing, she imagines gently massaging his smooth scalp and bulging, muscular traps with one of her herbal salves. Maybe tonight. *Calendula, Achillea, Urtica.* She touches her bruised lips at the memory of the mouth-to-mouth just hours ago. She wonders why he shaves his entire body these days. Obviously not for swim team! Probably some stupid Weaselly reason that'd bore her.

Georges, eager to return to his bicycle, nearly takes her heel off with the toe of his chucks. "Oops, sorry," he says, repentant.

She wants to deck him. Instead she grinds her teeth and keeps walking.

The flatrock blisters the soles of her bare feet. Another noisy pink herd of tourists is headed their way, mooing up the trail. One whale, two feet, three teeth, four tourons. And here they come, flashing their light-bright teeth at The Weasel, saying, "Hey there! How much farther til we're there?"

"A hundred fucking miles," Artemis says, and she pushes past everyone, past the tourists and past her boys. For she needs to take a dump.

Another clot of tourists has passed. She wordlessly trudges far behind the boys who took the lead when she took her pit stop, digging a cat hole beneath a juniper. They say hi to the other hikers, nice as can be, stop to chat with the enemy about the amazing rock formations, the hot day. When she catches up, Georges grins at her but she won't meet his eyes. On the move again, Georges takes up the rear. She watches The Weasel's neck turn splotchy red, watches his arms swing, his butt swish a little. She wonders where Maggot is. They're almost to the trailhead when a raven gurgles from the sky. She stops in the trail to look up, and Georges crashes into her.

"Oops," he says. "Sorry."

"Damnit, Georges, back the fuck off! I am so tired of your SHIT!"

His forehead is warped as if by frost heaves. Pale eyelashes cant down—then lift. Between the hairy caterpillars of his monobrow and moustache, his irises glow an electrocharged cerulean blue—blue as the bottom of a shallow lake, with the grey striations of undulating aquatic plants and the silvery flecks of flashing schools of fish. The black rings around his irises provide stark contrast against the marbled whites of his eyes.

My Goddess, Artemis nearly says aloud. The fetal son she aborted in '92 could've had Georges's blue eyes.

"What?" asks Georges of Artemis. "What've I done now? I said I'm sorry."

Artemis squints at the sky to get a sense of time. She's recently learned that men listen best between four and six p.m., when their testosterone level drops. They're probably just within the listening window. It's now or never.

Artemis clears her throat and looks at him. "Georges, there's something—"

But The Weasel calls from the trailhead: "LaRue! I think someone's stolen your bike!"

Damn, thinks Artemis. Everything's going to hell. The Weasel almost drowns, Georges is going to self-destruct, and the Medical Maggot still hasn't shown up.

Last night, at around eight o'clock at Wahweap Marina—the southernmost marina on Lake Powell, the one closest to the dam—two uniformed policemen standing beside their parked sedan waved down Emily Sevo while she was pulling out of the parking lot. It was clear that they wanted to talk with her. Emily, however, pretended she never saw the gestures. She resolutely steered her Toyota Landcruiser from the parking area and up onto the road that would take her to Interstate 89, checking her rearview mirror the entire distance.

Why had they wanted to talk with her? Had someone finally reported, after one-and-a-half years, excessive activity involving four houseboats, a black Landcruiser, and multitudes of heavy-looking wooden boxes being transported between them? She shuddered to think of all the evidence riding in the car with her that very minute, everything from photocopies of explosives manuals to a shoebox of cash to the four sets of camo Army Surplus fatigues and blue and green facepaint. No—she could not have stopped. All they'd have needed to say was, Mind if we have a look around?, and she'd be up shit-creek.

She reached Page on the other side of Glen Canyon Dam and thought she was in the clear. But when most of the cars turned south with 89 and she went east on

98, she saw that someone was following her.

She began to cough. They'd driven up quickly behind her, headlights brightening, then pulled back instead of passing. She was sure it was the Arizona state patrolmen. They followed her, 98 across the railroad tracks to 160, toward Kayenta, where she planned to refuel and turn north on 163. Some thirty dark miles passed in a panic—under the coal chute, Tsegi with its teal-trimmed inn and red pick-ups, someone in a checked shirt shuffling along the shoulder, then billboards for Kayenta's Holiday Inn, Monument Valley Tours and Tribal Park, a Navajo Code Talkers Display at the Burger King. Her fuel gauge hovered near empty but she passed up the Fina station. She drove at a prudent speed through town while compulsively checking the rearview. Then, holding a bandanna to her mouth as she coughed, she turned left onto 163, the road to Bluff, bypassing both Chevron and Conoco filling stations when she confirmed, by the lights of this windblown desert city, that she was indeed being followed by the patrol car.

Were they just waiting to see what she would do, where she would go next, with whom she might meet? It didn't seem like normal cop behavior. Maybe they knew something, but maybe they were just curious, or maybe, maybe it was just coincidence. Correlation does not imply causation. They'd never turned on their sirens or lights; she'd never driven over the speed limit. Sevo, she admonished herself, You have got to calm down. All this time, she'd had to behave like someone who hadn't seen them wave her down at the marina, someone who wouldn't know that those headlights belonged to a black-and-white sedan, someone who wasn't pre-guilty as sin for a hundred felonies about to be committed. Her nerves were overwrought. She had a headache that crawled down her neck and back and she'd begun to worry about coughing blood.

They turned on 163 and followed her out of Kayenta. Another twenty long miles. Tumbleweeds roll-bounced across the road. Then, just over the state line, where the smooth Arizona asphalt turned rough and bumpy on the Utah side, they'd turned around. She'd heaved the biggest sigh of relief in the world and began to breathe again without coughing.

Unfortunately, and almost immediately, a southbound Utah highway patrolmen passed her, swung a U-ey behind her, and pulled her over, lights and sirens attacking her nerves. She'd had to pull over. "Cut your engine," his voice had barked from a speaker. Reluctantly, she did. The coughing resumed, this time bringing up about a pint of mucus and a tart metallic taste. She rolled down her window halfway and spat. "Sorry," she said, thinking quickly. "I'm sick. I'm trying to get to a hospital." The officer walked up alongside her vehicle with a skull-basher of a flashlight. But as soon as he'd come abreast of her locked door, she'd taken a deep wheezy breath, changed her strategy, turned the ignition, slipped into second gear, and pealed out, thinking, I am going to regret this.

It is the hour of the bat. The blinding, kiln-fired afternoon subsides finally into the soft pastels of a cool riverside evening. The Weasel, Georges, and Artemis sit cross-legged on Rusty's roof, fitting themselves between the bars of the roofrack. Bats click and swoop over the churning river across the road and just above their heads as Georges sniffles softly to himself. The Weasel and Artemis attempt to console him.

Other hikers load up their SUVs and Big-Ass

Trucks and drive off. Georges watches them go, and each time another giant vehicle leaves its parking space, it destroys any evidence which might have been left behind by Melanie's kidnappers. He also scrutinizes the sand where the vehicles were parked for the telltale tracks and spoor of landsharks. Pretty soon, if they haven't already, the heat-seeking landsharks will be coming up from the river again. He hates sitting on top of an evil car, but it's safer right now than sitting on the sand below.

"She's not coming," The Weasel announces, morosely. He looks at his watch. "So I guess I'll head on out. You two need a lift somewhere? Georges? Can I take you to your camp?"

Artemis touches Georges's knee. "We're really sorry about your bike, Georges."

He stares at the ground.

His face is patchy and purpled by misery, and his eyes, awash in tears, nevertheless are alert in their sockets. Artemis watches his face, then, shrugging, removes her hand from his knee.

"Thank you," he says to Artemis. Then, to The Weasel, he whines, sounding very put-upon, sounding very much the victim and martyr he's trained all his life to be: "No thanks, I think I'll just walk back to town. My camp's only a few miles farther up the Potash Road."

Artemis winces unsympathetically and stares past Georges's wispy-headed silhouette. In the downriver gloaming, a tour van with sinister yellow eyes can be seen crawling along the river road, aiming a blue-white searchlight at the Wingate sandstone cliffs. An interrogating, giant circle of light exposes the coral-pink walls, pulls the pusillanimous stone from the gentle obscurity of night, forces one section of rock after another to stand naked before the perverted scrutiny of tourists. A giant voice can be heard now, booming and echoing up and down the curved walls of the great canyon: "Millions of years ago, *ago-go*, the river eroded, *ero-ro*, the sedimentary layers, *ayers-ers*, which were deposited. . . ." Our three listen for awhile, watching the tour van's inevitable approach. Artemis feels her pulse rise to her ear canals and throat; a whooshing invades her skull.

"Motherfucker!" she shouts. "I have had it with these tourists! YOU PEOPLE SUCK!" She's hyperventilating and needs to get a grip, she knows. It's not their fault they're stupid, contributing to light pollution and angering the bats with their loudspeaker's reverberations. At least these tourons are outside, right? Instead of watching TV? Breathe in, breathe out. It's okay. If she could only say something, or, better still, do something. . . . "Okay," she says. "Okay. Check this out, Rangers. Don't go anywhere. I have me an idear."

She jumps off the car and hoofs it across the parking lot. Keeping an eye on the slow progress of the tour van, she climbs the scrabbly slope using all fours. To the men on the roof of The Weasel's car, she looks like a black bear running up the talus. Her large rump bobs in the canyon's dusk.

"What the fuck. . . ?" The Weasel asks. "What the hell's she doing now?"

Georges shrugs.

Little myotis bats soar, dive, then swoop low for the mosquito cloud above the two men. The Weasel slaps at his bulging neck; Georges Nondairy blows at his slender wrists. They think their private thoughts about blood-sucking parasites while watching the dark humpy shape of Artemis climb the slope, shrink with distance, and become intermittently absorbed by the shadows of boulders. What is Artemis doing? United against a common mystery, the two men begin to bond inasmuch as two misanthropic men are perhaps capable of bonding when not at war or on a direct-action campaign.

The Weasel has never liked Georges: he considers pussy-footed ole Hayduke LaRue a flaky, unstable creature who goes whichever way the wind or a vegan girlfriend happens to be blowing; The Weasel still hasn't been able to determine why Maggot wanted him to contact this delusional loser. What could this self-righteous troglodyte possibly bring to their May-Day-in-Moab Rendezvous? But Georges has never liked The Weasel, either: Arrogant alcoholic asshole, was what he'd thought upon first meeting the hypocritical, longhair hippie years ago. The Weasel was a charismatic, macho redneck type who, Georges was certain, was using the movement and other activists to work through his anger and addiction issues—a not uncommon scenario in the EF! movement, to be sure, but unpardonable nonetheless for how the narcissist's personal issues distracted the tribe from effective political activism. It was irritating how The Weasel always needed to be in the Fishbowl during consensus meetings. How he'd always had his name on the facilitator's dry-erase board of speakers-up-next, and how, once he was given the talking gourd, would not shut up. A bloviating bore who agitated for escalation and tried to lead the protests following the annual rondies and played the loudest guitar around the bonfire. Still, at some point early on, the two had volunteered for some midnight shenanigans that subsequently went badly for The Weasel, but that week together had only reinforced their first impressions.

Now the two men—one balding from age and rising testosterone levels, the other from a prophylactic razor and too many close calls with arson projects gone bad—sit side by side on their metallic perch like two owls come home to roost—neither so very different from the other—pupils dilated to the night, ears straining for the footfall of their baffling former lover.

"I hope she doesn't do anything stupid," Georges says, with a loud sigh. "I hope she doesn't get hurt up there."

"She's incapable of getting hurt," The Weasel says.

The claim surprises Georges. He looks at The Weasel, whose head gleams like marble in the twilight. Georges remembers what happened earlier, when The Weasel got sucked down the brown currents of the Colorado, then Artemis gave him mouth-to-mouth. Georges clears his throat. "Are you in love with her?"

The Weasel doesn't say anything, so Georges continues in his buggy whine, his voice cracking with jealousy. "Cuz some people, you know, after they've been saved from danger or death by a rescuer, they might begin to think they owe their lives to someone else, see, and I've heard that that heady sensation can feel a lot like falling in love—" Georges stops himself. Some tiny but complicated molecule of his subconscious thinks he's talking about himself, and how The Weasel once saved him from testifying, or worse, which could mean that Georges was secretly feeling certain things toward The Weasel, which couldn't be.

The Weasel pulls his upper lip. "No, I don't think so."

A few seconds pass. "I'm not either," Georges says.

"You're a terrible liar!"

"Well, so are you! Your hands were all over her, up there at the crawdad pond!"

"We were stoned! Christ, Georges, just go with the

flow for once. You're so uptight."

Georges blows a mosquito from his ankle; it was stabbing through his sock.

Not looking at Georges The Weasel adds, "There is something about her though."

"I know," Georges says. He gets a seductive whiff of patchouli incense just thinking about Artemis, and wonders if there's a word that means olfactory hallucination.

"I just. . . nah, I don't know."

"No, go ahead, say it." Georges pulls at the crotch of his baggy black pants, makes himself more comfortable on the roof of the car. The patchouli scent gathers power: He is olfceived by odons and blushes clear down to his armpits as he relives that one evening twenty years ago when they made love in the pinewoods like five or six times while everyone else was drumming and singing and hollering around the bonfire.

"I wonder sometimes if she's immortal," The Weasel says, watching the sky.

Georges scowls, stunned, and considers this new information seriously. "What? Like an actual Goddess?"

"Shit, forget it." The Weasel clears his throat. He squints into the dusk seeking the ursine hump and shuffle of Artemis. "Jesus, she's way up there."

Artemis has arrived at the juncture of the scree and the Wingate cliff just as the tour van begins to sweep its obnoxious spotlight toward her. She's doing something up there, maybe dancing, as she claims a grand pedestal of sandstone. Dark things fly from her body. Then she stands absolutely still. The tour guide's voice: ". . . on the ancient rock-*rock-ock*, primitive peoples made petroglyphs-*glyphs-ifs*. . ." The spotlight finds Artemis. She is buck-naked and frozen in a standing grizzly-bear pose, hands raised and curled like claws, fangs bared. Someone shrieks from the open-topped tour van, and the shriek is amplified by the tour-guide's speaker; the echo shrieks back and forth between canyon walls. Then silence. The milky blue spotlight stays trained on the athletic, Mesopotamian physique and snakelike dreads and fearsome-griz stance of Artemis, but her skin is the exact color of sandstone. So one could convince oneself that she was only the eidetic suggestion of woman by stone and shadow, a pretty darn realistic tromp l'oeil. The tour guide says, "Hello-*hello*? Hello you there-*there*?" then to his clients, "I don't know. . . ." When Artemis belts out the loudest wolf-howl ever heard from the throat of a human, and that eerily realistic howl echoes up and down the canyon, the shrieks of tourists again ricochet between the walls, and the tour-van's driver hits the gas, roars off.

The men on top of the car shake their heads. Georges sighs. The Weasel smiles and holds his sore belly. And in the peaceful silence restored to the canyon, little myotis bats click overhead and listen for the bounce of sonar off a moth's wing, a mosquito's blood-tight abdomen.

Around the bonfire at Campsite #1, up Onion Creek Canyon, The Weasel gets the fire going. He's always been good at fire-setting, ever since he was a boy back in Kansas. He used to love setting fire to the prairie behind his folk's house and setting fire to boxes of oily rags in the garage and setting fire to abandonned cabins and sheds for the sheer joy and meanness of it. Arson is something he never outgrew; he just learned to use it more wisely and more safely.

But there was a violent sport he did outgrow. For

a while he went out every autumn with his father and uncles to hunt one poor critter or another, pheasants and turkey, or deer and coyote. Then one cold and overcast November morning he himself actually killed an animal—a hen turkey. Immediately sad, he ran to her, tossing aside the shotgun and scooping up her hot feathered body. She kicked her dinosaur legs with the claws that snagged his jacket; she bled all over his arms; he wept while her brown eyes queried him, then sank into her skull. First her neck, then her wings, then her body went limp in his arms.

Thus anointed with her blood, he never hunted again and he stopped eating meat. His father became cruel, calling young Mike a weak little pansy-assed faggot at the dinner table in front of the uncles and Mike's childhood friends. Taking the handgun his grandfather had bequeathed him, Mike Weiselmann ran away from home at fourteen and, since 1989, his only family has been the Earth First! tribe. It required four years of prison anger-management counseling for him to understand the source of his anger and to stop picking fights and stop hating his father so that he could move forward with his life. Steve, the counselor at the prison, used to tell him that rage in itself wasn't bad, just rage that wasn't skillfully directed. He told Mike that rage could be destructive and unhelpful if you rage out at everything but also if you hold it in. "Don't repress, 'less you fester." Rage, according to Steve, needed to be redirected creatively, kind of like fire—a simile that made sense to Mike. So Mike unrepressed his father-hating during his sessions and told Steve all about his hoboing teenaged years, his alcoholism and gang fights and militant activism, his one-night stands with older women and his eco-sabotage risk-taking behavior, and his fear of being "weak" or being seen as weak, and they worked through most of it.

In the end, as Mike was preparing for release, the man he'd begun to call Uncle Steve surprised him by saying, "You know, from everything you've told me about this Earth First! group—and I'm not saying that I approve of the illegal shit you did—but it seems to me that wasn't such a bad place for young men to come of age, testing their manhood in almost ritualistic protests, learning to stand up and speak out for what they believe in, planning projects and carrying them out as a group, and, in the process, learning about themselves and what it means to be alive. It's probably as good a rite for passage into manhood as anything our modern American society has got. It probably gives a boy the same opportunities to test himself and prove himself a leader as the Army or Marines, without reducing him to a serial number, or a murderer."

Now at thirty-seven Mike Weiselmann is among the youngest of the old-school EF!ers. He is a career activist, working for one of the Canyonlands organizations that signed onto the Center for Biological Diversity's 2006 lawsuit against Kempthorne. He never finished high school, never went to college, never worked anywhere that would have violated his conscience. His most prized possessions are his library card, his CD player, and his sense of justice. He also has a brand-new love: an orange tabby kitten back in Salt Lake, currently under Jeannine's, his neighbor's, care.

Fermin is the first domestic creature The Weasel has ever taken on as a responsibility, the first living being to entrust him with its protection, care, and nurturing. When he comes home from work these days, Mike comes home to someone, and he doesn't crank his Jesus Lizard or Pearl Jam or Seven Year Bitch quite so loud, and he's started eating better and drinking fewer near-beers, and he's been spending long Sunday afternoons in the sunlit apartment playing string-toy games with Fermin. Although it's only been a few weeks since Fermin showed up in his apartment complex, Mike loves his kitten like he's loved nobody and nothing else—except for the Earth itself. Uncle Steve would be proud of him for finally opening his heart to another. But it's hard, too, knowing that, if he'd drowned earlier today, Fermin would have never seen him again. (Okay, he concedes, suddenly embarrassed by the self-centered melodrama of his fears: Maybe the kitten doesn't really care who feeds him, pets him, and plays with him. Jeannine would've adopted him; Fermin would've been fine; and Mike Weiselmann—as he has suspected all along—is, in the grand scheme of things, quite likely dispensable.)

The twigs catch and The Weasel blows on the flame and adds some bigger branches and a few planks from pallets scavenged from behind a gas station in Green River, Utah. The fire blooms to cheery life and The Weasel sits on his sandaled heels, stirring the flames, loving the fresh heat on his hands and forearms and knees and toes. In the beginning, the Earth was Fire, and in the end, The Weasel is sure, the Earth will be Fire. Fire is the transformative elemental, the most powerful force in the Universe. He loves tracing serpent-lines through the new coals, handing off the flames from branch to his poker-stick to another branch, standing and lifting a torch to the stars—the stars: those distant, skillfully-directed explosions of fire!

Across the bonfire from The Weasel, Artemis grins and passes to Georges a cottonball with some dark goopy salve on it. "That first touron's shriek was phenomenal," she says, "but I sure wisht I coulda seen their faces. That would've been intensely satisfying." She looks up at The Weasel who holds a flame to the heavens like he's the fucken Statue of Liberty and she says, "Hey, Weez, you should probably put some of my salve on your sunburn."

It takes him a moment to come back to earth. "No, that's okay."

"Want me to do it for you?"

Squatting on his heels again, The Weasel winks at Artemis. "Maybe later."

A sullen and horribly jealous Georges Nondairy dabs at his skinned knees and says, "You want to know what I think? I think modern civilization has produced only three good things: Bicycle frames, bicycle wheels, bicycle lights, and bicycle saddles."

Back in the parking lot after Artemis's funny stunt, with still no sign of Maggot, and still no magical return of Melanie, The Weasel noted the late hour and proposed they camp together at Onion Creek for the night. It was a suggestion to boost Georges's mood. Georges would have to ride in the car with them to Onion Creek—it was past Castle Valley, but not as far as the Fisher Towers turn-off—too far to walk in one night. While Artemis amended with her Sharpie the graffitied message to "Phaenicia," she overheard Georges and The Weasel arguing by the car. Poor Georges refused to get in the car; a bona fide No Impact Man, he hadn't been inside a car in some twenty-five years, and he wasn't going to violate his ethics just because his cyclocentric lifestyle came to a brutal end. So, with his paws protected by nonleather bicycle gloves, he'd clung to the roof-rack, and The Weasel drove the festering Honda at 10 m.p.h. the whole way, while 8-cylinder SUVs and cherry-red rent-a-jeeps flashed their brights and blared their horns in passing. Not that Rusty the Gimp could have gone much faster. Finally they turned off the asphalt and onto the badly-rutted jeep trail to the campsites. At the bottom of an arroyo, about a mile in, the Weasel drove into a rock he somehow hadn't seen despite his car's perfectly-good headlight, and Georges fell off the roof into the rocky, creek-flooded road. Sopping wet, wounds burning and joints screaming, a miserable Georges walked the last mile with Artemis helping him along. Georges sniveling the whole way. He was so upset he couldn't appreciate how fortunate he'd been. His injuries could've been much worse. Good thing he'd been wearing his bicycle gloves; otherwise, his hands would've also gotten pulverized and embedded with sand and pebbles.

"I'm gonna have to disagree, little man," The Weasel tells Georges, after thinking about bicycles and civilization for a moment. He continues to stoke the coals with his poker-branch, sending sparks whirling into the column of smoke. "I despise civilization: I think it's the reason we're all fucked. However, if forced to identify three good things, I'd say that the three things I like most about civilization are books, CDs, Tevas, and handguns."

Artemis looks at each of the men, who seem to have become closer in the past hour. "Do you fuckheads not realize you're listing four things?"

Georges narrows his eyes at The Weasel. He hates being called little man. "You don't own a gun, do you?" asks Georges. "Because I can't be around people with guns. You know how some people—their brains, their minds, their, their their neuronal synapses—don't work well around watches? Well my mind is that kind of finely-tuned instrument. No watches, no radios, no tee-vees, no guns, no cars, see. It messes things up inside and makes it impossible to think linear."

"How about computers?" The Weasel asks, just to agitate and distract Georges.

"Holy cow! Especially computers! Computers are the worst of all the appliances!" Georges picks a chunk of gravel from his knee. "Ouch. Did you know that the more time you spend interacting with computers, the more your brain rewires itself to conform to them, and the less able you are to communicate with actual people? And did you know that some people can't even leave their house without their iPhone or Blackberry? Because they feel incomplete without the appliance?" Georges looks at The Weasel, who is smiling almost smugly to himself. Georges remembers: "But I asked you a question, didn't I? About guns?"

"I don't have a gun," The Weasel says. He frowns sincerely at Georges.

Artemis suspects that The Weasel is lying but doesn't call him on it. She gives Georges a freshly medicated cottonball. "Well, since I guess it's my turn," she says, "I think the best things about modern civilization—the only three things of value—are glass, typewriters, condoms, and anesthesia."

The Weasel thinks: Leave it to the woman to see the big picture, and he gets up to fetch more wood.

Away from the campfire and the susurrant voices, the evening feels cool against his skin and alive with the nocturnal commerce of creatures. The Utah night subsides to a purple-black that lets the day-kept starlight out. Nighthawks buzz and dive at moths, lacewings, and mosquitoes. Beyond their campsite beneath a massive cottonwood tree, where they parked and pitched a two-person tent from Goodwill's, shrill peepers sing and bullfrogs moan, crying WAAAANH, in the lush oxbow gloom of the gulch. *Please whoever you are help me to accept what I can't change,* Mike Weiselmann hears himself pray. *Please whoever you are gimme courage to change what I can and the wisdom to know the difference.* Those annoying AA meetings in prison weren't for nothing. He opens the Honda's trunk and collects the wood, eyeballing the three sixpacks of bottled beer he'd brought—to give away. All day, doubt has dogged him: Is Maggot on her way, or not? *Maybe. . . .* he thinks, but can't imagine a scenario that would postpone her for nearly twelve hours. *Please whoever you are make sure she's okay, bring her to us safely.* He's often wondered what to do if an activist doesn't show up for a rendezvous or action. With the hitchhikers and hoboes and the trouble they may or may not have had with the law, the last thing you want to do is call the authorities for help. But Maggot? It's not like she's coming by freight train or thumbing a ride from Thompson Springs.

Meanwhile, back at the campfire, Georges smiles at Artemis, who's lighting another joint. The firelight plays over her moonish face and sparks on the little glass vial of water and the other necklaces that draw the eye to her profound cleavage. Maybe she'll sleep with him tonight, after all. He likes the way she's tending to his battered knees; he was thrilled when she offered to walk him all the way to the campsite while The Weasel drove the car; he was overjoyed to hear that she was 90% vegan. "I have the diet of a black bear," she said, one arm around his skinny little ant-body while he hobbled down into another dark stony wash and out again. "So I guess I'm more freegan than vegan." Good enough for Georges these days, who prides himself on being not nearly as self-righteous as everybody seems to think he is. He liked the feel of her warm arm around him, her right breast pressed against his ribs, his hip and hers moving together. He'd like some more of that, please. The blonde with the yellow bikini top hasn't visited him in hours, probably because she feels spurned. Now we know for whom his tender vegan heart pounds!

The Weasel returns with the firewood. "Speaking of anesthesia. . . ."

"I know," Georges says. "I don't think she's coming."

"She probably just got delayed is all," Artemis says, wanting to believe it.

"By what?" The Weasel retorts. "A fucking twelve-hour traffic jam? She was so clear on the phone a few weeks back, almost demented with urgency. And now she doesn't even bother to show—it doesn't make any sense."

"What'd she say?" Artemis asks.

The Weasel feeds wood into the pyre and prods the burning planks to stir up the flames. Fountains of sparks leap into the night air and reflect in his glasses. "She was gung-ho, like, 'This is it! It's now or never! It's what we've all been waiting for!' She kept asking if I was with her, a hundred percent."

"*With* you? What the fuck does that mean?"

"Beats me." The Weasel shrugs.

Artemis reflects. "And what *have* we all been waiting for?"

Georges feels suddenly sad. He feels like crying—how confusing, to have emotions all over the map, from love to despair within minutes! He hugs himself, wrapping his arms around the baggy wool sweater that Artemis lent him when the air chilled. His knees hurt, Maggot's blowing them off, he hates himself for wearing this wool—traitor!—and he hasn't yet felt the presence of Edward, who'd promised he'd be here tonight. And, worst of all, is the theft of his beloved Melanie. Such a gaping hole in his life! "I don't know what I'm going to do," says Georges, again on the verge of tears.

"About your bike," Artemis guesses.

"About everything! I can't imagine life without Her," he cries. "I was supposed to ride Melanie to the Yukon, see, to start a state-of-the-art, eco-friendly, minimal carbon footprint community bok choi farm. To lead an ailing planet out of the darkness and feed the starving polar bears, who, as we're all aware, can't get to the seals anymore because there's no ice for them to travel on. So the ice is melting, the polar bears are starving, more people are driving, and even more people are having babies who'll also be driving in a mere fifteen more years, so more ice will melt so more polar bears will starve. If there are any left! What am I going to do?"

"Polar bears eat bok choi?" Artemis asks, her voice slanted toward mockery.

There she goes again—why does she do this to him? He says, "I have drawn up elaborate architectural plans for these high-tech greenhouses in the Arctic tundra, see, and I've worked out all the construction paradigms and water-cycling extrapolations and sun-angles over twelve months, mentally drafted architectural blueprints in synchrony with latitudes above 60° North, and I know important, very handy revolutionaries who can make this project happen. But I have to be there! People will be looking to me to present the blueprints and coordinate the objectives of the Arctic Autonomous Zone!"

"I thought you only got this directive this afternoon," Artemis says. She looks at The Weasel and when their mocking eyes catch, she smiles and The Weasel smiles, too.

"Now wait a minute," The Weasel says, turning suddenly to Georges. "I thought you were against technology."

"Fine. Go ahead and mock poor Georges. But what I'm saying is we need to relegitimize technology that hasn't happened yet." He taps his skull importantly. "While you've been effing with tourons, while you thought I was just getting stoned at the crawdad pond and hiking down Negro Bill or riding on top of that evil machine, my mind has been actively working everything out, see. I'm very good at multitasking and seeing the grand scheme of how every action has an equal and opposite reaction, which is why I'm uniquely qualified to be a competent leader."

"Right on, little man," The Weasel says. "Sounds like a bomb-proof plan. They're lucky to have you."

Georges cringes; he knows when he's being condescended to.

"So Rangers, you hungry yet?" Artemis stands and shakes dust and ash from her skirt. "All this talk of bok choi is rousing the ole appetite. I was thinking of cooking up some kind vittles in the coals. I don't have any bok choi but I've got potatoes, corn and leeks. Sound tasty?"

"Yes, please," Georges says.

The Weasel nods and says, "I'll help." He looks up into the benevolent face of this older woman with whom he might be falling in love, and with whom he might've actually slept once, at a rendezvous, when he was horny and fifteen and drunk as an autumn honeybee. He sees the fiery gold moon rise over her right shoulder, over the rim of the shallow canyon with the night-black buttes and spires of the Fisher Towers in the distance. His bruised stomach clenches into a nervous, hungry fist. But he's not hungry for vegetables.

It is the evening of the day they were supposed to meet. Emily Sevo, running on fumes nearly twelve hours behind schedule, stops at a gas station in Bluff, on the edge of the Navajo Reservation. She fuels up and buys a hot dog, Snickers bar, and potato chips—because why not? She'll be dead within the next twelve hours anyway, so may as well load up on all the fat, sugar, and salt she's deprived herself of for most of her svelte and healthy life. She spent the night and all of today famished and anxious and coughing blood near her car, concealed in a fold in the land up a two-track in Monument Valley, and now, finally, she's headed northeast again on 163. She hurries through the exchanges with the cashier and jumps back into the Toyota Landcruiser, heart pounding wildly against her sternum, lungs like water-filled bellows gurgling for air. She puts the SUV in gear, turns on the headlights, and hauls ass out of town on 191 toward Blanding, checking her rearview compulsively, thinking, It will be a god-damned miracle if I don't get pulled over and we actually pull this off. She wonders if the others came. And if they're still waiting for her at the trailhead. She wonders—again—how she will tell them.

The Landcruiser devours the electric tape of lit highway beneath its waxed hood, surging ahead at 80, 85, 90 miles per hour. Emily eats her hotdog like a boot camp recruit and spills a ketchuppy-mustardy goop on her synchilla jacket; she swipes at the spillage with a flimsy napkin. Checks the rearview: still no headlights. Did she really ditch the Utah patrolmen last night? She admits now (to no one in particular) that she might have panicked. Maybe she should've just spoken with him and explained her medical emergency calmly. Maybe he was only going to say your taillight's out, or it seemed you were weaving across the double-yellow. Maybe a breathalyzer test, that's all. Because she'd ditched the cop on a side road into Monument Valley, and had half-slept there all night and hidden most of the day, now an entire stateful of cops would be looking for her. Stupid!

As if on cue, as if attracted to fear-of-cops thought-bubbles, a patrol car passes her going the other way, headed southwest. In her sideview, she sees the brakelights flare; up ahead she spots a cluster of yard lights. Lets up on the accelerator. She hopes for a driveway, a break in the fence line. Without tapping her telltale brakes she pulls off the highway, almost overshoots a ranch road, fishtails, guns the car fifty meters up the drive and behind a sad lighted row of cinderblock houses, pulls a U-ey with such centrifugal force that the passenger-side tires leave the dirt, then shuts her lights and engine. She cracks a window for air and hears the clucking of chickens disturbed. Dogs bark. A loose flap of corrugated-metal roof bangs in the wind.

Beyond the glass confines of her windshield, the stars are bright and impartial witnesses, withholding their verdicts. She wants so much to believe that the universe is on her side, but also understands that she's on her own. She tears open her bag of potato chips and crunches through a few as she watches the road like a movie. The cars on the highway, the ones that were behind her a minute ago, have gone blithely by. She is strapped for time now and can't go far up a dirt road and wait as she had last night, so she has to trust this makeshift cover of darkness and dwellings. The jackrabbit's strategy of sitting still. She eats a few more potato chips. They make a satisfying noise.

The patrol car speeds past. She should stay put for another twelve hours, but she blew it last night and can't risk missing her friends or the record spring run-off for which she'd timed her launch. So she finishes her potato chips and licks her fingers with loud smacking sounds. Then she rolls her SUV back onto the highway— following the cop by only a couple of miles at most. *This is crazy*, she thinks, bringing the Landcruiser to a prudent 65 miles per hour and reminding herself not to let adrenaline dictate her speed, lest she catch up to the cop who passed her. *Crazy exciting!*

She eats the rest of the hotdog and gobbles up the decadent Snickers bar—*Happy Birthday to Me!*—all the while nervously checking her rearview. Still no headlights. There are no headlights at all—is that odd? Shouldn't someone be on this highway—191 to Blanding—on an early evening in May? All those cars earlier and none now. None behind her, none ahead. Maybe this damn highway shouldn't have been built after all: Nobody seems to need it, and a whole bunch of people hadn't wanted it. Or maybe she's thinking of that vile wildlands-slicing highway, 95 to Hanksville, Monkeywrench Alley. At night, all roads are tunnels and all roads look the same and all roads make the wilderness too accessible because once upon a time everything was wilderness. Well, okay then, Sevo, she says, trying to calm herself. What's the plan? You're twelve hours behind schedule, a record-high spring run-off is maxed out right this minute, and you've got a hundred miles of night-driving on this two-laner north to Blanding then Monticello and Moab where cops are trolling for a black Landcruiser. Then you've gotta convince three friends to come along with you. A nearly impossible task! To settle her nerves, she pops in an Indigo Girls CD and cracks a bottle of New Belgium beer—a little something she'd brought with her from Colorado—but doesn't take a sip. Because—checking the rearview—she sees two pinpoints of light, very far back but rapidly approaching. Reluctantly she hurls the bottle out the window. She hears the glass shatter behind.

Back at the Onion Creek campfire, the hour is late and the minds have become floppy, beer-sodden and pot-addled. Something about the primitive ritual of sitting with one's tribe around a warm, dancing pyre and sharing coal-fired corn-on-the-cob, blue potatoes, and leeks, among other Kingdom Plantae substances, stimulates contemplation and honesty, or just plain silliness.

"I've always wanted to be a hero," The Weasel announces, between crooning out verses of a Danny Dolinger song. He continues to strum his nylon-stringed child's guitar as he speaks. He wears his red and blue "SuperWeasel!" cape tied around his neck and his speech is slurry. Several empty beer bottles lie on their sides at his feet. "I've always wanted my life to mean something. And my death, too. Instead, I've wasted almost a quarter of my life rotting in a prison cell. I'm afraid I'm going to spend the next four decades rotting in an office, getting nothing of consequence achieved, then I'm going to end up strapped to a urine-soaked mattress in an old-folk's home, tubes running up my nose and veins and dick, machines breathing and peeing for me and beating my heart, and that will be that."

"THERE IS NO WAY I'M GOING TO END UP IN A NURSERY HOME!" Georges shouts, far too loudly, into the quiet night. The frogs stop *WAAANHing* when they hear him. Wearing his bicycle gloves, Georges nibbles at a blue potato with a crunchy charcoaled skin. He weaves from side to side, too close to the fire, swallows, and says, "YOU KNOW WHAT WOULD BE SUPERB? IF WE HAD SOME MUSTARD! MUSTARD IS THE BEST."

"Georges, you're yelling." Then to Weasel, Artemis says, with kernels glued to her cheeks and holding her cob with two hands, "I thought your nonprofit was doing good work up there in Salt Lake." She sports an aluminum cookpot like a beret on her head, with the handle at a jaunty angle. She dives into her corn and rips out a few rows. Slurping and grunting.

"Sure we are," The Weasel says. He strums a tragic

E-minor chord and follows it with an A-minor. "We're really good at the cartography of the destruction of wild places."

"Well, someone's got to do that," Artemis says around a mouthful of kernels, only sort-of joking. "But I know what you mean, though, about wanting it all to matter." She feels a rant coming on. "Some people measure success in life by the health and happiness of their kids—who do we have? Others set career goals and get after them, like those people who've always wanted to make a million dollars, or buy forty acres and design their own prairie-castle, or discover the cure to the common cold, or invent a better machine to get coal from the ground—but how do we measure success? We measure success by what we can stop! By what doesn't happen as a result of our efforts. And it's always a temporary success. Because when we win, some patch of nature is preserved but only until the next time some greedy bastard comes along wanting something from it. When they win, they win forever. And do we even know what we've lost? What we're still losing? I'm just wondering if Mama Earth is ever gonna just rise up and say, *Enough of this shit! I have had it!*"

"WOW, THIS IS DEPRESSING!" Georges yells. "All this talk of us versus them. YOU KEEP FORGETTING: WE'RE ALL IN THIS TOGETHER!" he quips, rocking side to side on his bony hips as like a squirrel he nibbles at his potato skin.

"I hate that phrase," Artemis says. It's been hours since they've cleaned up Georges's knees, but she's stoned and forgets so she hands him a freshly-medicated cottonball with her cornsticky fingers and he takes it. The salve in which she's dipped these balls is a sweet-smelling lavender-calendula-honey blend that she made herself, and it doesn't sting. "We're not actually all in this together. Some people aren't in this mess at all! They are above it! And what does it mean, anyway? That our current state of ecological fuckuppedness is somehow tolerable because we're all sharing the experience? That's such new-age bullshit."

"MAYBE YOU'RE RIGHT," yelps Georges, dabbing at his knees with one hand, licking potato starch off his other hand. Maybe if he agrees with her, she'll sleep with him, she'll let him kiss her and touch her all over, love on her til sunrise, and she'll mash those lovely breasts against his cold little hairy chest. He is still hungry. Always hungry. "ARE THERE ANY MORE SPUDS?"

Artemis digs one out of the coals for him. "Careful," she says. "Oh, here's a leek, too."

The Weasel adds an armful of juniper branches to the fire. The fire explodes. "Whoa nelly," he says. A bullfrog moans from somewhere close. Whenever there's a gap in the conversation, the night beyond the bonfire seems so tranquil, so expansively vast, so full of ears. The Weasel has a vague sense that he's somehow fucked up his life forever and there's no going back. He cracks another bottle of beer and chugs half down in one gulp.

"What do you think?" Artemis asks him, after he and his fire have settled down a bit.

"Ahh," The Weasel says, clamping the bottle between his sandaled feet so it won't fall over. He pokes at the fire and says, "Me? Man, I don't know. I don't know what it all means." He looks at Georges, then at Artemis. "Shit, I almost died today."

"Yeah," she says, finishing her corn and spreading her toes toward the heat. She tosses her cob into the fire. "And. . . ?"

"I mean, I don't know what my life is about. I

haven't done shit, and everything I do gets undone. I'd like to do something important, something great for the earth, something heroic before I die, but—strangely—I felt ready for it, you know, for death, even though I haven't really lived yet. But there's. . . this kitten I'm taking care of, I guess I would've felt bad for Fermin if something had happened to me today. Other than my cat, though, I have no one and nothing to live for anymore, so why the hell not?" He closes his eyes. It's just too hard to fight the inevitable. Too hard to win the war against the bottle. Against inconsequentiality and death. He is so very tired. He'd like to surrender everything.

Artemis recalls thinking The Weasel lied when Georges asked if he had a gun, and she doesn't know why she thinks that. Woman's intuition, maybe.

"WHO WOULD LOOK AFTER YOUR KITTEN?" Georges shouts across the fire.

The Weasel opens his eyes.

"Damnit, Georges! Mike Weiselmann is telling us he doesn't want to live anymore, and you're worried only about his kitten?"

"Well," says Georges, gnawing on his leek.

"It's a practical consideration," The Weasel says, picking up his guitar again to strum a bright G. "A logical question. My neighbor would look after him. Or a coworker, I guess, but Jeannine loves cats."

"What, exactly, are you saying?" Artemis scowls across the fire at The Weasel, whose shiny orange head is partially obscured by smoke.

"Don't worry," he says, eyeglasses and guitar-varnish glinting in the firelight. F-chord, D-chord, back to G. "I'm only saying, I almost died today, and it was okay. I guess maybe I'm just coming to terms with my mortality, as every middle-aged man must eventually do.

And, if, for instance, I had the opportunity to risk my life for a damn good cause, I might actually have the courage now to jump in and do it."

"You risked enough going to prison."

"YEAH! WE'RE ALL REALLY PROUD OF YOU FOR NOT SNITCHING!"

"You don't have to fucken shout," Artemis reprimands Georges, who tries to hide behind his disappearing leek.

The Weasel carefully sets aside his guitar. He and Georges exchange meaningful looks, then The Weasel slugs back the rest of his beer. Artemis glances from one face to the other and back again, thinking, *Hunh, interesting.*

"You're welcome, Georges," The Weasel finally says, lowering his empty bottle with a clink among the others. He gets up for his fifth or fifteenth beer and to put on a coat beneath his satiny cape. When he returns to the fire, Georges is talking about a movie he saw at his cousin Darryl's house a few years back, called *Children of Men.* It pissed Georges off.

"SO IN THE MOVIE, all the humans are infertile by the year 2027," Georges begins to shout, then remembers to lower his voice. "But there are plenty of dogs, cats, horses, sheep, and birds. Now how can that be? 'Whatever befalls the beasts, befalls mankind,' right? 'Splain to me how on earth all humans could be infertile but no other mammal is infertile."

"It was a virus, wasn't it?" The Weasel asks.

"BUT IT DOESN'T MAKE ANY SENSE!"

"Shush, Georges," Artemis says.

"It was a human-specific virus," explains The Weasel.

"I don't think so. But the other ridiculous thing about this movie was this idea of The Human Project, see? The military-funded Breeders sneaking in their message. But pro-repro at a time when the earth is severely overpopulated? When every city is wall to wall with desperate starving people, and everyone's homeless and fighting in the streets? And every city, every little town in the whole world has erupted into dog-eat-dog chaos? I DON'T THINK SO."

Artemis says, "Well, people equate a newborn's face, a baby's very presence, with hope. And people need symbols of hope. They need to feel that life is, and will be, worth living. Others believe they can cheat mortality through their children. Achieve a kind of genetic immortality."

"I HATED THE 1980s," Georges hollers. Artemis shushes him again, then she and The Weasel wait for him to explain, but Georges won't; he looks insulted.

"Why, Georges?" Artemis asks, rolling her eyes.

"Are you gonna shush me again?"

"Just tell us why you hate the '80s, Georges," The Weasel insists.

"Well that was the decade when the human population surpassed the number of years the earth is old! Four and a half billion! It goes without saying that, not coincidentally, that was also the decade of 'Another One Bites the Dust' and Reagan's Reign of Terror. Do you realize, in another three decades, our population will be twice that, unless we completely overhaul our modus operandi?" Georges looks at them from beneath his furry monobrow. He licks the droopy fringe of his moustache and says, "You know, I'm not sure I actually want to live in a world of nine billion people. I think Zero Population Growth is the only way to go."

"Maybe you should do your part for ZPG and kill yourself," The Weasel suggests.

"Jesus, Mike!" Artemis gasps.

"MAYBE YOU SHOULD DO YOUR PART AND KILL YOURSELF," Georges volleys back.

"Maybe I will, my little man. Maybe I will."

"Will you PLEASE stop calling me that?"

"Hey, enough with the bullshit, you two. Just because population is the single biggest factor in whether the planet's gonna survive us or not," Artemis says, wiping her sticky hands on her skirt, "doesn't mean that low-impact activists should off themselves."

"I have no idea what you just said," The Weasel admits. He sets another just-opened beer on the ground and returns the guitar to his lap. He holds the neck, strums a G-C-D progression. He's never been very good on guitar but likes to think of himself as a campfire entertainer.

"The Earth needs people like us to fight for Her," Artemis clarifies.

"The Earth doesn't need us," The Weasel bitterly retorts, hammering on E-minor, then returning to G. "The Earth would be fine without any humans at all. And if people in countries that consume the most stuff don't rein in their 'nads and capitalist urges, we're all fucked."

"It's not American or European or Japanese children who are the problem, it's our greed. It's adults who own the companies and make the commercials that tell kids to want cheap plastic crap and manage the overseas factories that abuse child-slaves. That needs to end right away! Instead, we need to be teaching our kids how to take care of people and the land where we live."

"Well, sure. And how are you going to do all that?"

"NOT THAT I HATE KIDS," Georges shouts, stuffing the rest of the leek into his mouth, "BUT

BOYOBOY AM I GLAD I NEVER HAD ANY! GAWD!"

Artemis stares at him; she's glad she never told him about her 1992 procedure. She doesn't shush him this time; she takes something from her skirt pocket and says, "Here." It's a telfa pad from her first-aid kit. Earlier, she pawed through her first aid bag but couldn't find the bandaging material, and thought she'd neglected to bring any, which would've been a major oversight for one of the movement's herbalistas. With her bandage scissors she cuts lengths of white adhesive tape from the roll, and transfers the ribbons from her fingertip to his.

Georges finishes bandaging his knees. He yanks down the legs of his longjohns over the bandages, down his shins to his itchy ankles welted up with mosquito bites despite the socks. He contemplates his knees and thinks of his roofrack ride on the Honda, and how scared he was when he got bucked off and fell, elbows and knees flying, into the stony jeep-trail full of cold water. Now one of his elbows is starting to feel swollen and painful.

He says, "Maybe I should've just gotten into the darned car. What's the difference, anyway, between riding inside a car, and riding on top? It always comes down to the choices we make, doesn't it? What's really the better eco-choice: eating organic tofu made from intensively-raised soybeans grown a thousand miles away and transported by gas-guzzling, carbon-dioxide-farting trucks to a factory where they are mass-boiled and pressed and packaged in plastic by underpaid workers then transported again by trucks along roads where little animals try to skitter across transported to grocery stores that use electricity from coal-burning to refrigerate their packages of tofu—or eating a handful of beetle grubs from under that log over there? BUT THEN I'D BE KILLING A SENTIENT BEING, RIGHT?"

If he could eat nothing at all—air, sunshine, a little clay, maybe—that would be better for the earth and consistent with his sense of right and wrong. But then, he would die.

He says to his friends, "Eh, bien. . . I'm morally opposed to nearly everything I do."

"Not this again," Artemis says. "*His life is against his ethics* and all that." She takes out her mojo bag, her special little pouch, and some rolling papers. To The Weasel she says, "And I was wondering when his French would come creeping back."

"C'est vrai! MY LIFE IS AGAINST MY ETHICS."

"Nature of the human animal," The Weasel summarizes, and G-A-D-C answers his guitar. "We aim for perfection, but ultimately, we're all fucked up, fallible, and flawed. We contradict ourselves at every turn. Every thing we do, every act, every thought and word, all of it, all of us—we're imperfect. It's what makes us so annoyingly human and despicable and fascinating. It's all just part of our soiled flow through time and across the earth's continents."

"You make the march of civilization sound like sewer effluent," Artemis observes.

"I'm so glad the Elders of the Movement got together to talk about all this," Georges says, without a trace of the irony the others expected. He finds his potato, which had rolled off into the shadows, brushes it off, and eats it. Then, remembering Melanie and the ride across North America that will never be, tears fill Georges's eyes as he chews, watching the fire. The crisp leaping edges of the flames double and blur and look watery.

"Fire plus Water," Georges murmurs, sniffling and wiping his eyes. "Fire and Water."

"Hey, that's my *nom de plume*, you fuck. That's my *nom de guerre*." Artemis bangs the pot on top of her head with her steel bandage scissors. "Gloria Fire-Water! *Ah-woooo!*"

"Who needs a pseudonym if their name is Artemis Jade Bison-Wallow?" The Weasel asks.

Artemis bangs on her potted head—wang! wang! wang!—then howls in a chanty-sing-songy voice, "Don't dam the river, leave the river alone! Don't dam the river, the river is a hooooome! *Don't dam de ree-vah, let de ree-vah surviiiive, de ree-vah, de ree-vah she's aliiive.*"   She   looks at her comrades who appear to be as unmoved as the stars. She sets aside her scissors. "Born in the Rockies," she explains. "Of high mountain streams."

"Melanie—" Georges chokes up. "She's gone. I just can't believe it."

"Have a beer," The Weasel suggests. G-C-D adds his guitar.

"Have a joint," Artemis proffers.

Georges this time takes neither bottle nor joint. "It won't take the pain of the loss away."

"But you'll forget about the loss for a few hours," The Weasel says. His right hand leaves the guitar to bring the beer-bottle to his lips.

"So this is why activists are a bunch of addicts."

Artemis and The Weasel watch Georges carefully. Georges feels that he has said something important; for once, Georges is right. "To deal with all the loss," Georges elaborates. "All the deaths of wild beautiful places, all the could-not-saves." He stares at his fingertips which protrude from his bike gloves. Then sucks the residual potato from them.

"Here, here," The Weasel says, raising his bottle in a toast.

Artemis scrutinizes him. "You know, I thought you stopped drinking," she says.

"I did. Then I shtarted up again," he says, slurring for self-deprecating effect.

"When?"

The Weasel consults his watch. "About two hoursh ago."

"That's sad," Georges says, then frowns. "You know what's weird, and not weird in a good way, weird in a suspicious way? That states have legalized medical marijuana. Which means the State has decided marijuana is useful for maintaining its power over people. Which means. . . oh, wow, I never thought of this before, but my mind, my brain, it's like everything is so crystal clear: Pot is soma. Pot is soma. That's why it's legal! Pot makes people less likely to revolt, or work toward changing the system, so now it's legitimized!"

"That's just your marijuana-induced paranoia talking, little man."

"They're winning! They've got us hooked on drugs that make us lazy, talkative, hungry, and apathetic! It's over. It's all over y'all."

"Our lives aren't over yet." Artemis lights the joint and smokes it. "We might have a few protests yet to go to, a few more letters to write."

"Protests and letters," Georges says, sneering. "As if either of those did any good!"

"Protests and letters have done a lot of good," Artemis counters, waving the red eye of the joint at him. "Need I remind you of the anti-vivisection movement of Great Britain? Or women's suffrage in the U.S.? The Civil Rights marches, and the millions who turned out for Obama's inauguration celebrations? We are counted by what our bodies do. Action is everything. Thought is. . . . just thinking."

"Hey, don't lecture me," Georges says. "I'm the EF! Historian."

"Actions begin with thought," The Weasel says. He sets down his bottle.

"But if we get bogged down with self-doubt, second-guessing, and deliberations, then the thought counts for nothing," Artemis says. "Zilch."

Georges blows his nose again and wipes his nose and moustache. "So, a bunch of animal-rights people are sitting around a table, smoking cloves under a bare bulb, arguing about whether or not to release some caged foxes from a fur-farm. They call themselves 'The Animal Deliberation Front.'"

"So what is your next great, world-saving action, Artemis?" The Weasel asks her, ignoring Georges's old joke, but only because he'd heard it a hundred times before.

"Well, I don't rightly know yet." She smokes her joint and stares at her feet; with her head bent over, the firelight is reflected in the shiny metal of the pot on her head. The plumy incense of *Cannabis* buddage mingles with the woodsmoke. "I'm, as they say, between jobs." She passes the joint to Georges, who for all his ranting a moment ago takes it, touching his fingertips to hers and getting an obvious thrill from the contact.

"Sometimes," Georges says, inspecting the joint, "it's not so much what we do that's important, but what we don't do. What we don't consume. The fast food we don't eat, the redwood decks we don't buy, the children we don't have, the cars we don't drive, the animal-murdering pharmaceutical pills we don't pop. . . ." Georges puts the joint to his lips and inhales as his eyes seek Artemis's approval. Exactly what the State banks on! He wonders if he should decline the soma. He needs to make a stand. He can't.

"I feel like our conversation's circling the drain," The Weasel observes. "Didn't Artemis already cover all this crap before? What's the point?"

"The point is," says Georges, thoroughly lit, "The point has always been that it's kinda hard to define a lifestyle by what we don't do. Much less a movement." He passes the joint to The Weasel.

"Have you-all noticed lately how our movement just kind of. . . lost its spunk and fizzled? It seems to have lost its identity sometime in the late '90s. Earth First! used to be a bunch of rowdy rednecks defending the wilderness. They used to get shit done."

"Excusez-moi," Georges interjects, when he notes that Artemis hangs on The Weasel's every word. "But were you even born yet in the '90s?"

"Quiet, Georges, I'm pontificating. Now—who knows what Earth First! is? Anarchists, People In Black, with their gender issues and social justice concerns, boycotts and backstabbing, all the focus on snitches and computer files, *if an agent knocks* kind of crap—and all the shit-hot wilderness defenders are now working under different banners and slogans, because the name 'Earth First' so polarizes the public they can't get any useful work done."

"Shit-hot wilderness defenders such as yourself," Artemis says, accepting the joint from him.

"Yeah, maybe," The Weasel says, and he returns to his guitar to noodle a little bluesy tune in the key of F.

"People still do tree-sits," Artemis points out. "They do road blockades and outreach, marches and demos and occupations and banner-hanging."

"Banner-hanging!" The Weasel shouts, with an amused snort. "Julia Butterfly does not a movement make."

"Don't dis my shero, man. I'm just saying that the

movement is constantly evolving, like all the species, like the Earth herself. My friend Anoo told me this amazing thing once. She said that under the Christian doctrine of cosmology, everything was created the way it is just once, a one-time deal. But creation in the evolutionary model keeps on creating! You can't cling to something, Mike Weiselmann, and think it's not going to change. You cling too tightly to something, that's the recipe for misery. Because everything changes. Even the environmental movement."

"I'm not an idiot. I'm just saying that the Deep Ecology movement seems to have been hijacked by the transgendered anarchists. Is all."

"And what's wrong with that?" Georges asks. "Aren't the PIBs fighting for the Earth?"

Mike Weiselmann adjusts his satiny cape.

"What's most important?" Artemis asks. "Do you put Earth First! first, or the Earth first?"

"Anarchism isn't a spin-off of Earth First!," Georges cuts in to inform his younger comrade. "It kicked the whole dang thing off."

"I don't think so, little man." The Weasel starts to feel ganged-up on and defensive.

"I happen to know that EF! started because of five guys talking about Ed Abbey's 1975 novel, see, and before that Ed Abbey wrote his University of New Mexico Master's Thesis on Anarchism and Violence, way before he wrote his most famous novels or even *Desert Solitaire* in '68. We've come back to the beginning, see? It's all a big circle! Actually a spiral, but you get the picture. . . ."

"Maybe it's just me who's gotten cynical." The Weasel drains the last of his beer and sets it alongside the other bottles with a musical clink. Any bottles still standing fall over like bowling pins. He studies the sky:

Why did he start drinking again? After all the work he's done to get clean? Now he's come back to the beginning too, and he feels defeated—not at all the elation Georges feels about coming full circle on something. A few hours ago, the Big Dipper was way over here, but now it's all the way over there on the other side of the heavens. The hour is late. Maybe it's too late.

He sets down his guitar and says, "What are we doing here?"

They stare at him.

"I mean, what are we doing? It's all talk, talk, talk. We're wasting our time. We're sitting here, getting drunk and stoned and eating our root vegetables and having a lovely time debating this shit and that shit. But it's all just talk. Meanwhile, the machines devour the earth. I feel like I'm wasting my life." He appraises his friends morosely, then adds, "I gotta take a piss."

While The Weasel is getting something from his car, then wandering behind their tent looking for a likely loo, Artemis whispers to Georges, "I'm worried about him. Aren't you? He seems like someone about to do something brash and stupid. . . ."

Georges leans toward Artemis, who is talking and smoking down her joint, and takes one of her pendants between his fingers. It's a brash move for the likes of Georges Nondairy. But she permits it.

"I've seen this before in burnt-out activists," she says. "It's an existential crisis—"

"What's this?" he asks, interrupting something she was saying about The Weasel.

She looks down. "It's Escalante River water. From near Glen Canyon, before it was dammed and everything got flooded." Artemis takes it gently from him and inspects the glass vial in the firelight. "It was a gift from Maggot," she says, taking the pot from her head. "Anyway, I think it was. She left it in my sleeping bag."

Behind the tent, beneath the fluttering leaves of the cottonwood tree and the moon unmoored and all the thousands of cold callous stars, The Weasel pees on a Mormon-tea bush then zips up. He stands still and silent as a statue contemplating his purpose on the planet. He comes up with nothing. He has no purpose. He has known pain and caused pain and feels devastated that his species is wrecking the earth and all that he loves. When has he ever been truly happy? Sure—little glimmers here and there, stumbling into random wormholes—but true happiness? Real joy? He doesn't even know what that means.

At the car he scrounged up his stashed handgun and holster and wears both now under his ridiculous cape that somehow makes him feel both like a cartoon superhero and pathetic. He takes the bequeathed gun from its sheath and lays it flat on his palm. He tilts it in the moonlight and the moon pours little rivulets of its light along the shiny metal. He hears the others talking, the gentle crackling of the fire, the cottonwood spades brushing against each other, a distant frog. Then he hears something else and looks up.

"Hello?" he asks, softly.

Again, he hears a very tiny twig snap from the bottom of the shallow arroyo, from near a cluster of pools obscured by willow and grasses and the shadows cast by them. His heart beats drunkenly and disorderly. A shrub seems to have rustled, too, but he can't be sure.

"Who's there?" he whispers, afraid the others will hear him and think he's lost it. (Well, hasn't he? What exactly did he intend by fetching his weapon?) Artemis laughs by the fire; someone has taken up his guitar and plucks unmusically at its strings, boing, boing. Georges hollers out the name of a song.

Mike Weiselmann tilts his glasses and lifts his face while his myopic eyes probe the moonlit gulch for movement. There are too many boulders and shrubs and ledges, too many shadows that could be about the size of man or beast. His heart jumps: There, to the right! Liquid movement, a silent streaming of a phantom's shadow gliding over flatrock. Is it a cougar? It's huge! Should he stay put or run like hell? Wave his arms and yell something? He should run. Yes. But he cannot run. His feet are stakes in the earth, pounded deep; he's not going anywhere. He searches the gulch. It's gone. No— over there now! How did it leap that crevice without a sound? Its shadow approaches, a long blue stain flying low over white sand and pebbles. Closing the distance: Ten meters, seven, five, three. Help, he wants to cry out. Help.

On enormous paws the giant silent cat stands before him with twin moons for eyes. The eyes are bioluminescent green-gold and unblinking. Mike holds his breath and stares. Help. Run? Shout! But nothing happens. It occurs to him that the catamount maybe isn't what she seems—markings on the face, a spotted flower-pattern across her moonsplashed pelt, a switching tail with banding. This isn't a cougar at all! This is, *my god*—!

Purring, the jaguar licks her whiskers with a large tongue. The purr is more like an airy rattle. *What will happen now?*, he wonders. It's quiet back at the campfire. No frogs sing, no cottonwood leaves shuffle. Mike has a sense of the planet hurtling through space and the stars wheeling overhead: The jaguar has come within inches of Mike's free hand, the loose trembling hand beside his thigh—body parts that no longer seem attached to his body.

The jaguar lowers her great head and gently bumps him.

Something tells his fingers to dig into the thick velvet of her spotted forehead and scratch around her ears. Enraptured, she purrs and rubs, smearing her cheek-scents on his hand. Her whiskers vibrate in the moonlight. Her purring gets louder. In the amplified rumbling, Mike thinks he hears a voice, as if there is singing in one feline throat coming from two voiceboxes at once, and the voice says to him, Mike Weiselmann, you've been tapped for a special mission, to rescue a drowning soul. You must be brave, kiddo. You must be a fucking warrior.

"Okay," says Mike Weiselmann.

He feels his body again and hears the trees, the fireside chat, a car coming up the road.

The jaguar is gone.

The frogs have all fallen silent: While The Weasel runs in slow-motion back to the campfire, stunned and speechless and moving as if he's in a dream, a loud truck guns up the jeep trail at high speeds. Highbeams spotlight the cliffs, disappear, reappear on a sagebrush hillside, swing left, disappear. A steel chassis, strike plates, and wheel rims smash against rocks, shock absorbers pound and creak in the ruts and rises. A heaving monstrosity made of metal and glass clambers up and over hills, around the bend, down into the creekbed—SPULL-LASH!—grinds a gear crawling up the other side, then slows, downshifts. . . idles, revs the engine, yes, the asshole in the SUV is turning into their campsite.

"Where the hell have you been, Weez?" Artemis asks, clutching her pendants to her breast and watching the visitor's vehicle make the turn. "Get lost out there?"

"Who's this asshole," The Weasel says, and picks up an empty bottle—not with the jaguar hand, but with the hand that holstered his handgun. He never wants to use his gun, ever, not ever again. But he holds the bottle's neck as if ready to break it off. Or crack it over someone's head.

Headlights pin the tent and catch our three around the fire like stunned hares. Georges slips sideways into the smoke and shadows, whimpering behind Artemis and The Weasel.

The driver's tinted window hums down. "Jesus, people! GET IN! QUICK!"

"It's Maggot!"

"GET IN, YOU ASSHOLES!" Maggot shouts, then coughs, then shouts again. "They're right behind me, they're on my tail!"

The Weasel drops his bottle, Artemis relaxes her fist of pendants, Georges emerges from behind his friends. They crowd around the driver's open window: Artemis reaches in with her lips to lay a wet kiss on Maggot's mouth; The Weasel touches the elbow crooked on the door. Maggot coughs and says, "Yeah, yeah, enough of the lovefest. I'm serious, the little fuckers are like five minutes behind me, max. Get your shit, douse the fire, let's go!"

They stand beside her Landcruiser as if paralyzed.

"HELLO, what the fuck's the matter with you?" she wheezes. "Get in the car! We're on an important mission here, people!"

The Weasel says, "I knew there was a damned good reason—"

"COME ON, GET YOUR SHIT AND GET THE FUCK IN!"

The three disperse to grab backpacks and sleeping bags, water jugs and food and guitar, first aid kit and panniers, and they throw all their belongings into the back of Maggot's car. The Weasel returns to his Honda and gathers up the maps from under the front seat. They encircle the fire and pour potfuls of creekwater on it and kick sand into it, every motion accelerated, frantic, and breathless—but alas, they are not fast enough.

The frogs go quiet: Once more, another big vehicle is hauling ass over the rough two-track. Fast sweeping headlights show on the cliff, disappear, reappear on a sagebrush hillside, swing left, disappear as the engine roars louder.

"DAMN IT!" Maggot lurches her Landcruiser forward, down an incline and into a gulch. She shuts the engine and the lights, closes the doors, rips open a plastic package (bought just hours ago in Blanding, "Gateway to Adventure!") and throws a camouflage net over the car. Coughing and wheezing something fierce, she runs up the bank grabbing at a swatch of sagebrush, asking forgiveness as she rips it from its trunk. The chase-vehicle guns around a bend— headlights flood the night—down into the creek and up the other side. SPULL-LASH! Maggot and Artemis sprint to the turn off to Campsite #1 and sweep away the Landcruiser's tire tracks, backing up, sweeping, backing up and sweeping even as the vehicle, a white or silver Ford Bronco with a ski rack or something on top, slows for the left turn. Maggot finishes erasing her tracks and backs herself between sagebrush shrubs, disappears down in the gulch where her covered but hulking vehicle, ticking and hardly inconspicuous in the bright moonlight, waits. There's a terrific tickle in her throat and, suppressing her cough, tears spill from her eyes.

Georges stays in the tent, where he went back for his handlebar bag, and whose interior smells like unwashed socks. His molars click and his shoulders hunch protectively around his narrow little birdcage of a thorax. He feels vulnerable and terrified. He imagines huge tattooed skinhead rednecks finding and mocking and dragging him to the middle of the dusty campsite and kicking his teeth in. He wants to run but now it's too late. He's trapped in the glowing green tent, which is lit by the pursuer's headlights.

Artemis and The Weasel take up positions around the fire. The fire billows smoke into their eyes. The Weasel turns away from Artemis, surreptitiously takes his pistol out and turns the safety off, reholsters his weapon palming the handle and waits, thinking, *Okay ya little punk scrappers, ya redneck fuckers, ya rich city fratboys, whatever you are, come on, come on.* He'll make this one exception to his new no-gun rule, but he doesn't like the idea one bit. He looks at the hand the jaguar had touched. Then he sees the cherries light up on top of the Bronco, red and blue strobes turning the canyon into a discotheque. Oh, no, not cops, Jesus!

Once the staties have turned and parked, but left their engine running, their lights on, Artemis welcomes them with a grand parade-wave of her arm.

"Hey there!" she calls out, friendly as can be. "What's going on?"

The Weasel holds his breath; everything is moving too fast for him. From sitting on his ass for hours wasting time around the fire, filling the great empty expanse of boredom with noodling on his guitar and getting shitfaced, to the jaguar and this—and what the hell is she doing now? She's approaching their car.

"Good evening, ma'am," the driver says, getting out of the vehicle. Inside, one can hear radio traffic

relayed. He swaggers toward her with his left hand on a holstered billy-stick or club and his right hand extended. Artemis politely shakes his hand. He scopes past her shoulder at The Weasel standing rigidly by the fire.

The Weasel raises his empty, jaguar hand in a friendly but somewhat stiff gesture.

"Sorry to trouble you, ma'am, but there's a dangerous criminal come up this road not five minutes ago we figure. He's driving a black Toyota Landcruiser,

2010 model." The officer surveys the campsite's layout, takes in the Honda, the one tent, the cottonwoods, the smoking fire. "You seen it go by?"

The Weasel swallows hard, adam's apple feeling too plump and swollen for his throat; inside the tent, Georges curls his fingers around his toes; down in the gulch, crouched a fair distance from her car and concealed behind a massive boulder, Maggot rolls her eyes, thinking, *Damn, it's over. So close. Damn fucking damn. So damn fucking close.*

But Artemis has been talking ever so cheerfully and helpfully to the officer: "Yeah, yeah, he went by like four minutes ago maybe, like a freaking bat outta hell, not even slowing for the rocks in the creek bottom there. He went straight on up thataway." Artemis points to where the jeep trail continues upward, past their campground to who knows what lawless canyonlands lie beyond. "Seemed a bit reckless, if you ask me."

"Everything okay here, ma'am?" the officer asks, looking pointedly over her shoulder.

"My husband and I were just putting the fire out. Headed for bed." She nods at the tent and sighs happily. "It's been a long, fun-packed day of canyoneering and seeing the sights, going to Arches and the water-slide and mountain-biking all over Moab. This is our favorite vacation spot of all time. We love it here."

"He all right?"

The officer keeps staring at The Weasel, so Artemis turns to see what interests him. The smoke churns in the twin cones of the Bronco's headlights, nearly obscuring the rigid man standing with one arm behind his back, not speaking, still wearing his 'SuperWeasel!' cape tied around his neck, over his coat. The cape looks a little ridiculous. And the concealed right arm? Suspicious as hell.

"He's a little drunk I reckon, mostly just dog-tired, but yeah, he's all right."

"Let me see your right hand, buddy."

The Weasel shows him his right hand.

The officer squints at him. His sharp little eyes sweep over the campsite to the dust and sand and gravel of the turn-around. He twists in his shoes, then turns and walks around, studying the criss-cross of various tracks with his sharp little eyes. "What is—? What are . . .?"

"Is this guy really dangerous?" Artemis thinks to ask. "Like should we not sleep here tonight?"

The police officer looks at her, then says, "No, no, you'll be all right." Walking slowly, he circumnavigates the campsite then gets back into the vehicle while unbeknownst to him Georges in the tent and Maggot behind the boulder both nearly faint. The officer shuts the door—window's still down—and says something to his partner, who gets on the radio. He salutes Artemis neatly with two fingers and says, "Well I sure thank you ma'am, and again, sorry for the trouble."

"Oh, you're most welcome. No trouble at all."

They turn off the strobes, back up, back all the way out of the big turn-around to the jeep trail, roll downhill toward the creek, force it in gear, and spin their wheels crawling out of there, groaning up the hill, unfurling red lights and dust deeper into the upper reaches of the canyon.

After our four campers can no longer hear the Bronco's whine and the slamming of wheels and chassis against rocks and ruts; after the headlights no longer swing across cliffsides and the dust has settled, Artemis raises her arms to the heavens and shakes her unfettered bosom.

"Am I good, or am I GOOD?" Artemis shouts.

"Gotta admit, I have a singular talent."

Her comrades crawl from the shadows—out of smoke, and gulch, and tent.

"Jesus, that was close," Maggot says. A half-minute passes where she can do nothing but cough. Then she hucks up something salty and dark and takes charge. "Okay, I'm gonna need your assistance getting out of this ditch, then we're gonna have to seriously race those jokers outta here, cuz they are gonna realize in about two minutes that whatever tracks they were following aren't there anymore. And they are gonna turn around."

Georges goes back to get his handlebar bag and puts it in her car.

"What the fuck did you do?" The Weasel asks Maggot.

"Never you mind that, it's only gonna get stickier. Come on, help me here, STAT folks, let's go." Maggot gathers up the camo netting and tosses it in back. She gets into her Landcruiser, puts it in 4WD-LOW, and ignites the engine. The others get behind the rear bumper and when she rocks forward, they push, and push, and the wheels dig and dig, spin a little, climb, then up and over the mound she goes, no problem. Artemis gets in up front, shotgun, and The Weasel and Georges jump in the backseat—then Georges slips right back out again.

"Get in, Georges, come on."

"No, uh, I. . . . see, I can't actually technically get into a vehicle, per se, because. . . ."

The Weasel reaches over, grabs Georges with both hands around the skinny arms aswim in the sweater, and yanks him into the vehicle. "AAIIIIGGGH!" shrieks poor, terrified Georges. Maggot disengages the four-wheel drive, drives the shifter into first, and guns the gas. She releases the clutch and squids out of the campsite, leaving behind an opaque dust cloud that shimmers pearl in the moonlight. Reaching for the door handle, The Weasel crushes Georges against the back seat; he catches it finally and yanks. The door slams shut. And they're off.

"So," Artemis says, once they've breached the asphalt, no headlights following.

"So," Maggot says, glancing at Artemis with a sly smile. She spits into a bandanna.

Artemis is ecstatic to see that the Medical Maggot still wears a butchy crewcut. By the wan light of the instrument panel the hair appears to be bright blue. She has the gaunt rugged physique and flat chest of a marathon runner. One peacock-feather earring sweeps Maggot's neck; perhaps the other was lost just now in their flight from camp.

"So, Maggot," Artemis tries again.

"Just call me Emily, okay? I'm a little too old to go by 'Maggot.'"

"So Emily," The Weasel interrupts from the back seat. "Why don't you fill us in?"

"Well, shit, where do I start?" She glances in the rearview and accelerates to 90 miles an hour going west, toward Moab. The river road gets curvy but why should that slow her down? She thinks she hears someone in the back seat say, Mon Dieu. She should've just asked everyone to meet in Moab. Would've been so much easier. Or Bluff, or Kayenta—or, for that matter, the Wahweap Marina. But there's that other matter. And first she has to see where people are at with this shit. Who's down with the big job and who isn't. If she could have done the job alone, by goddess, she would've. Because honestly, who needs these complications? Who needs wild cards like the damaged psyches of these washed-up ecofreaks?

"I'm working on a little river restoration project," Emily-Maggot says. "And I need a team. The problem is, parts of this project—well, okay, most of it—are somewhat frowned upon by certain governmental entities, thus necessitating careful preparations over the past twenty years, and especially intensive preps over the past year and a half, and also necessitating the involvement of three others. I chose you three based on a set of criteria."

"Which were . . . ?" The Weasel asks, if a bit tremulously. He sniffs his cat-scented hand.

"Euh," says Georges.

"What's up Hayduke LaRue?"

"It's uh, Georges Nondair*EEE*, and I think I, I have to take a piss or something." His voice is screechy and high-pitched. "Oh Mon Dieu, how fast are we going? Like a thousand miles an hour? I don't think mammals are meant to go this fast."

The Weasel shoots his comrade a judgmental eye-bullet. Poor little Georges is clinging to his door handle, knees folded up under his chin, shoulders hunched around his ears, rubber soles on the seat cushion. His face is blanched. He stares fixedly straight ahead.

"This is Georges's first car trip," Artemis tells her.

"I think I'm getting car-sick," Georges whimpers, and makes a deep abdominal sound.

"Only going ninety here, Georges. And there should be an empty juice bottle rolling around back there somewhere. Piss into that. If ya gotta barf, roll down the fucking window."

"Nice bedside manner, Doc," The Weasel says.

"Anyway, my criteria were: One, I had to know the person for at least twenty years; Two, they had to have environmental activist backgrounds and strong eco-ethics; Three, at some time in the past they had to have demonstrated that they could keep a secret and weren't tempted to gossip for self-aggrandizing purposes; and Four, they had to have no children, no spouses, no current activist campaigns, no real homes, no pets, no attachments, and no jobs. And if they'd run out of hope and become depressed and cynical—suicidal even—all the better."

"Hunh," The Weasel says, and Fermin's little orange face, green eyes, and white whiskers float into his mind—then merge with the grand noble face of the talking jaguar. He swallows. Should he tell them what happened back there? "So basically number four is, 'They have to be a no-count worthless loner. A kind of isolated eco-loser. Someone who won't be missed too much."

"Well, yeah. Myself included, however."

"Why?" Artemis asks her. "For what project?"

"Doesn't it bother you? That she's basically calling us losers?" he asks Artemis.

"I'm more curious about this river restoration project. Sounds like a hoot."

"Sounds like a suicide mission."

"Well, girls and boys, we've got a hundred and sixty miles or so. Plenty of time to chat. Actually, it's going to be a bit longer. I need to make a special stop first." Emily reaches up, adjusts the rearview, then, relieved, settles in. She buckles her seatbelt and reminds the others to do similar, but Georges refuses. "Suit yourself, little man," she says, coughing a little, and he grimaces, thinking, *Why does everybody call me that?*

"You got bronchitis or something?" Artemis asks her.

"No, lungworms."

"What?"

"Just kidding." Emily coughs and brings forth a

big noisy glob, which she deposits in her bandanna. "It's just some damn lingering cold."

"So where are we headed?" The Weasel asks. "Can you at least tell us that?"

"Lake Foul, my friends. Lake Foul. With one very small detour to visit the daughter I gave up when I was too young and dumb to know what the fuck I was doing." She smiles at Artemis; something sparkles from Artemis's chest. Frowning, she reaches across the seats to fondle it. "Is that—?"

"Yeah," Artemis says, lifting it over her maneful of dreads. "You left it in my sleeping bag that time. . . . You have a daughter?"

"Crazy, right? I met her for the first time last year. She lives in Green River, Utah."

"And did you know that there are now 100 million more automobiles in the U.S. today than there were in 1980? And another 240 million acres were stolen from prairie dogs and badgers for car dealers, highways, parking lots, and mechanized agriculture? Motor vehicles are the worst evil the world's ever seen, aside from maybe the Inquisition, Manifest Destiny, and the Holocaust, okay and the A-bomb I guess, too, but cars, everybody wants one, see, they think cars are convenient and harmless, but the cumulative effect is horrific. There are over 6,775,000,000 humans on the planet now vs. 4.5 billion in 1980, with a projected 9 billion by 2040! I can't wrap my mind around that. Can you? It goes without saying that 1980 was a very, very important year. Why, you ask? Because that's when the world human population surpassed the number of years the earth is old. Not coincidentally, the '80s was also the Reign-of-Reagan decade when Pink Floyd's 'Another Brick in the Wall' and Queen's 'Another One Bites the Dust' climbed to the top of the Pop Rock charts. Clearly, the '80s were a tipping-point decade. *Bawh-buh-buh! And another one's gone, and another one's gone, another one bites the dust!"*

Somewhere between Moab and Green River, after 191 T's at I-70 in Crescent Junction, Georges began to free-associate. Nobody asks him questions, nobody comments, nobody prods or provokes him. In the night, tumbleweeds and jackrabbits flit across the headlit highway, and Emily expertly dodges each one. Georges keeps yammering on as if he's talking to someone who hangs on his every word. It is a strange enough soliloquy that Emily Sevo begins to think that Georges is about to suffer a psychotic break. And it alarms The Weasel and Artemis for its broken-record repetition.

"C'est dommage, things have already gone too far," Georges laments. "Maybe uncoordinated campaigns and singular acts of ecotage won't make a dent at all. Burning a billboard today is like putting a band-aid on a patient wracked with cancer, right Emily? You're a doctor. You'd know. It might make us feel better, but it's too little, too late. God, my head, my head! Can't you hear that high-pitched ultraviolet whine? How can you not? It's like listening to a flock of lifeguards blowing all their whistles at once! Make them stop already!

"What? Well that's because we know the damage we inflict upon the Earth is suicidal and yet still we do not change our ways," he says, holding his head in his hands and rolling it back and forth. "Americans, Abbey wrote over twenty years ago, are 'a stupid, fat, and brutal people,' or something like that, but Americans today? A lot of Americans are hip, smart, over-educated, energetic, and compassionate toward pets, and yes, for the most part, well-fed. We're a bunch of hypercaffeinated info-junkies," Georges looks at The Weasel and summarizes, "and we know all kinds of facts and still we don't change. Take global warming. Or war—that barbaric anachronism!—killing people for petroleum! Or the depletion of the ocean's fishes, the topsoil of the Great Plains, the Oglala aquifer. But it's easier to read about action and think about taking action and elect someone else to take action than to take action.

"Are we cynics and nihilists? Am I suicidal? I think not.

"Okay, well, maybe I am. As a population, though? You're right, that's another matter. It's obvious that as a group, we're suicidal. Either that, or we are simply too lazy to renounce the conveniences of modern transport, entertainment, the internet, packaged addictions and cheap plastic crap and gadgets, see? 'Eschew surplusage.' Or perhaps we're afraid that if we refuse to subscribe to the New Millennial hive-mentality, the system will kick us out, imprison us, or shoot us dead on the street. Stoplight videocams are loaded with film and with bullets. Did you know?"

No one says anything, so Georges peers out his window. The moonlit landscape of undulating sagebrush and far-off cliffs zips by under the stars at rocket speed.

"YessirrEEE," Georges answers himself. "That's scary enough to deter me. Are you guys hungry? I'm jonesing for some mustard. Stone-ground, Grey Poupon kind of mustard. Slathered across a blue potato or between two slices of dark rye bread. I can feel him, can't you? Feel him like he's squashed right up between me and The Weasel. I can almost smell the underarm sweat from his button-down shirt and the tobacco from his pipe."

It is quiet for a full minute, for a mile and a half. Then Artemis asks, "Who, Georges?"

Georges grins. "Edward Abbey, of course! Cactus Ed has come back."

It must be sometime between one and two in the morning, Artemis reckons, by the time they glide off the highway ramp into Green River. The men are asleep in the backseat. Curled on his side, Georges's head rests in The Weasel's lap. The checkerboard city flashes its yellow traffic lights into a pearly fog; not a single other vehicle is creeping down any of the wide moistened streets; porch lights are on but the neighborhoods sleep and cottonwoods snooze, oblivious to any mischief. No other lights shine from inside the tight little houses.

Maggot—Emily—takes a few turns then lurches left into a driveway. She shuts the exhausted engine and it ticks soothingly to itself. "I'll just be a minute or two," she whispers to Artemis and gets out of the car.

"You want me to come?"

Emily's face hardens and her eyes gleam. Holding open her door, she says, "I am going to say goodbye to my daughter."

"Where's she going?" Artemis asks.

Emily taps the seat a few times with her key fob. "She's not going anywhere."

"Come on, Emily. Stop jerking us around."

Emily chews her lip. "My daughter and I, we have to part ways now. I'll fill you in afterward, okay?"

"Okay, fine. Go say goodbye."

"I hate goodbyes," Emily confesses. "I suck at them. Even when clearly it's time to go."

"Do you want me to come with you, or not?"

"Yes," Emily says. "I want you to come with me."

Artemis gets out and they gently shut their doors so as not to wake the menfolk or the residents of the neighborhood. Emily doesn't go to the front door but bypasses it, skirts the porch around to the side of the house, where she lets herself in by a latched gate. "Come on," she says. "Her bedroom's around back." They sneak into the backyard, creep across the dewy lawn, and follow the brick wall and the row of sweet blooming daffodils to the corner and a window that gives onto cottonwoods and the Green River out back. "She's expecting me," Emily says.

When they reach the window, it's open, the light's on, and a young woman—in her mid-to-late twenties, Artemis guesses—tosses out a duffel bag and softly says, though her voice is choked with emotion, "I'm coming with you guys."

"What?" Emily says, whispering harshly. "No."

"Yes."

"No! Absolutely not; I will not allow—"

"Mom, for christ's sake! You recruited your best friends, the people you love most in the whole world—besides me, of course. So I'm coming, too."

"It's going to be so fucking dangerous," Emily hisps back, a rattlesnake. "My friends are seasoned activists, people who're used to taking risks, people who've already lived so much of their lives. . . ." Emily looks with inscrutable significance at Artemis and says, "I'm sorry, I haven't. . . , and here I am. . . . Damn it." Emily bends her head to her hands and rubs it. Artemis notices, by the light from the bedroom window, that Emily's short fuzzy hair really is blue—a dyed bright blue, perhaps to match some of the iridescent hues of her earring.

"Mother, I am coming with you. Period." The daughter hooks a leg over the sill and pushes from behind. She gets her other leg over rather nimbly and jumps down. "So," she says and extends a hand to Artemis. "I'm Morgan Flynn. You must be Artemis." They shake hands. Morgan's hand is strong and warm. Artemis says she's pleased to finally meet her.

But Emily is less than pleased. "No, Morgan."

"I can. And I will. And you just have to accept it, okay? Let's go." Morgan flips her hair and pushes past the two old friends and they turn, staring at the back of the strapping young athlete, her Levis and the Carhartt jacket over her plaid flannel shirt. "Let me at least drive, okay? You-all must be exhausted, and I'm like totally wired on espressos."

"Damn it, Morgan, don't make this harder," Emily says with finality, one last attempt to hold onto her parental authority. "You promised that if I made this stop you'd let me go without protest. It would be farewell without any melodrama, remember? We're saying goodbye right here and right now."

Morgan stops at the corner of the house. She turns slowly. "I am not going to let you have all the fun! Or spend the last wild night of your life without your daughter by your side. You contacted me for a reason. This is the reason. I've thought about it a lot. Yeah, I'm scared, and I'm really sad, Mom, but I understand why you don't want to live anymore. And why you want to do what you want to do. I totally get it, okay? I'm meant to share this night with you."

"God, Morgan, you are so fucking headstrong."

"I take after some bitch doctor we both know."

Artemis turns to Emily. "You don't want to live anymore?"

"She didn't tell you?" Morgan says, striding up to them on her long legs, loose hips rolling. "She's got terminal breast cancer, in what stage now? Some advanced stage. It's metastasized all over the place. The oncologists gave her at best eighteen months, and that was—" she pauses to melodramatically consult her watch.

"Morgan, I am warning you, you have no right—"

"You have cancer?" Artemis asks, touching her friend's sleeve.

Emily's hard face has melted into another kind of mask, soft and pliable-looking, but without expression. She looks at the lawn between her boots.

"Wow, will you look at that?" Morgan says, tapping her watch. "Exactly eighteen months ago! Probably to the day. Which also happens to be her fiftieth birthday, did she at least tell you that? Of course not. It's like having a clam for a friend, isn't it, Artemis? Anyway, she gets this outrageous idea in her head: Sell the house in Denver and all her stock and belongings and withdraw her savings to buy a bunch of motorized houseboats— to take out the dam, right? And I say, Mom, you're nuts! Why don't you just travel the world on a cruise ship like normal retired white people do, or kick back on a Hawaiian beach with some mai-tais and flirt with the massage therapists, but no, not this activist. She has to take out the g.d. Glen Canyon Dam! So I say, Fine. Just visit me every month before you decide to do yourself in accomplishing nothing. But then I starting thinking about it, right?" Morgan addresses her mother again. Morgan's eyeliner has smudged beneath her eyes; she's been crying. "And I read all those books. And you know something? You're freaking right. The dam has got to go. And I'm gonna help. So here's the new plan: I'll drive you guys down, drop you off, make sure things are underway, then I'll take care of the Landcruiser for you, drive back home, get rid of the license plates and everything, so there's not a single clue as to who did what. Brilliant, right? You've got to admit it now, you need me to come along."

"You'd be an accomplice. You'd be in grave danger, Morgan, and I can't do that to you."

"Emily?" Artemis says, stunned. "*The Glen Canyon Dam?* That's your river restoration project?"

Emily rubs the bristly crewcut over her head. It makes a scratchy sound. She rubs it and rubs it and says to her daughter, "Well, shit. That's the stupidest, most hair-brained idea I've heard." She looks lost, blindsided by this fly in the ointment, this sabot in the cogs of her plan. She coughs and checks in with Artemis. She touches the pendant around her neck.

Morgan looks at her mother's chest and says, "Hold on. Is that—?"

"Yeah. Escalante riverwater from the tributary where Frank and Millie met."

Emily lifts it over her head and loops it over Morgan's, settles the gold chain on her daughter's neck. The elegant, blown-glass dacryovial rests upon Morgan's sternum.

Morgan touches the pendant. "You mean, Naked Millie in the photo?"

Emily nods. Morgan inspects the vial of nondescript brown water and places her palm over it, over her heart. She looks at Artemis and smiles, then looks at her mother. "This so means I get to go, doesn't it."

En route along 24 to Hanksville and points south, our five heroes discuss the plan and right away set to arguing about whether or not they must give their lives, and if Emily has in fact stockpiled enough explosives, and if four boats are adequate for the task.

Artemis is initially giddy with excitement—she can't wait to get behind the wheel of a fifty-foot motorized house boat!—while Georges can't stop sobbing. The Weasel, sober now, tells him to knock it off, because breaking down into a puddle when the fates have tapped you for action isn't the warrior's way. He tells Georges, "Buck up, kiddo." Then, in his own moment of weakness, The Weasel tells everyone about Fermin, his kitten, and Emily becomes disproportionately irate, reminding him that, when she called only three weeks ago to confirm, he swore he had no responsibilities toward anyone—no partner, no children, no pets. He avows that, when she called, he didn't have any dependents, but a few days later Fermin turned up, so that's the situation and now they have to deal with it. She says, No they don't. He says, Oh yes they do. Then she says, "Damn it, Mike, it's just a cat." The Weasel retorts that there's no such thing as "just a cat." Then he says, that's like telling a parent their kid "is just a child," and Georges pipes up and puts in his two cents about animal rights and the ever-expanding circle of moral consideration. And so on.

For a half-hour, the kitten is the biggest issue; it's as if their own lives aren't worth advocating for—or it feels too anthropocentric to do so—but Life itself, in particular its manifestation in a rambunctious kitten, is. The kitten is a symbol of all they want to hold onto. Especially The Weasel, who is stunned that, by choice, he'll never see Fermin again, but also Georges, who imagines the kitten's experience of Weiselmann's empty Salt Lake apartment as May blooms into June and June bakes into July and The Weasel never comes home. Georges hyperventilates as he absorbs the anxiety the kitten will feel. How animals can live in a world of so much uncertainty and so many unanswered questions baffles him. He weeps, he sobs, he blows his nose and gasps for air.

Emily ignores Georges's second round of sobbing and says, "My only regret is that I'll never get a chance to see Morgan fall in love and make babies, and do everything else she's told me she wants to do." She looks at Morgan with dry eyes. "Man, I wish I could've watched you find your way in the world."

"Don't worry, I'll find my way." Morgan in the driver's seat looks at her mother and bites her lip. She says, "I'm just glad you finally let me get to know you. I'm glad we've had this year together."

"I never got a chance to bike to the Canadian arctic and save the polar bears," Georges says. "Now who will go?"

"I never got a chance to say goodbye to Fermin."

"Enough with the cat, already," Emily says.

"You don't have to be such a cold-hearted bitch," The Weasel snaps back.

"I never got a chance to swim with the whales," Artemis says.

"Fuck it all, this cat thing is a wrench in the plan. Are you people ready to talk tactics yet? Or do we still have unresolved issues regarding mortality and shit?"

"Doctor Hardass requests that all delicate flowers leave the operating room."

"You don't know me, Mike Weiselmann. So shut the fuck up."

"I still have unresolved issues," Georges says.

"Then fucking deal with them, LaRue."

"Can we please try to remember that we're all on the same team?" Artemis says. "And that our enemy is a concrete monster seven hundred feet tall and a thousand feet across? Weighing whatever five million cubic yards of concrete weighs?"

"We may as well be tilting at a windmill," The Weasel murmurs. He fidgets with the lock and the door handle. Then he says, "This is ridiculous. Let me out. I need to think."

Morgan looks to Emily.

Emily glances at her watch and says, "Ignore him. Keep driving."

So Artemis tries to do what Artemis does best: Big picture stuff, conflict resolution, weaving the tribe back together after a hole's been torn in it. Artemis has always had the gift of the gab, but she's never been put to the test like she is now. While The Weasel takes off his SuperWeasel cape and stuffs it behind the small of his back, she launches into a speech in such a way that she hopes no one feels preached at or condescended to. It works for about five minutes.

It turns out they are only human—they are animal—interested in life, and terrified by death. Actually not so much death, per se, but the act of dying. These pagans are fortunate in that they've never taken hell or the devil or other fairy tales literally. But their fear of crossing the threshold—their instinctual fear of change—makes them angry, and so they fight, and come up with a dozen good reasons why this dam-ramming plan will never work despite its necessity and nobility. Suddenly, their lives don't feel inhabited at all; their lives on a deadline feel incomplete and hollow, and this awareness, of the imminent termination of life, cancels out all earlier declarations of peacefulness after almost drowning and the bullshit about wanting to be leaders and heroes. Wanting to die for a cause, to find meaning in one last act of heroism? Bullshit, bullshit! They shout at each other out of fear, out of anticipatory bereavement, and out of the shock of knowing that today—tonight—really is their last. If they so choose.

As the four old activists yell and weep and argue and cajole and try to rile up or comfort each other, Morgan drives them south, smiling when she catches her mother's eye. Emily reaches for Morgan's hand for a reassuring squeeze. They've had much longer to accept tonight's outcome, Emily realizes, with a proud glance at her daughter; she shuts up and lets the others wrassle, hiss, and howl in the backseat. Sooner or later they'll exhaust themselves.

But they don't. So, finally, when the cacophony of back-seat activists becomes unbearable, Morgan flips the turn signal and pulls the Landcruiser into the parking lot of a Kum-n-Go somewhere on Utah State Road 276. Everybody gets out. They walk a ways, then stand on the sweet dirt of the earth under the stars, at some distance from the lume of the convenience store neons and other signs and beyond the reach of streetlights. It is the deepest, coldest, inkiest hour of the night—nearly morning—and the stars are more numerous and brighter than any of them have ever seen before. The moon is huge. The sagebrush has never smelled so good.

After a minute of stargazing and huffily breathing together, Mike Weiselmann recalls the way the stars wheeled overhead when the jaguar came to him, and he tells Emily not to worry about him. He's in. He won't be backing out at the last minute. She says, "You fucking swear to me, Mike Weiselmann?"

He nods and says, "My neighbor will take care of the cat. Fermin will be fine." But he says this through tears, sobbing, his shoulders heaving as he wraps his arms around his tummy, which is still sore and bruised-feeling from when Artemis pumped water from his lungs.

Artemis puts an arm around The Weasel and he

slobbers on her dreads and neck as he clings to her. Her skin and hair smell of woodsmoke and incense. She presses her furry cheek against his smooth one, which is hot with sunburn, and whispers in his ear, "Hey now, listen up, Weez. If I survive tonight, I'll go on up to Salt Lake and get Fermin, okay?"

He nods through his tears. Because he's convinced himself that Artemis is, in fact, and for no logical reason, immortal, he says, "You're going to like Fermin. He's a really great cat."

So they place their faith in the kitten, and they place their faith in each other, and pacts made long, long ago, when they were courageous, arrogant, self-righteous, lusty twenty-somethings who hadn't a clue what their lives meant or would someday come to mean. They place their faith in the sagebrush and the sandstone earth at the center of the universe, in the yearning straining roiling brown river that desires more than anything to be free, in the transience and mutability of all things. They place their faith in the ancient submerged terrain from which glowing nymphs with lanterns come, graceful water-sprites who will guide them with absolute confidence and certainty deep into the canyonlands for the long-awaited healing of wounds and draining of bathtubs that should never have been filled. They agree to do what must be done, and Emily says, "When you've got Toxic Shock Syndrome, you gotta pull the tampon plug."

During a lull, Artemis—feeling light-headed, dehydrated maybe—detaches from the group and ploughs silent and prehistoric as a sturgeon across the dark sage plain toward the truck. Alone and dizzy, with the cool soil and cryptogam squeezing up around her toes, she entertains a fantasy. Or suffers a residual cannabis-induced hallucination. Or is bonked in the head by persuasive Fates who, once she's on the ground seeing fireflies, show her a front-page newspaper clipping.

The Arizona Times-Herald, May 3, 2062
GOVERNOR ATTENDS
DAM-RAMMER CEREMONY

Escalante River, AP—On the 50th anniversary of the simultaneous removal of both Glen Canyon and Hoover Dams, the four river activists who bravely gave their lives for the greater good of the American West were finally exonerated and memorialized today with a sandstone monument and well-attended ceremony. Gloria Fayah Wauta, the barefoot 102-year old marine biologist and reclusive author of *The Last Four Power-Boats on Lake Powell: A Biography of the Dam-Rammers,* gave a short speech and enjoyed a standing ovation. Afterward, she presented the Governor of Arizona with a 1962 sepia-toned photograph of the resurrected slot canyon in which today's ceremony took place (continued on page A-12).

Artemis regains her usual but especial vibration of consciousness only a second later, but is surprised to find herself sprawled upon the piles of gritty-mossy soil. As if having been decked by a seismic event. Never underestimate the power and reach of the media! Her fanned hands stamp impressions in the cryptogamic earth; her dreads tangle with the perfumed wands of a nearby mouse-footed sage. Did she pass out? She gets up and brushes herself off. Looks back: Her comrades are a black cone humming a tune, arm-in-arm and heads bowed together it seems, under the starry tarp of night. Frowning, rubbing her naturally lumpy noggin, scratching at the tickling retreat of a nervous flea, Artemis continues her forwardish progress toward the truck, feeling bedazzled by the brilliance of the stars and by the clear-as-cut-glass AP news item delivered to her by the Fates. At the truck she excavates a sage bundle from her backpack and returns to the group.

She tells them where she collected the sage. She tells them she dried the sage-bundle over the woodstove in her writing studio back on the Coast. (She's never called her shanty a writing studio before, but, now that she knows she's going to write a whole goddamned book. . . .) She does not, however, tell them about the celestial associated press—why would she? Except for Morgan, nobody else will be living after this morning. And how does she feel about that? About surviving while others will perish?

She lights the sage, blows on it, coaxing it along til it crackles and smokes and little dots of orange pulse in the bunched twigs. They waft each other, one smudging the next around the tight circle. Artemis watches, memorizing their features: the sobbing alabaster bust of Mike Weiselmann with the moon jiggling in his glasses and his watch glowing green on his wrist; the gaunt and butchy Emily Sevo with a grim set to her jaw and an arm hooked around her daughter's waist; and poor weenie little Georges Nondairy with his wispy forelock floating above his forehead like a sea-creature's deeley-bop, moustache disappearing into his mouth and pulled taut by his lower teeth, nervously blinking, throat making little animal noises.

"Holy motherfucking balls of fire," The Weasel whoops. "Are we gonna blow this thing, or are we gonna blow this thing?"

413

"That's the spirit," Emily Sevo says, clapping The Weasel on his shoulder.

Evidently, the plan has lit a slow fire under The Weasel's ass. Now that the tinder's caught, and the big dry beams of his pyromaniacal soul are burning, he drags the group back to the truck, where he once again dons his SuperWeasel! cape and takes out the maps Maggot requested. As he begins to organize the group's movements and logistics, he supercharges the group's morale with a burst of new energy, like jet fuel on an arson project.

He always knew he was meant for great things. He always knew he would be a hero. It is the time of The Weasel! The great jaguar's eye guides him from the hole in the sky where the others may only see a moon. He is once again part of the magic. They all are.

Before leaving the Kum-n-Go, they go inside to fill up on a weak coffee-flavored slurry and go potty and stare at themselves in the mirror over the sinks. Unbeknownst to the others, it is at the Kum-n-Go's outside phone booth where Georges, with sweat beading his brow, makes a quick call to a cousin who works for the Army Corps of Engineers in Louisiana.

Georges asks his blunted cousin Darryl for a favor: to keep his eyes on the tee-vee cuz there was predicted something like a massive earthquake and a dam failure at Glen Canyon in Arizona, see, and a mega-tsunami is gonna barrel down the Colorado River through Canyonlands and overtop the Hoover Dam, and that people 'round those parts and livestock and pets should definitely definitely be gotten out of the way, evacuated—EVACUATED, hear?—just in case. Cousin Darryl sounds sleepy and disbelieving and pissy at having been woken up.

Georges says, "Listen up now Darryl, didn't I

predict the December 2004 tsunami in the Indian Ocean? Didn't I predict the Haiti earthquake of January 2010? And everybody thought George LaRue was an addle-pated bugwit who'd lost his mind. But I was right, wasn't I? Well this is sort of the exact same thing, see? Well—not exactly, but I've gotten very clear transmissions and instructions! This is going to happen! And the Army Corps of Engineers won't listen to me, Darryl, but they will listen to you." His cousin grunts into the receiver and says, "Okay then." Okay then, says Georges, and he makes his cousin swear on the bible. "Fine, I swear on the Bible," his cousin says, but Georges, unconvinced, says, "Swear on Sparky's grave." His cousin pauses, swallows audibly, then somberly says, "I swear on Sparky's grave." Georges lowers his voice. "If you forget your promise, you'll rot in hell with landsharks for all of eternity." "Okay," Darryl says. Georges signs off with a soft-spoken, "Give my love to Aunt Martha," and he hangs up.

Georges looks through the storefront windows of plate glass. There are aisles of windshield washer fluid, antacids, candy bars, and condiments. Hmm, he thinks. The others haven't reappeared yet, so he goes into the store and says hi to the young man behind the counter, where cigarettes and nudie magazines are stocked in tidy, colorful array. But Georges is not tempted by what tempts many men; he goes instead, directly, to the ketchup, mayonnaise, pickle relish, and mustard shelves.

On leaving, he wishes the cashier a good night.

Georges trots back to the shiny black Landcruiser to wait for the others to get back from the restrooms. He doesn't even check beneath the car. Bravely, victoriously, he scooches onto the back seat and the The Weasel is there, sipping his coffee and mindlessly whapping a folded map against his leg. Whap-whap-whap. Georges clicks his door shut. He takes his condiment from beneath his oversized pink T-shirt and opens it.

"What's that?"

"French's Mustard." Georges removes all the security packaging and squirts a bunch of mustard into his mouth. Oh, yes.

"That's gross," Mike says.

They sit together, almost primly, not saying anything. Two Victorian gents at tea both too polite to speak the thing that must be spoken. A minute ticks by on The Weasel's Ironman watch, with its green glow-in-the-dark bezel casting an otherworldly light on his adam's apple. Whap-whap-whap goes the map. Downing glop after glop of mustard, Georges's legs bounce up and down. He really, really, really wants to tell The Weasel what he just did—*make the mindful telephone call? carry out the mindless theft? or both?*—but he doesn't.

The Weasel says, "You scared, little man?"

"I can't swim. . . very well. And also, there may be. . . . Are you scared?"

"No." He considers telling Georges about the jaguar, but decides against it. He says, "I'm just a little sad."

"About your kitten."

"Yes, Fermin," The Weasel says. "I think it's true. It's our attachment to things that makes us miserable. Really there's nothing else. Anyway, it's gotta be all or nothing. We can't half-ass this. The river's depending on us, and also, I am not going back to prison."

"I woulda never survived that," Georges says. "I think maybe prison's more scary than what's lurking at the bottom of Lake Powell, waiting for us."

"Maybe. But you might have surprised yourself."

While Georges thinks of lots of scary things and

the few things he's attached to, like his bicycle and the numinous blonde in the mustard-yellow bikini, Mike Weiselmann remembers some things Uncle Steve said in the slammer, and he says, "Constant change is the law of the universe. Transformation is God's other name. Things come, things go, and we're all just a part of the flow." The Weasel stills his map to say, "Fire is one instrument of the Tao."

"And dynamite?"

"That, too." Mike watches Georges squirt mustard in a line down his forearm then lick it up and inspect his forearm hairs. He wonders if Georges really understands what they're talking about, and what they're about to do. Mike's worried that he and the women are asking a mentally-handicapped human being to do something beyond his intellectual or moral comprehension; if Georges really understands what's at stake, would he still do it? If they find out that he doesn't understand, will they still include him? Won't they have to?

The store's glass door opens and the women spill into the night, with fluorescent and neon and moon light playing on their hair and shoulders. The Weasel asks, "So I guess we're really doing this?"

Georges scissors his long forearm hairs with his fingers. "Know what I think is dumb?"

Mike waits for Georges to answer. When he doesn't, Mike sighs and asks, "What, Georges?"

"That Alcoholics Anonymous prayer they make people recite. Why should anyone accept anything we think we can't change? Who decides what can be changed, and what can't?"

As Mike considers Georges's question, he watches the three women walk abreast, Emily Sevo in the middle, all of them swaying in step across the lit parking lot toward him and Georges in the vehicle. Each step they take seems choreographed and exaggerated: Three right feet lunge forward with heels lightly touching the ground, three back feet leave the pavement, toes last; time slows, slows, slows waaaaay down to a fluid close-up of each passing nanosecond, as if in this one sage-scented pocket on the Plateau the spell of gravity has been temporarily lifted. It's the same strange feeling he had back at camp when the jaguar came to him. Here, the three women are rock stars or astronauts taking the stage in slow-motion footage. Their heads are backlit and shimmer with coronas from blazing blue, red-orange, and moongreen spotlights; they glow with halos cast by sun-stars a billion miles away. Morgan's long straight hair rocks side to side behind her broad shoulders. Emily's buzzcut shimmers like the velvet fuzz of a watershrew. Artemis's surly wild dreads lift and twist and weave and fall like charmed but harmless watersnakes. Three feet swing forward again. Skirts and coats rock in synch on their bodies. Three left feet, then three right, and as the women become ever-so-slowly larger and ever-so-slowly begin to block the light from the store and fill the windshield with their invincible silhouettes, Emily reaches and encircles one arm around her daughter's waist, and she slides the other arm around Artemis's. She pulls them close to her. Morgan bends her mouth to her mother's ear. Artemis bends her head toward Emily, too. Their heads join, then their torsos, then their hips. The women are laughing about something as they reach the SUV.

"What did you say, Georges?" Mike Weiselmann asks, then finishes his coffee. Because it seems to him that Georges said something important. Something that for once makes sense.

"That stupid prayer, about accepting what we can't change. It's probably something Lyndon B. Johnson wrote with Richard Nixon and Barry Goldwater near the end of the Viet Nam War and they sold it to AA for a million dollars. A disempowering New Age mantra to keep the masses from rising up and doing anything about stuff that's wrong or abusive and seems beyond our control, see, but actually isn't? And then darn that pseudo-punk-activist Sinead for putting it in her song! Because think about it: If change is the one universal constant," Georges says, petting his arm-hair as if it were a ferret, raising his voice to a squeak, hyperventilating, "then how do we know what can, or can't, or won't change? I mean, think beyond the individual ego-self here! Think social effects! Think cultural change and revolution! Think conspiracy theory."

Is it possible that Georges is smarter than Mike's prison counselor Uncle Steve, the mentor he believes saved his life in and beyond the slammer, and gave him new tools to live by? Could the self-righteous, free-associating, wheedling vegan in his ridiculous striped socks actually know something about the nature of the universe which even Uncle Steve did not know? Well, why not? Mike Weiselmann rubs the back of his smooth head and clears his throat and says, his voice cracking and raspy, "Jesus, Georges. I think you're right."

"I am?"

"Yes," Mike says. He drops his voice to an earnest baritone: "You're right, little man."

Doors pop and swing open; lights and laughter and a lunatic gust fill the car. There's a mirthful air about the triumvirate of heroines, as if they've been sharing silly secrets and telling jokes and laughing their asses off in the bathroom. Mike wishes he could be one of the girls and be silly, too, especially on the last night of his life. How can they be laughing in the face of their imminent deaths? What did they talk about in the loo? How can

Morgan be okay with losing her mother forever within the next couple of hours?

Georges says, "Really? I'm right?"

Mike conjures the bright green eyes of Fermin, the moon eyes of the jaguar. Something happened back there at the camp and something is happening right now. Something bigger than he as a human can understand. He morosely watches Georges's stunned face, his underslung, haggard, two-caterpillar face and corduroy forehead, dimly lit by the tiny yellow-white lights of the vehicle's interior. The happy lower caterpillar twitches on his smiling lip; the baffled upper caterpillar pinches above the nose. Pressed between are two lively eyes, small and set deep beneath a puckering of wrinkles.

"I'm right?" he asks Mike, again, and all else, everyone else in this car, recedes from him.

Nobody's ever told Georges he's right. Well, nobody in, like, twenty or thirty years. Maybe longer. He can't recall the last time someone believed in him, understood his brilliance, totally grokked his wisdom. It makes him feel less alone and not quite so alienated or insane. His face grows hot with this unexpected compliment from one of the men he admires most in all the world, the man who went to prison instead of snitching, the man therefore who saved Georges from certain violation and violent death by cell-mates. Such rare blushing praise!

"Incoming!" Artemis shouts. She has been talking to Georges. "Hello, NondairEeee! Yo dipshit! How many times I gotta ask? Will you please move the fuck over?"

He doesn't budge so she gives him a push, and the little plastic container of mustard falls between Georges's and The Weasel's thighs.

"I'm right?" Georges repeats, as he scootches,

reluctantly, toward Mike. The others get in up front—Morgan riding shotgun and Emily reclaiming the wheel—and Artemis slides her substantial goddess-butt onto the bench in back; the vehicle rocks. Because of the width of Artemis's hips, Georges has to keep scooting til he's mashed beside The Weasel, lest Georges's trailing appendages get squashed like a bug's.

With Georges smushed right up next to him, some new feeling, something fraternal and playful, comes over Mike. He calls Georges, "little bro," saying, "You're right, little bro, you're right!" and knuckles Georges's wispy-haired pate. Georges giggles. Hilarious, high-pitched, shrieking giggles. Egged on by Georges's uncharacteristically childlike reaction, Mike tickles Georges under his thin arms and along his knobby sides.

"What's that smell?" Morgan asks. "It stinks like a hotdog stand in here."

"No! No, don't! Stop! Stop it Weasel, I'll pee my pants!" Georges screams, giggling, drawing up his knees and kicking his chucks and laughing harder than he's ever laughed before. But he doesn't mean it. He doesn't want the tickling, or Mike's attention, or the echoing words "You're right," ever to stop. Not ever.

"Jesus, you two," Artemis says, and throws a quizzical glance up front. "Did you get into my pharmacopeia again?" Emily pulls a stern and wincing what-the-fuck face; Morgan smiles like a Madonna upon her child, almost condescendingly. Artemis thinks, How alike they look, Emily and Morgan!

Mike turns on Georges. He tickles Georges's love-handles, which are just two slips of depleted skin folds, thin as bandaids, hardly a molecule of adipose anywhere. He digs his fingertips into the soft place beneath the ribcage where Georges's liver quietly metabolizes what little the body ingests; it's tender from the occult infections, and Georges shrieks and gasps and cries, "Eeek! Eeeeek! Stop! Hoooooo!" Then Mike lifts Georges's oversized pink T-shirt, pushes up the layers of undershirts, and puts his mouth on Georges's concave furry belly, and blows. He makes a farting sound against Georges's skin.

"Eeeek!" Georges wails with delight and the intolerable ticklishness of the zerbert. In the wee pre-dawn hours of May 3, 2012, Georges at sixty-three years has never felt younger or freer or been happier in his life. He gets his chucks under Mike's pectorals and armpits and kicks like a donkey. "Stopitstopitstopit!"

Mike snorts. His bludgeoned armpits start to feel bruised, and his abs are still sore from yesterday when Artemis pounded on his belly, but he keeps tickling Georges. He hasn't had this much fun in years. It's been ages, ages since he's laughed so hard his abs seized, ages since he's snorted and wept. He lets Georges kick his chest as he tickles Georges ferociously, and their game continues til Mike's soft palate can't take the snorting anymore.

"Maintain composure!" Georges shrieks, kicking harder now and wheezing and gulping for air. "Maintain—ack!—composure!"

Suddenly Mike surrenders. He sits back on his end of the cushion, upright and statuesque, and sets an elbow on a convenient ledge on the door paneling. He curls a loose fist and looks at his hand and grins. He says, "All right, little brother."

Georges yanks his shirts down over his hips and sits up, bringing his shoes to the floor and his skinny, bandaged knees almost parallel with Mike's knees, which bulge with muscle.

"You lads done yet?" Emily Sevo asks. "Shall we

proceed? And did somebody spill some mustard or something? It smells disgusting in here."

Mike and Georges look at each other. Georges protectively clutches his wrists to his chest and starts to crack up, but Mike's eyes slide to the profiled face of Artemis. Artemis has been unusually quiet. A shadow against the indigo night, her elegant profile thrums and wavers just beyond Georges's twitchy, undershot quarter-profile and protruding moustache. Hers is the poised, multifaceted visage of the hundred mutable Goddesses which lies just beneath the surface of all our faces, beneath all our masks and our personas, our dragons and our myths. It is the face of the Mother of God and it has a hundred names: Innana, Hecate, Demeter, Hera, Diana, Isis. . . the Jaguar Goddess. . . . Georges, seeing a strange expression wash over Mike's face, turns. He looks upon Artemis's face. He feels the awe he saw in Mike's expression.

Emily starts the Landcruiser and puts it in gear. Idling, she looks to Artemis, and says, "Hey, you."

Artemis starts humming, and Emily recognizes the tune. Artemis's eyeballs roll back in their sockets, eyelids flickering. She finishes the hummed verse of a Dana Lyons river song and emerges from the trance; she steadies and focuses her eyes to check in with each of the other three who will tonight give their lives to the river. She asks them, "Can you feel it?"

"Yes," Emily says, nodding.

"Yes," Mike and Georges say.

"Can you feel the boom and crash? Can you see the tiny trickle, the falling water drops, at first just a little drip-drip through the puka in the wall, so minuscule, so terribly small, you'd think it wouldn't matter at all? But the hole is the way out, the portal to the sea, the gateway to give in to what must follow, the holy crack in the concrete beast that lets the river finally the river with all Her force lets her push through like something being born, it's the force of the newborn river aching for Mama Pacifica that topples the dam, it is the WATER not us, not us at all, and can you hear the rumbling rush, can you feel the joyful roar of a river liberated at last?

"Can you feel it?" Artemis asks again.

"Yes."

"The canyons drowned for fifty years, they breathe again! They feel the sunlight on their shoulders, down their walls, all along their sandy bottoms? And trees dead for fifty years come back to secret grottoes, and birds, and lizards, and bees, and tiny monkeyflowers? I say, Can you feel it?"

"Yes, yes."

"So, great, are we ready, then?" asks Emily, ever the practical one.

Artemis grins at her. "Sure, Sevo. We're ready."

"Oh, shit!" Emily yelps. "Now what?"

One by one they look up to follow Emily's eyes and peer out the windshield: The Kum-n-Go clerk is running furiously toward them across the parking lot, cellphone pressed to his ear, yelling, waving his other arm like a rodeo clown.

"Oh, no!" cries Georges, not feeling so invincible anymore. "He knows! Hit it, Maggot!"

Emily turns the steering wheel hard and pulls out onto the black asphalt. She drives at a heady rush, a dizzying speed. Over the Eastern rim of the world there lies the tiniest, bluest, earliest suggestion of dawn. She peers at Georges in her rearview. Squashed between the other two he looks weenie and sheepish.

"Georges?" she asks.

"Nothing! I didn't do anything, okay! I made a phone call, that's it!"

"So why was the cashier—?"

"Let it go, Emily," Artemis says, looking over her shoulder. "He's gone back inside."

"What did you do, Georges?"

"What? It was only a small thing of mustard."

"SHIT, shit shit shit, Georges! That guy was calling the cops! Damn it, I swear to god, it's the little shit, it's the tiny insignificant crap that always—"

"Calm down, Emily," Artemis says. "Nobody's calling the cops over fucken mustard. Have some faith."

They are silent. Perhaps Artemis is right: The road to the west side of the Glen Canyon Dam is all theirs. There are no cars behind them, no cars before them. It was a small thing. They have huge things to think about. They are on a profoundly important mission that will change the river, if not the gorgeous American West for decades to come.

"Nice work, Georges," Artemis says, remembering what he said earlier about wanting to one day steal something small before he died. Something of no consequence. For whatever reasons the little man had, he did it. Successes come in all sizes.

"Are you being facetious?"

"No." She slides an arm around him and smiles.

He pulls back, suspicious. "You guys are always making fun of me."

"Poor little Georges. Poor adorable little Georges."

"Who, me?"

Morgan turns in her seat. "Yeah you, Georges. Cute as a baby chickie."

"I'm cute?"

"As a baby chickie," Artemis confirms.

"What about me?" Mike asks.

"You're hot, Georges is cute," Morgan pronounces while Emily cusses. Artemis settles into her seat, satisfied that the two delicate male egos have been adequately tended to. Now they're ready to get down to the business of the Goddess.

Georges, too, finally relaxes. He nestles between his two loves, feeling warm and accepted and—strangely— safe. Like nothing can harm him ever again. It's as if losing Melanie, his sweet trusty bicycle, his gallant white steed, was not that big a deal after all. And only yesterday the loss seemed so overwhelming! This re-evaluation of what's important and what's not surprises Georges. He recognizes how lonely he's been for the past twenty years and notices with glee that, right here, right now, in this thrilling moment, he's not lonely anymore. He smiles with the memory—was it only last night?—of Artemis in the tourist's spotlight against the redrock canyon wall, naked and snarling like a bear. And the sensation of riding on top of The Weasel's car, wind in his hair; his wounded knees tingle a little with the bite-memory of the rock and the ministering afterward by Artemis. Now Georges Nondairy has friends, and a purpose in life—to free the river he's lived beside for most of his life—and he rides fearlessly inside a car (inside a car!) between The Weasel and Artemis. And his lifted merchandise—somewhere around here—is proof that he can do whatever he puts his mind to. *Le petit voleur*—cute as a baby chickie, according to Morgan and to Artemis herself!—no longer feels invisible or belittled. He feels invincible again.

The Weasel, warm and smooth and comforting, and sticky-wet with mustard-goop along their thighs, braces Georges on one side; on his other side, Artemis's massive shoulder and arm and round breast and hip embrace him, spicy and tingling and exciting. Georges is elated. He loves being the filling in the middle of the sandwich.

He leans toward Mike and says, "We're going to be effing heroes."

"Yeah," The Weasel says. "But unfortunately, we'll be eco-terrorists first."

A little while later, Emily Sevo pulls into the marina parking lot. She parks. They get out and trickle down to the dock. Morgan is crying. The Weasel looks at the boats; they look seriously bad-ass and imminently flammable. Georges, suffering through pangs of puppylove, follows Artemis to the water's edge.

A pearly white dawn covers the sky like a baby blanket. To the East, the bloody muscular edge of the redrock rim begins its contractions against the horrific, dead-bone-colored, convexly-bowed dam that, at least for one more hour, blocks the wild tortured river and plugs up the frothy, amoebic sediments of Lake Powell. Artemis looks upon that vile disgusting repulsive concrete menace and thinks, "This is it!"

Emily appraises the four eager houseboats lined up along the docks. The solid-looking boats rock heavily and gently, almost innocuously, on the water. But their drizzly nonlinear reflections scatter and fragment, and break up against the oily shadows of the boats into a zillion tiny pearls and glowing scales and iridescent insect wings. Five hundred feet—leagues below—in the shaded depths of the scene, one can almost hear the restless clicks and bubbles rising from chilly soft things astir in the sand.

Holding her daughter's hand as the five line up beside each other to face Goliath, Emily says to her comrades, without a hitch in her voice: "So, what do you think?"

And Georges, Georges of all people, says, "Let's blow that concrete motherfucker to smithereens."

A Brief History of the Rise and Demise of the Glen Canyon Dam, the Dam Being a Leviathan Concrete Arch Dam in Arizona that Imprisoned the Colorado River for Fifty Years.
—A report for Mrs. Henderson's World Civ class by Artemis Sevo Flynn, Jr.

19 October 2057

Stupidly constructed in an unstable, dynamite-blasted, sandstone canyon with 4,901,000 cubic yards of concrete, the Glen Canyon Dam once loomed 710 feet high with an imposing crest length of 1560 feet. The "concrete menace" that crouched in the canyon was a formidable 300 feet thick at the base, as thick as a football field is long. Like the world's most dangerous criminal or nuclear weapon, it was encircled by bristling barriers, state-of-the-art electronic security and surveillance technology, and heavily-armed personnel. The dam's purpose was to box in the Colorado River to generate electric power for such necessities as neon lights and computers, store water for lame-brained irrigation projects in the desert, and provide recreational boating opportunities for annoying rich people.

The nefarious "industrial conglomerate" Merritt-Chapman & Scott started construction on the dam in 1956. The river began to sludge behind the dam, drowning the main canyon bottom and its tributaries sometime in 1963. Eventually this obnoxious Arizona dam would cause the river to back 180 miles clear up into Utah. The dam bridge was completed in 1964 and the dam "dedicated" in 1966.

Eco-novelist Edward Abbey entertained the idea of taking out the dam and blowing up the dam bridge in his 1975 action-packed classic, *The Monkey Wrench Gang*. On March 21, 1981, Abbey gave a rousing speech and watched a group of Earth First!ers unfurl a 300-foot black plastic "crack" from the top of the dam. The radical environmental movement was born.

In late June 1983, the Colorado River flooded and bravely fought the dam, a battle that left the monster's spillways damaged and the dam trembling in fear and licking its wounds. Ominous predictions were made, however: If the river had breached the dam, a 230-foot mega-tsunami could have roared downcanyon and overtopped the Hoover Dam, putting millions of lives at risk.

In 1996, the guilt-ridden Sierra Club, which had approved the dam in a deal that then-executive-director David Brower called the biggest mistake of his career, demanded a release of river water to re-create natural flow cycles. A restored flow, they argued, would clear the silt deposits. It would also scour the banks of tamarisk and other noxious shrubs, and drain and rejuvenate the polluted, motorboat-infested waters of Lake Powell while resurrecting native fish populations and the natural beaches downstream in the Grand Canyon. Longterm experimental dam-operational plans were drafted in 2006 in a Bureau of Reclamation EIS, as a result of the Center for Biological Diversity, et. al. v. Kempthorne litigation.

In 2009, predictions emerged that, if we continued to overpopulate and develop the American West without rethinking current water policy and practices, the Colorado River reservoirs would desiccate by 2057, and the West would become an inhospitable wasteland. Thanks to what happened just three years later, none of these dire predictions came to pass.

In May of 2012, four river activists each drove a houseboat loaded with explosives at suicidal speeds into the crest of the Glen Canyon Dam during the peak run-off of a hundred-year flood, bombarding and chinking the leviathan's convex brow just enough for the waters of the reservoir to spill over the concrete rim in a thunderous cascade. The explosion and cataclysmic release of the river shook the bedrock as far away as Kayenta, Arizona, and Kanab, Utah. "At first I thought it was a freaking earthquake or something," a tourist from Panguitch reported later from the South Rim overlook of the Grand Canyon, from where he'd heard the explosion and videotaped the deluge. The rumbling vibrations rattled the Glen Canyon Bridge (Interstate 89) off its abutments; after dangling for 3 hours into the chasm, the sections finally separated and collapsed. Meanwhile, as the reservoir was drained downriver in one fell swoop, a mighty blast of canyon air (reported by a hotdog vendor at Hite Marina as "an eerie whooshing not unlike a giant vacuum cleaner") sucked at the northernmost bridge where the controversial and bitterly contested Utah Highway 95 once traversed the canyon. The sucking jounced the bridge and set up the periodic sine-waves that later proved fatal to the bridge. Neither bridge was ever rebuilt.

The breaching of the Glen Canyon Dam set off a 350-foot mega-tsunami that blasted through the Hoover Dam as if it were made of sand. All of this without any loss of life to pets, livestock, citizens, tourists, or boaters either upstream or down, owing in part to the celebrated efficiency of the federal emergency preparedness agencies and in part to the brave men and women of the Army Corps of Engineers, who seemed to know exactly what was going on for once—some sources say, because of a tip called in by a Louisiana engineer.

However, the media reported that none of the people we now call eco-heroes was believed to have survived, but mystery still enshrouds the case of the four "Dam-Rammers" because nothing from their exploded bodies was ever recovered. Gloria Fayah Wauta, a Jamaican-American marine biologist with unexplained burns across most of her body, later turned over to authorities debris from the battered boats she'd found in the Gulf of Baja California, floating with a pod of whales. ◗